The Destruction of
Bacterial Spores

The Destruction of Bacterial Spores

A. D. RUSSELL

Welsh School of Pharmacy,
University of Wales
Institute of Science and Technology,
Cathays Park,
Cardiff CF1 3NU, Wales

1982

ACADEMIC PRESS

A Subsidiary of Harcourt Brace Jovanovich, Publishers

London   New York
Paris   San Diego   San Francisco   São Paulo
Sydney   Tokyo   Toronto

ACADEMIC PRESS INC. (LONDON) LTD.
24/28 Oval Road,
London NW1

United States Edition published by
ACADEMIC PRESS INC.
111 Fifth Avenue
New York, New York 10003

British Library Cataloguing Publication Data

Russell, A. D.
The destruction of bacterial spores.
1. Spores (Bacteria)
I. Title
589.9′046   QR79
ISBN 0-12-604060-5
LCCCN: 81 69592

Printed in Northern Ireland by
W. & G. Baird Ltd.

Preface

The bacterial spore is a complex structure. The sequences of events occurring during the process of sporulation and during those stages (germination and outgrowth) leading to vegetative cell development have long held the attention of biochemists and microbiologists. A considerable amount of time and effort has been devoted, at the cellular, biochemical and molecular levels, in order to achieve a better understanding of the spore and of sporogenesis, sometimes with a view to harnessing the findings to achieve more efficient use of sterilization and sporicidal treatments.

Generally, spores possess an above-average resistance to inimical processes. Following a brief initial account of spore structure and sporogenesis, the effects of chemical and physical agents are discussed, with emphasis placed on factors influencing destruction, mathematical aspects, applications and the mechanism(s) responsible for spore inactivation or resistance. The most important processes are undoubtedly thermal (moist heat, dry heat), radiation (ionizing, ultraviolet), chemical (liquid phase, vapour phase) and hydrostatic pressure. In recent years, there has been renewed interest in the possible use of combined sporicidal treatments, and these are described and discussed in a separate chapter. Finally, sufficient data have now accumulated for some preliminary conclusions to be reached about the recovery and revival of sublethally injured spores.

It is inevitable in a work of this type, which deals with the effects of chemical and physical agents upon a single type of organism, that some overlapping occurs between chapters. In the author's opinion, this is not necessarily a disadvantage, since studies in one field frequently impinge into investigations in another area.

It is hoped that the book will be of value to microbiologists in the food, dairy and pharmaceutical industries and to those who undertake academic and applied research into spore destruction.

January, 1982   A. D. Russell

Contents

10. *Recovery and Revival of Damaged Spores*

Acknowledgements

I wish to thank the following for permission to include Figures or Tables: American Society for Microbiology (Fig. 1a,c,d; Tables 4.6, 6.2, 10.1 and 10.5); Academic Press (Fig. 1b; Tables 4.4 and 6.5); Chapman and Hall (Table 6.4); the Czechoslovak Academy of Sciences (Fig. 2.4); the Editors, *Developments in Industrial Microbiology* (Table 3.6); the Editors, *Journal of Food Science* (Table 3.3); Dr R. S. Stafford (Fig. 5.4); and Almqvist and Wiksell (Fig. 6.1).

I also wish to express my gratitude to Dr W. B. Hugo, University of Nottingham, for allowing me to expand and develop into the present volume a chapter of the same name that appeared in his book, "Inhibition and Destruction of the Microbial Cell" (Academic Press, 1971).

Finally I must thank my typist, Mrs P. Bevan, together with Ms Caroline Boydell of Academic Press for the helpful and efficient manner in which they have carried out their duties.

Every reasonable effort has been made both to trace copyright ownership and to obtain permission where necessary to reproduce copyright material, and the cooperation of all those cited is gratefully acknowledged.

To Margaret and David
with gratitude

1

The Bacterial Spore

I. *Introductory Comments*

Since their existence was first discovered, a great deal of research has been carried out on bacterial spores. The reasons for this interest are not difficult to find: spores are highly resistant to various chemical and physical agents, so that scientists designing methods of achieving sterilization of various medical and pharmaceutical products and of certain foods have of necessity been forced to take this resistance into account; the relatively recent utilization of ionizing radiations and of various gases for sterilizing certain of these products has rejuvenated interest into the mechanisms of resistance of spores to these and to other, more traditional, methods. Moreover, the complex chain of events which occurs during sporulation and during the germination and post-germinative processes provides a fascinating study for the biochemist, molecular biologist and microbiologist. There is the concern being felt as to infections acquired in hospitals, and bacteria such as staphylo-cocci, Gram-negative organisms and anaerobes (including spores of the genus *Clostridium*) are frequently implicated as aetiological agents. Clos-tridia that are the most important in this context are probably *Clostri-dium perfringens (Cl. welchii)*, the causative agent of muscle sclerosis, and *Cl. tetani* (Howie, 1961), the aetiological agent of tetanus.

Many spore-formers are important as food-poisoning agents, and in this context *Cl. perfringens, Cl. botulinum* and *Bacillus cereus* can be cited (Hobbs, 1976; Hobbs and Gilbert, 1978; Roberts and Derrick, 1978; Roberts and Gibson, 1979; Sofos *et al.*, 1979). Botulism is a compara-tively rare disease but is often fatal; it is caused by ingesting the thermolabile neurotoxin produced by vegetative cells of *Cl. botulinum*, arising from the consumption of contaminated foodstuffs such as can-ned meats (Sofos *et al.*, 1979) or fish (Hobbs, 1976). Food poisoning caused by *Cl. perfringens* is associated with fresh meat which has been lightly cooked, but only rarely with cured meats (Roberts and Derrick, 1978). *Bacillus cereus* has become increasingly implicated as the agent of a type of food poisoning associated with a toxin that is similar to that caused by staphylococcal enterotoxin (Hobbs and Gilbert, 1978).

A recent interesting paper (Levinson *et al.*, 1978) has discussed the applications of bacterial and fungal spores, with particular emphasis on the production of antibiotics, enzymes, toxins and bacterial insecti-cides.

This chapter will consider briefly the structure of bacterial spores and the various stages which take place during sporulation, germination and outgrowth. Subsequent chapters will deal with the susceptibility and resistance of spores and of their germinated forms to chemical and physical agents.

II. *Spore Structure*

The most important spore-formers are members of the genera *Bacillus* and *Clostridium*, but certain other bacteria, e.g. *Sporosarcinae*, can also form spores (Robinow, 1960; Halvorson, 1962). True endospores are also produced by thermophilic actinomycetes; for example, *Thermoacti-*

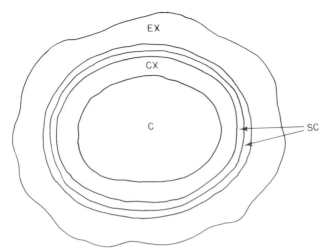

Fig. 1.1   A "typical" bacterial spore* (not drawn to scale) EX, exosporium; SC, spore coats; CX, cortex; C, core.

nomyces vulgaris endospores are highly refractile, do not take up simple stains, have a typical endospore structure, contain dipicolinic acid (see later) and are heat resistant (Cross *et al.*, 1968; Attwell *et al.*, 1972).

Only the two former groups will be discussed in this book.

Tipper and Gauthier (1972) have presented a useful description of the structure of bacterial endospores. Figure 1.1 depicts a so-called typical bacterial spore, and cross-sections of some spores are presented in Fig. 1.2. Spores are considerably more complex than vegetative cells. The germ cell (protoplast) and germ cell wall are surrounded by the cortex, around which are the spore coats, of which the outer is the more dense. In some spores, e.g. *B. polymyxa*, a layer (exosporium) beyond the spore coats may be found. In other spores, e.g. *B. cereus*, an exosporium is also present, but surrounds only one dense spore coat (Robinow, 1960). The interior of bacterial spores is essentially the same; thus, the major differences between various species consist of variations in the organization of the number and form of the outer layers.

Of the various layers, the cortex is of considerable importance in controlling the heat resistance of spores (Chapter 2) and the spore coats are implicated in the resistance presented by spores to at least some antibacterial agents (Chapter 6). These aspects will be fully covered in those chapters.

Bacilli and clostridia grow in a vegetative form until the culture medium becomes limited by exhaustion of an essential ingredient,

(*For more detailed descriptions, see Fig. 1.2).

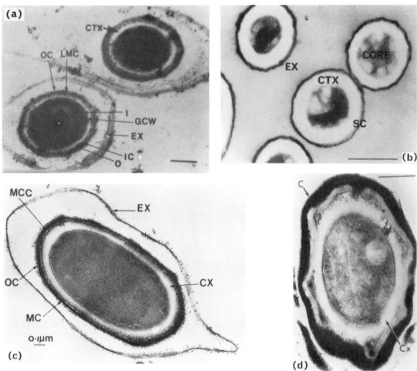

Fig. 1.2   Spore ultrastructure:
(a) Thin section of *B. sphaericus* wild-type sporulating cells (from Imae *et al.*, 1976).
    Bar = 0·25 μm. I, inner forespore membrane; GCW, germ cell wall; CTX, cortex;
    O, outer forespore membrane; IC, inner coat; LMC, lamellar midcoat; OC, outer
    coat; EX, exosporium.
(b) Thin section of *B. megaterium* KM spores (from Crafts-Lighty and Ellar, 1980).
    Bar = 0·35 μm. EX, exosporium; SC, spore coat; CTX, cortex.
(c) Mature spore of *B. cereus* T (from Ohye and Murrell, 1980). Bar = 0·05 μm. EX,
    exosporium; OC, outer coat; MC, middle coat; MCC, mother cell cytoplasm (inner
    coat); CX, cortex.
(d) Mature spore of a conditional serine protease mutant of *B. subtilis* (from Santo *et al.*,
    1972). Bar = 0·05 μm. C, outer spore coat; CX, cortex.

when the cells are induced to form spores (Mandelstam, 1969). Stages
in spore development are described in Section 3.

Unique chemical entities in the bacterial spore are dipicolinic acid
(DPA; Fig. 1.3) and spore peptidoglycan (Fig. 1.4). These are considered later.

A. Spore Core (Protoplast)

In a recent review of the molecular structure of the bacterial spore,

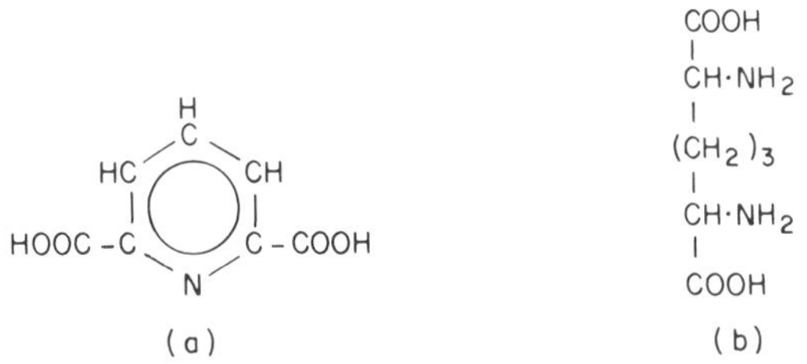

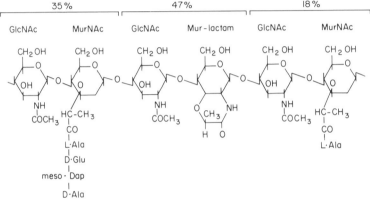

Fig. 1.3   Chemical structures of (a) Dipicolinic acid (DPA), (b) Diaminopimelic acid (Dap).

Fig. 1.4   Chemical structure of spore peptidoglycan.

Warth (1978) has pointed out that the core, in terms of its macro-molecular constituents, is a relatively normal cell. It appears that most, if not all, spore enzymes are similar to the corresponding enzymes in vegetative cells. The lipid composition of spores and vegetative cells is likewise similar. The spore cores of *B. megaterium* (Setlow, 1975) and *Cl. bifermentens* (Setlow and Waites, 1976) contain a substantial amount of low molecular weight, basic proteins which are rapidly degraded during germination. The core is also the location of deoxyribonucleic acid (DNA) and ribonucleic acid (RNA) and these unique spore proteins appear to be associated with spore DNA (Setlow and Setlow, 1979).

In 1969, it was stated that there was then no good direct evidence to indicate the location of dipicolinic acid (DPA; Murrell, 1969). Since that time, several important investigations have been made. Scherrer and Gerhardt (1972) studied the location of calcium in *B. cereus* T and *B. megaterium* QM B1551 spores by electron probe X-ray micro-analysis, and found that calcium was distributed throughout the spore but was located mainly in the central region corresponding to the spore protoplast. On the assumption (see Murrell, 1969) that most of the

DPA is associated in a chelated form with calcium, this finding provides indirect evidence for DPA location in the core rather than in the cortex. Germaine and Murrell (1973) showed that DPA sensitizes spores to ultraviolet (UV) light (see Chapter 5) and increases the rate and extent of thymine photoproduct ("spore photoproduct") production from DNA. Since DNA is found in the spore protoplast, this finding suggests a proximity of DPA to DNA, so providing further indirect evidence for the presence of at least some of the DPA in the core. Ultraviolet radiation has also been used in a more direct context; Germaine and Murrell (1974) devised a method involving the mechanical breakage of UV-irradiated spores containing radioactive DPA and a subsequent determination of the distribution of "photochemically-bound" radio-activity among the major spore components. This provided evidence for a core location. Beta-attenuation analysis has also indicated that DPA is present in the spore protoplast and not the cortex (Leanz and Gilvarg, 1973). Finally, Johnstone *et al.* (1980) have used high resolution electron probe X-ray microanalysis to show that the core of *B. megaterium* spores contains most of the calcium, potassium, magnesium, manganese and phosphorus present in the spore. These authors point out that to preserve electrical neutrality a major portion of divalent metal ions must be associated with DPA, a strong chelating agent, which provides additional evidence for a location of DPA in the core.

These findings thus demonstrate conclusively that DPA is located primarily in the spore core. Additionally, they lend support to the expanded cortex theory of spore heat resistance, a salient feature of which is the low concentration of divalent metal ions in the cortex (see Chapter 2 for a full discussion).

B. Cortex

The cortex is a zone present between the spore core and the spore coats. A dense inner layer (primordial cell wall, cortical membrane, germ cell wall) develops into the cell wall of the emergent cell when the cortex lyses during germination and outgrowth (Section IV).

The cortex consists largely of peptidoglycan (mucopeptide, murein), which is similar to, but not identical with, that found in vegetative forms. In disrupted spores, the cortex and usually the germ cell wall are dissolved by lysozyme, and the repeating unit of peptidoglycan depicted in Fig. 1.4 has been obtained from the digestion products of several *Bacillus* species (Warth and Strominger, 1969, 1972; Rogers, 1977). An interesting feature of this structure is that some 45–60% of the muramic acid residues do not have either a peptide or an N-acetyl substituent but instead form an internal amide known as a muramic lactam. Whereas the vegetative cell walls of spore-formers differs from organism to organism, the structure of the cortex appears to be constant (Warth, 1978).

Removal of the spore coat layers allows spores to remain viable. Exposure of such forms to lysozyme results in the digestion of the cortex and germ cell, and if this is carried out in hypertonic solution containing Mg^{2+} and Ca^{2+} the core is liberated as a protoplast (Fitz-James, 1971).

In conditional spore cortex-less mutants of *B. sphaericus* deficient in *meso*-diaminopimelic acid (Dap; Fig. 1.3) synthesis, the muramic lactam (and hence cortex) content increases with an increase in the external concentration of Dap, and characteristic spore properties are associated with different spore properties, including octanol resistance (*ca.* 25% of maximum cortex content required) and heat resistance (*ca.* 90% of maximum cortex content required) (Imae and Strominger, 1976).

C. Membranes

During sporulation, two membranes (inner (IFSM) and outer (OFSM) forespore membranes) surround the forespore. In dormant *B. megaterium* spores, about 80% of spore phospholipid and 66% of spore lipid are present in the inner membrane (Ellar, 1978). The forespore membranes have opposite structural polarity to each other (Wilkinson *et al.*, 1975). Evidence has recently been presented which suggests that the outer spore membrane persists in the spore integuments (outer layers) of *B. megaterium* (Crafts-Lighty and Ellar, 1980).

D. Spore Coats

The spore coats comprise a major portion of the spore, occupying about 50% of the spore volume (Murrell, 1969). They consist mainly of protein (Hiragi, 1972), with smaller amounts of complex carbohydrates and lipid and possibly large amounts of phosphorus (Warth, 1978). Warth *et al.* (1963) demonstrated that in various *Bacillus* species the spore coat consisted of two layers, an outer coat and an underlying laminated inner coat. In *B. sphaericus*, the spore coats consist of an amorphous inner layer, a lamellar midlayer and a structured outer layer (Holt *et al.*, 1975).

Several studies have been made of the structure and mechanism of assembly of spore coats (Aronson and Fitz-James, 1968, 1971, 1975, 1976; Aronson, 1981). Extracted spores, i.e. spores in which the spore coats have been removed, retain their DPA and refractility and are equally resistant to heat and radiation, indicating that the coats have no role to play in these contexts (see Chapters 2, 4 and 5 for further information). Conversely, such spores may be more sensitive to lysozyme and to octanol (although in at least some organisms, the cortex may be implicated in resistance to octanol: see above and Chapter 6) implying a role as a type of permeability barrier, and may show differences in response to germinants (Warth, 1978). Aronson and Fitz-James (1971) described the removal of both spore coat layers by treatment of *B. cereus* T spores with dithiothreitol plus urea; such spores became sensitive to lysozyme. Mixture of these spores with an ammonium sulphate fraction of spore coat protein under defined conditions results in deposition of coat material on the stripped spores and a partial reimposition of resistance to lysozyme.

As pointed out later (Section IIIB) spore coat synthesis begins at about the time of forespore formation (Aronson and Fitz-James, 1976) but completion is a later event, occurring at the same time as the development of refractibility and octanol resistance, but before heat resistance. Vinter (1958) has shown that cystine is taken up from the medium and appears in a crude coat fraction; the coat fraction enriched for half-cystine is the most resistant to solubilization. This increase in cystine incorporation into the insoluble coat fraction occurs late in sporulation but in *B. cereus*, at least, it appears likely that the incorporation results primarily from disulphide interchange (see Aronson and Fitz-James, 1976 for a comprehensive account of this).

E. Exosporium

In *B. cereus*, the exosporium (an outer, membranous structure) comprises loosely fitting outer, intermediate and basal layers (Warth, 1978). In *B. cereus* T, the formation of the cortex, coats and exosporium occurs together (Ohye and Murrell, 1973), although classically cortex formation is associated with Stage IV and the completion of spore coat formation with Stage V (Ohye and Murrell, 1973; see Section IIIB).

The formation of exosporia in sporulating cells of *Cl. botulinum* is initiated laterally in the sporangia before the synthesis of the spore cortex (Stevenson and Vaughan, 1972).

A typical exosporium is present on spores of some *B. megaterium* strains but not others (Beaman *et al.*, 1972). Lund *et al.* (1978) have recently described the structure of the exosporium in a pigmented *Clostridium* and found that in negatively stained preparations it appeared as an open-ended sac surrounding the spore. This is similar to that described as "a flimsy integument draped around the rigid spore body" of *Cl. pasteurianum* (Mackey and Morris, 1972a), and to the exosporia of other *Clostridium* species (Hodgkiss *et al.*, 1967; Walker *et al.*, 1976).

From the rather limited information available as to the chemical composition of exosporia, it appears that the exosporium of *B. cereus* T contains protein as a major component, with significant amounts of glucose and lipid (Matz *et al.*, 1970).

III. *Sporulation*

It is impossible to review here all the studies that have been carried out on bacterial sporulation, and what follows should be considered as being in the nature of a summary. The interested reader is referred to the excellent reviews of Murrell (1961, 1967, 1969), Halvorson (1962), Sussman and Halvorson (1966), Kornberg *et al.* (1968), Hitchins and Slepecky (1969), Fitz-James and Young (1969), Mandelstam (1969, 1976), Hanson *et al.* (1970), Halvorson and Szulmajster (1973), Szulmajster (1973), Freese (1977), Piggot and Coote (1976), Ellar (1978) and Warth (1978). Additionally, the papers published in the American series, *Spores* I (Halvorson, 1957a), *Spores* II (Halvorson, 1961), *Spores* III (Campbell and Halvorson, 1965), *Spores* IV (Campbell, 1969), *Spores* V (Halvorson *et al.*, 1972), *Spores* VI (Gerhardt *et al.*, 1975) and *Spores* VII (Chambliss and Vary, 1978) should be consulted, as should those published in the British series, *Spore Research 1971* (Barker *et al.*, 1971), *Spore Research 1973* (Barker *et al.*, 1974) and *Spore Research 1976* (Barker *et al.*, 1977). These volumes provide important information on various aspects of germination and outgrowth as well as on sporulation.

A. Factors Affecting Spore Formation

Vegetative cells of various *Bacillus* species undergo sporulation when nutrients in a culture medium become exhausted (Grelet, 1957). However, vegetative growth of *Bacillus* and *Clostridium* species does not always lead to spore formation, for sporulation is greatly affected by the environment (Murrell, 1969) and provided that the culture medium is kept in the proper condition, vegetative cells can grow without sporulation (Halvorson, 1962). Sporulation normally occurs after the end of exponential growth of cells in an appropriate medium, and when cells are transferred from a rich to a poor medium (Freese, 1977). What has been termed "microcycle sporulation" has been shown to take place with outgrowing cells which, in a poor growth medium, do not undergo cell division but rather prespore septation (Mychajlonka and Slepecky, 1974).

Several factors influence spore formation:

(a) Temperature: in general, the optimum temperature for sporulation is equivalent to that for growth, but the range is narrower (Ordal, 1961). As shown in Chapter 2, the heat resistance of spores can change as the temperature of sporulation is varied.

(b) pH: in general, the optimum pH for sporulation is equivalent to that for growth, but the range is narrower, e.g. in *B. coagulans*, maximum sporulation occurred at pH 6·5, although the organism grew equally well over the pH range 5 to 7·5 (Ordal, 1961). Nakata (1963) observed little difference among growth curves of cultures of *B. cereus* T buffered at pH 6·4, 7·0 and 7·4, and reported that the sporulation process also was not significantly impaired within this pH range tested. In general terms, however, sporogenesis is more fastidious than vegetative growth with respect to pH (Foster, 1956; Murrell, 1961).

(c) Oxygen requirements: as cells sporulate, they have an increasing energy demand in order to sustain the endogenous changes leading to the formation of a spore (Halvorson, 1957b, 1962; Ordal, 1961). Oxygen inhibits the growth and sporulation of anaerobic spore formers (Vinter, 1969).

(d) Manganese: various authors have reported that manganese stimulates sporulation, e.g. in *B. cereus* (Ordal, 1961), *B. stearothermophilus* (Thompson and Thames, 1967), *B. megaterium* (Weinberg, 1964). Weinberg (1964) studied the manganese requirements for sporulation of a laboratory strain of *B. megaterium*, and found that considerably higher concentrations of manganese were required for spore formation than for normal vegetative growth; over the manganese range in the growth medium of $0·01 \times 10^{-6}M$ to $10 \times 10^{-6}M$, the numbers of viable spores increased from 10^2 to $6 \times 10^7/ml$.

(e) Carbon and nitrogenous compounds: the presence of certain carbon compounds may increase sporulation (Murrell, 1961). An interrelationship may occur between the induction of sporulation and spore yield and the level and nature of carbon and nitrogen sources (Vinter, 1969).

(f) Composition of sporulation media: a study with the more common mesophilic *Clostridium* species has demonstrated that a cooked meat medium based on Hartley's digest broth will support sporulation of more species than other media investigated (Roberts, 1967). Yao and Walker (1967) have described a liquid medium for the production of spores of *B. stearothermophilus* at 55°C. Several strains of *B. sphaericus* have been shown to grow and sporulate in a simple, defined medium containing sodium acetate as sole carbon source. Chemically defined medium have been designed for the growth and sporulation of *Cl. perfringens* (Ting and Fung, 1972) and *B. sphaericus* (White and Lotay, 1980).

The composition of the sporulation medium may influence the resistance of the spore crops to harmful agents, such as heat (Chapters 2 and 3) and radiation (Chapters 4 and 5).

B. Stages in the Sporulation Process

Sporulation is a multiphase process in which the stages occur in a fairly synchronous manner (Ellar and Lundgren, 1966). The process can be considered as involving, in essence, the production of a refractile cell, followed by synthesis of DPA (pyridine-2,6-dicarboxylic acid, Fig. 1.3; Powell, 1953) with the later development of heat-resistant cells (Halvorson, 1962). In *Cl. roseum*, the formation of DPA follows by several hours the appearance of refractile bodies (prespores), with mature (heat-resistant) spores being formed an hour or more after the maximum amount of DPA has been produced (Halvorson, 1957b). As discussed in Chapter 2, such studies led to the hypothesis that DPA was directly implicated in heat resistance, although despite much research, its actual role in the spore still remains unclear.

The version outlined above is, of course, a simplistic one and considerable research has been carried out to elucidate the cytological and other changes that take place during the formation of a spore from a vegetative cell. Table 1.1, based on the findings of Ryter (1965), Vinter (1967), Mandelstam (1969), Hitchins and Slepecky (1969) and Slepecky (1978), shows that there are seven stages (I–VII) in this process, as depicted diagrammatically in Fig. 1.5. Stage 0 represents the time at the end of logarithmic growth of the vegetative cell culture. Mutants of *B. subtilis* that do not produce both protease and antibiotic do not progress beyond Stage 0 (Waites *et al.*, 1970). Thymidine deprivation prevents sporulation events in thymine-requiring mutants of *B. subtilis*, and serine protease is also not produced, this enzyme being among the earliest events occurring in sporulation (Dancer and Mandelstam, 1975; see also Millet, 1970). There appears to be a link between the induction of sporulation and a specific stage in the DNA replication cycle (Keynan *et al.*, 1976); the amount and rate of sporulation in starting cultures depends on DNA replication and the

Table 1.1.   Summary of stages in the sporulation process[a]

Stage	Characteristics
0	Vegetative cell.
I	Pre-septation: DNA in axial filament form. Extracellular products (including amylase, proteases and antibiotics) appear.
II	Septation: separation of chromosomes resulting in asymmetric cell formation.
III	Engulfment of forespore: membrane of developing spore becomes completely detached from that of mother cell to give the spore protoplast. Appearance of characteristic enzymes.
IV	Cortex formation begins to be laid down between the two membranes of the protoplast. Refractility begins to develop, commencement of peptidoglycan synthesis (see text in present chapter and in Chapter 6).
V	Synthesis of spore coats. DPA deposition, uptake of Ca^{2+}. Development of resistance to organic solvents (octanol, chloroform).
VI	Spore maturation: coat material becomes more dense, increase in refractility, development of heat resistance.
VII	Lysis of the mother cell, and liberation of the mature spore.

[a] This should be read in conjunction with Fig 1.5. Additional information appears in the text.

successful termination of existing rounds of DNA replication is essential for sporulation to occur (Keynan *et al.*, 1976; Dunn *et al.*, 1978).

In Stage I, the pre-septation stage, the nuclear material in bacilli is present as an axial filament, although this is rarely observed in clostridia (Johnstone and Holland, 1977). Stage I terminates when a septum starts to form asymmetrically in the mother cell, resulting in the synthesis of the forespore membrane and the compartmentalization of DNA in Stage II. Transfer of *B. cereus* spores into fresh medium prior to the beginning of Stage III gives renewed growth, whereas cells that have attained Stage III continue spore development (Fitz-James and Young, 1969; Hanson *et al.*, 1970; Szulmajster, 1973). Sporulation in *B. megaterium* is not influenced by the composition of the medium after Stage II is reached and removal of all nutrients after Stage II does not influence the time taken for the completion of sporulation (Greene and Slepecky, 1972).

In Stage III, the forespore protoplast is engulfed, and poly-β-hydroxybutyric acid granules are often seen in the cytoplasm of vegetative cells at this point (Walker, 1970). The result of engulfment is the

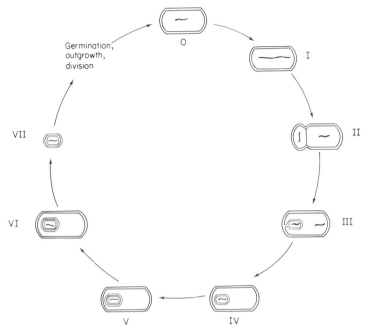

Fig. 1.5 Stages in the sporulation process (based on Halvorson and Szulmajster, 1973; Mandelstam, 1976).

0. Vegetative cell;
I. Axial filament formation (pre-septation);
II. Formation of septum;
III. Engulfment of forespore (encystment, envelopment);
IV. Cortex formation;
V. Coat formation;
VI. Maturation (development of refractility and heat resistance);
VII. Release of forespore.

existence of the forespore as a discrete cell, bounded by two membranes, within the mother cell; these membranes are the IFSM and OFSM, the former later becoming the cytoplasmic membrane of the germinating spore (Ellar, 1978).

Stage IV involves the synthesis of the cortex, which is needed for spore refractility and for DPA accumulation (Slepecky, 1978). During this phase, peptidoglycan is laid down between the IFSM and OFSM, possibly in two phases as found in *B. sphaericus* (Holt *et al.*, 1975): the first phase is the formation of vegetative cell-type polymer and the second the spore-specific peptidoglycan of the cortex. In conditional cortex-less mutants of this organism, the spore cortex cannot be detected unless the medium contains Dap, and the muramic lactam content reflects the real content of cortex in the spore (Imae *et al.*, 1976). Muramic lactam appears during cortex synthesis in sporulating cultures (Wickus *et al.*, 1972).

In Stage V, synthesis of the spore coats takes place; although deposition of at least part of the coat layers occurs during earlier stages (Aronson and Fitz-James, 1976) the bulk is synthesized in Stage V (Ellar, 1978). In addition, DPA accumulates and there is an uptake of calcium. Coat synthesis normally linked to Stage V appears to be associated with the final stages of coat assembly (Aronson and Fitz-James, 1976). Resistance to octanol appears in Stage V after refractility but before the development of heat resistance (Hanson *et al.*, 1970). In spore coat mutants of *B. cereus*, lysozyme sensitivity is related to defects in coat coverage rather than to the absence of specific coat layers (Aronson and Fitz-James, 1975).

Stage VI is termed spore maturation. Here, the coat material becomes more dense in appearance, spore refractility increases and heat resistance develops. Dehydration occurs, and resistance to UV radiation develops (Holt *et al.*, 1975).

Liberation of the spore, by lysis of the mother cell, takes place in Stage VII.

C. Initiation of and Commitment to Sporulation

Commitment may be defined as "the point of no return", i.e. the events associated with the developing system cannot be reversed. Initiation, on the other hand, is a different term, since it implies the commencement of the sporulation process but does not necessarily imply that the process is committed to forming a mature spore (Szulmajster, 1973).

Cooney and Freese (1976) showed that early sporulation events can be overcome and growth resumed if the sporulating culture is diluted into fresh medium, whereas later the cells are committed to continue the sporulation process. Greene and Slepecky (1972) point out that a point of commitment occurs during sporulation beyond which spore formation must take place. The specific point of commitment varies depending on the carbon source used (Cooney and Freese, 1976) or the organism being examined (Greene and Slepecky, 1972). Conversely, Sterlini and Mandelstam (1969) have opined that there is no single point of commitment for sporulation, but rather a separate point of commitment for each of the characters, so that after initiation of sporulation the cells become committed to one sporulation event after another.

Hutchinson and Hanson (1974) have postulated that a necessary and initial signal for the onset of sporulation is a decrease in the energy level of the cell. Initiation of sporulation is linked to the cell cycle and takes place only when DNA is being replicated (Mandelstam, 1969, 1976; Piggot and Coote, 1976; Dunn *et al.*, 1978). Decoyinine, a specific inhibitor of guanosine monophosphate (GMP) synthesis, induces sporulation of *B. subtilis* and of some mutants blocked at Stage 0 (i.e. grow vegetatively in complex or synthetic media) in the presence of C, N and phosphate sources. Decoyinine initiates the sporulation process when added to exponentially growing cultures, and is thus a useful experimental tool (Freese *et al.*, 1979).

D. Macromolecular Syntheses

Kornberg *et al.* (1968) have shown that protein synthesis takes place during sporulation, and have cited evidence that at least part of this synthesis is closely related to sporulation, because (i) protein synthesis during the stationary phase in a sporulating *B. subtilis* strain is 2–10 times more rapid than in an asporogenous mutant, (ii) some of the protein synthesized during sporulation is found in the mature spore, and (iii) addition of chloramphenicol prevents the further development of the forespore (see also Chapter 6). Singh *et al.* (1977) stated that enzymes which were absent from, or at low levels in, dormant spores were the same as those absent in early forespores, although the mother cell compartment possessed significant levels. Nevertheless, it was also pointed out that high levels of other proteins are accumulated by the forespore; these proteins could be synthesized in the mother cell and transported into the forespore, or alternatively they could be synthesized on forespore ribosomes using mRNA which in turn is synthesized either in the mother cell or in the forespore. Stable mRNA appears to be involved in the synthesis of spore coat proteins (including enterotoxin) in *Cl. perfringens* (Labbe and Duncan, 1977). Enzymes such as those of the TCA cycle appear early in sporulation whereas late enzymes include those involved in the synthesis of DPA and cortex peptidoglycan (see Szulmajster, 1973).

During the sporulation process in *Bacillus* and *Clostridium* species, maximum levels of DNA and net RNA synthesis occur at *ca.* 3 and 2 h, respectively, after inoculation of the sporulation medium; the rate of RNA synthesis subsequently decreases as sporulation progresses (Labbe and Duncan, 1976). Unlike *Bacillus* sp., however, net protein synthesis (sensitive to inhibition by chloramphenicol) continues during sporulation in *Cl. perfringens* (Labbe and Duncan, 1976). During sporulation, there is some degradation of pre-existing proteins, although this may be rather less in anaerobic than in aerobic spore-formers.

The peptidoglycan layer (primordial cell wall) closest to the inner forespore membrane has the chemical structure of vegetative peptidoglycan rather than that of spore peptidoglycan, and appears to develop during outgrowth into the cell wall of the new vegetative cell. The peptidoglycan in *B. sphaericus* vegetative cell walls is devoid of Dap, and is cross-linked between its L-lysine residues by D-alanyl-D-isoasparaginyl residues; lysine and aspartate are absent from the spore cortex peptidoglycan which contains *meso*-Dap and which, unlike vegetative cell peptidoglycan, is lysozyme-sensitive (there is also a more lysozyme-resistant spore peptidoglycan fraction, probably primordial cell wall, containing lysine and aspartate). During sporulation, enzymes functional in the synthesis of precursors of peptidoglycan are found, one period of synthesis (for vegetative peptidoglycan) starting at spore septum formation and coinciding with forespore engulfment; this period is associated with L-lysine ligase. A second period, involving Dap ligase activity, is associated with cortical peptidoglycan synthesis. Dap ligase is found in the sporangial, but not in the forespore, cytoplasm, whereas L-lysine ligase is present in both, but especially in the forespore cytoplasm (Linnett and Tipper, 1976; Tipper and Linnett, 1976). Correlation of these biochemical changes with morphological changes has been made (Holt *et al.*, 1975). Peptidoglycan synthesis is required early in sporulation (Dancer, 1979).

E. Use of Spore Mutants

Spore mutants have been extensively studied as an aid to a better understanding of sporulation and of the genetic aspects (Balasse, 1971; Piggot and Coote, 1976). Events leading to the formation of mature spores are controlled genetically.

Asporogenous mutants (Sp$^-$) are incapable of producing mature spores, and may be blocked at any stage in spore development. Oligosporogenous mutants (Osp) produce spores at a low frequency (of varying degrees) under normal sporulation conditions, and likewise may be blocked at any stage. Studies with Sp$^-$ mutants of *B. subtilis* have revealed that mutants that do not produce both antibiotic and protease do not proceed beyond Stage 0 (see Schaeffer, 1969), whereas the synthesis of alkaline phosphatase is linked to the transition from Stage II to III and glucose dehydrogenase is associated with the transition from Stage III to IV (Waites *et al.*, 1970). Sp$^-$ mutants of *B. subtilis* blocked at Stage 0 produce cells having the same volume as the developing sporangia or they divide to produce cells of half this volume (Dunn *et al.*, 1976). The majority of cells in an Osp culture reach a particular stage in the sporulation process and then stop, or alternatively go on to produce aberrant forms; if the cells are blocked at a certain stage, then the biochemical sequence is stopped accordingly (Coote, 1972).

Several conditional temperature-sensitive *spo* mutants have now been characterized (Piggot and Coote, 1976). For example, a conditional serine protease mutant of *B. subtilis* produces active serine protease and sporulates normally at 30°C, whereas at 47·5°C the protease is inactive and the cells do not progress beyond Stage 0 or I, with no septum formation (Santo *et al.*, 1972). Orrego *et al.* (1973) describe a thermosensitive strain of *B. subtilis* (ts-4) which is blocked at Stage 0 at the non-permissive temperature. Similarly, a conditional temperature-sensitive RNA polymerase mutant of *B. subtilis* has been investigated (Santo *et al.*, 1973) which has normal growth and sporulation at the permissive temperature (35°C) but not at the non-permissive temperature (47·5°C) where sporulation is inhibited at Stage II. Young (1976) has described two temperature-sensitive mutants of *B. subtilis*, one of which is blocked at Stage II and the other at Stage IV to V when held at the respective non-permissive temperature. Wild-type strains of *B. cereus* have been found that grow and sporulate at 37°C to give heat-resistant spores, whereas at 44°C there is only a very low yield of spores (Issaharry *et al.*, 1974).

Temperature-sensitive mutants affected in spore outgrowth have also been produced (Albertini *et al.*, 1979; see Section IVC).

IV. *Activation, Germination and Outgrowth*

Three sequential processes are involved in the transformation of a bacterial spore into a vegetative cell, viz. activation, germination and outgrowth (Halvorson and Szulmajster, 1973). Each event is considered below.

A. Activation

Activation is a treatment which results in a spore which is poised for germination but which still retains most spore properties (Keynan and Halvorson, 1965; Keynan and Evenchik, 1969). It is thus a process responsible for the breaking of dormancy in spores (Keynan *et al.*, 1965), but is reversible.

Methods of activating bacterial spores include the following:

(i) Heat. This is the method usually adopted (Evans and Curran, 1943; Curran and Evans, 1944, 1945) and is described in more detail in Chapter 2.

(ii) Calcium dipicolinate (Ca-DPA). Riemann and Ordal (1961) and Lee and Ordal (1963) reported that Ca-DPA caused germination of spores of many species of *Bacillus* and *Clostridium*. These Ca-DPA-activated spores represented an early phase of germination, and some of their properties were quite different from those of germinated or dormant spores.

In contrast to L-alanine-initiated germination (considered later), Ca-DPA induces non-nutrient-initiated germination (Dring and Gould, 1975). Ca-DPA induces germination of heat-activated spores of *Cl. pasteurianum* (Mackey and Morris, 1972b).

(iii) Ethyl alcohol. The activation of spores of *B. megaterium* QM B1551 with aqueous solutions of ethyl alcohol, the deactivation of activated spores with hot absolute alcohol, and the reactivation of deactivated spores with aqueous ethyl alcohol or with sublethal heat have been reported (Holmes and Levinson, 1967; Hyatt and Levinson, 1968).

(iv) pH effect. Keynan *et al.* (1964, 1965) found that the optimum pH for the heat activation of *B. cereus* T, as measured by the greatest percentage decrease in optical density, was between 2 and 3. Below pH 2 or above pH 8·5, activation was inhibited. In the presence of 0·5N hydrochloric acid at 25°C, the colony count of *B. stearothermophilus* NCIB 8919 increases to the value of the total (microscopic) count, this increase being accompanied by a progressive release of DPA (Brown *et al.*, 1968). Spores of *B. acidocaldarius* will germinate in acid without any necessity for prior activation (Handley, 1977).

(v) Dimethylformamide and dimethylsulphoxide. Both these substances induce rapid activation of *B. pantothenticus* spores (Widdowson, 1967).

(vi) Mercaptoethanol and thioglycollic acid. Both these substances produce activation of spores of *B. cereus* (Keynan *et al.*, 1964).

(vii) Water vapour. Hyatt *et al.* (1966) found that activation of spores resulted from exposure to water vapour.

B. Germination

Germination, an irreversible process, is a change of activated spores from a dormant to a metabolically active state within a matter of minutes (Hansen *et al.*, 1970). The germination of spores has been determined experimentally in various ways, e.g.:

(a) loss of heat resistance (E. O. Powell, 1957; J. F. Powell, 1957);
(b) loss of heat resistance accompanied by changes in staining properties, decrease of refractive index and decrease in dry weight (Powell and Hunter, 1955);
(c) decrease in optical density (Rode and Foster, 1961, 1962a,b);
(d) release of DPA (Powell and Strange, 1953).

Such primary changes in spores are usually described as germination, but might be better considered as being an "initiation of germination" or, simply, as "initiation" (Murrell, 1961). The first biochemical step in germination is termed a biological trigger reaction (Halvorson, 1959). Germination can be initiated by a variety of apparently unrelated chemical and physical stimuli (Rode and Foster, 1962a,b; Gould, 1969) such as nutrient initiators (L-alanine, purine ribosides, sugars, etc.), non-nutrient initiators (Ca-DPA), enzymatic initiators (lysozyme—see Chapter 10 on injured spores; *B. cereus* spore lytic enzyme) and physical initiators (hydrostatic pressure—see Chapter 8; other mechanical procedures) (Gould and Dring, 1972; see also Riemann, 1961).

It is impossible to describe here the wealth of information that has accumulated concerning the germination requirements of bacterial spores. Some of the earlier work will be considered briefly. Hills (1949a,b) showed that the germinative properties of yeast extract were due to specific substances such as L-alanine and adenosine. L-alanine is required for the germination of spores of various *Bacillus* sp. (Harrell and Halvorson, 1954; Wolf and Mahmoud, 1957; J. F. Powell, 1957; Hyatt and Levinson, 1961). Freshly-harvested spores of *B. cereus* were found by Powell and Hunter (1955) to require either inosine or a mixture of alanine, tyrosine and adenosine for optimum germination, whereas after a short heat treatment, adenosine alone caused rapid and complete germination. Levinson and Hyatt (1955) found that L-alanine and Mn^{2+} stimulated the germination of spores of *B. megaterium* QM B1551, and that D-alanine completely reversed L-alanine stimulation, but only partially reversed stimulation by Mn^{2+} or by heat. Subsequently (Hyatt and Levinson, 1961, 1964), it was shown that heating of these spores caused a decrease in the glucose or L-alanine concentration required for germination. Pre-heating of spores of *B. megaterium* strain Texas is essential for rapid germination by a mixture of L-alanine and inosine (Rode and Foster, 1961). The effect of this "heat activation" is considered in more detail later. 2-Phenylacetamide is a potent germinant for *B. macerans* spores (Sacks and Thompsom, 1971). Mutants of *B. megaterium* QM B1551 have the same germination requirements as the parent strain (Vary, 1972).

L-alanine binds rapidly to *B. subtilis* spores, the amount bound increasing as the external (free) concentration of L-alanine increases. Uptake proceeds to the same extent at $0°$ and $42°C$, so that an energy-dependent active transport process is not involved (Downing and Dawes, 1977).

L-alanine is essential for the germination of *Cl. bifermentans* spores (Gibbs, 1964), only this amino acid initiating germination when used alone (Waites and Wyatt, 1974). Inosine alone triggers the germination of *B. cereus* 569 spores (Weinberger *et al.*, 1980).

Thus, specific chemical agents trigger the rapid germination of spores (Stewart *et al.*, 1981). D-alanine will inhibit L-alanine-induced initiation of germination (Hallmann and Keynan, 1962). D-cysteine inhibits L-cysteine-initiated germination of *Cl. botulinum* spores (Rowley and Feeherry, 1970). The initiation of germination in *B. cereus* spores is inhibited by specific inhibitors of the electron transport chain, uncoupling agents and substances acting on oxidative phosphorylation (Dring and Gould, 1975). Ethyl picolinate does not affect the initiation of germination but inhibits the outgrowth of *B. cereus* T; when added to the medium before inoculation of the organism, it reduces markedly the uptake of ^{14}C-phenylalanine, ^{14}C-uracil and ^{3}H-thymidine, whereas pre-incubation for a short period prior to addition of ethyl picolinate enables the cell to assimilate these precursors and outgrow (Pandey and Gollakota, 1977, 1978).

During germination, the resting spore excretes solid material equivalent to *ca.* 30% of its dry weight into the medium, and also swells slightly (J. F. Powell, 1957). The main constituent of the excreted material is the calcium salt of DPA (Powell, 1953). Germinated spores and spores which have lost their DPA undergo characteristic changes in structure: electron micrographs show resting spores of *B. megaterium* to consist of undifferentiated oval bodies uniformly opaque to electrons, whereas germinated spores show two prominent, collapsed and folded areas which appear to be non-rigid (Rode *et al.*, 1962).

The sequence of events during spore germination has been studied by various authors, and is generally as follows (Levinson and Hyatt, 1966; Hashimoto *et al.*, 1969, 1972; Gould and Dring, 1972): loss of resistance to heat and to toxic chemicals, potassium release, calcium and DPA release, increase in stainability, phase-darkening, hexosamine release and loss of turbidity. This sequence may be modified by alteration of the porulation medium (Levinson and Hyatt, 1966).

An excellent portrayal of germination has been made by Vinter (1967) who stated that:

"Differentiation of the spore itself during germination is started by the alteration of peripheral spore layers connected with the loss of impermeability, hydration of the spore structures, activation of lytic enzymes, degradation of cortex (see also Hashimoto and Conti, 1971) and finally the release of mucopeptide [peptidoglycan] fragments and calcium dipicolinate. During this stage of differentiation, the spore also becomes sensitive to higher temperatures and higher radiation doses".

Thus, the marked changes in the envelope structures of spores accompany their germination and post-germinative development. During germination of the spores, part of the peptidoglycan structure is depolymerized, and Dap-containing peptides of the complex multi-layer envelope system are released from the cell into the medium, the source of these peptides being the spore coat and/or cortex. As Vinter (1965 a,b,c) points out, most of the spore envelopes thus lose their function of protection of the cell during germination and post-germinative development. There is a sequential alteration in the structure of the cortex and the outer and inner spore coats during the germination of *B. subtilis* spores (Santo and Doi, 1974).

During the first few minutes of germination, also, the synthesis of high-energy compounds takes place (e.g. aminoacyl-tRNA, ATP and NADH) as does rapid macromolecular breakdown, including that of significant amounts (about 20%) of dormant spore protein (Setlow and Waites, 1976) as a result of proteolysis by enzymes present in the dormant spore (for an excellent account, see Setlow, 1977). Dormant spores of *Bacillus* and *Clostridium* species contain virtually no ATP (Hausenbauer *et al.*, 1977).

An interesting discovery has recently been made by Dion *et al.* (1978), who showed that sporulating cultures (Stage IV) subjected to cold shock or to toluene and then transferred to a rich nutrient medium will allow intrasporangial germination and outgrowth. As pointed out by these authors, this implies that, at this stage (IV: spore cortex synthesis) of sporulation, the spores must possess those metabolic components that are required for vegetative growth.

Oxygen uptake becomes detectable during germination, and the sequence of germination changes has been followed closely by changes in the slopes of the curves concerned with respiration rate data (Levinson and Hyatt, 1956; Mandels *et al.*, 1956).

C. Outgrowth

Outgrowth is defined as the development of a vegetative cell from a

B

germinated spore, and occurs in a synchronous and orderly manner when germination takes place in a medium that can support vegetative growth (Hansen *et al.*, 1970; Keynan, 1973). Gould (1962) reported that, after germination, germinated spores became swollen and shed their coats to allow the young vegetative cells to emerge, elongate and divide. Spores of large-celled *Bacillus* species left behind ill-defined structures, whereas spores of small-celled *Bacillus* left behind well-defined coats after the new vegetative cells had emerged. Hitchins *et al.* (1963) recognized four stages in the post-germinative (outgrowth) processes: first, swelling, followed (in this order) by emergence from the spore coat, elongation of the emergent organism and division of the elongated organism. They further found three stages in the swelling of spores of *B. cereus* and *B. subtilis* during the germination and post-germination processes: (a) swelling during germination, which involved a rapid increase of about 20% in packed cell volume (pcv); (b) pre-emergence swelling of up to 100% increase in pcv prior to emergence from the spore coat; (c) elongation. Swelling, as a result of water intake, is the first morphological change to take place during outgrowth; if, however, conditions are unsatisfactory for outgrowth, the germinated spore does not swell and will remain as such for a few days until conditions become favourable (Keynan, 1973).

Santo and Doi (1974) studied the ultrastructural changes which take place during the germination and outgrowth of *B. subtilis* spores, and showed that there was a sequential alteration in the structure of the cortex and in the outer and inner spore coats. The cortex usually diminishes and disappears as outgrowth continues (Strange and Hunter, 1969). About 30 min after germination, just before DNA synthesis, prominent mesosomes have been observed (Santo and Doi, 1974) and when nuclear replication reaches full activity the mesosome develops into what has been described as "a single, complicated versatile system" (van Iterson and Aten, 1976).

Recently, Umeda and Amako (1980) have examined spore outgrowth and the development of flagella in *B. subtilis*, and have noted with spores incubated on solid or in liquid media that cell separation and the formation of flagella appear to be closely related events.

Much is now known about macromolecular syntheses that take place during the outgrowth process. RNA synthesis is the first after germination (Vinter, 1970) and this is closely followed in *Bacillus* species by the onset of protein synthesis, with DNA synthesis occurring some time later (Hansen *et al.*, 1970). During outgrowth, all types of RNA are snythesized. The antibiotic actinomycin D (see Chapter 6, Section IIIB) does not inhibit germination when added at zero time, but completely stops RNA and protein syntheses during outgrowth. This implies that dormant, and newly germinated, spores possess little or no functional mRNA (cf. Jeng and Doi, 1974); however, spores contain a DNA-dependent RNA polymerase and this is responsible for synthesizing the mRNAs necessary for transcription of early functions during outgrowth (Halvorson and Szulmajster, 1973). Spores can incorporate ^{14}C-thymidine into DNA soon after germination and incorporation continues at a slow rate up to 30 min after germination; this rate then increases rapidly. The early DNA synthesis depends upon simultaneous protein synthesis, is sensitive to chloramphenicol and puromycin, but not to actinomycin D and appears to be a repair type synthesis which is later followed by the onset of normal replication (Rana and Halvorson, 1972 a,b). RNA synthesis during outgrowth appears to occur in two phases, the first involving rRNA and tRNA synthesis and the second mRNA; the majority of 50S ribosomal proteins are synthesized very early during outgrowth, the rate varying with different proteins (Shaw and Armstrong, 1972). During outgrowth, cells can synthesize a large number of different proteins, and later the pattern of protein synthesis begins to resemble that of vegetative cells (Torriani and Levinthal, 1967). In temperature-sensitive mutants of *B. subtilis* affected in outgrowth, outgrowth proceeds normally at the permissive temperature (35°C) both in terms of cytological changes and of RNA, protein and DNA syntheses, whereas at the non-permissive temperature (47°C) RNA and protein syntheses are reduced and DNA snythesis cannot be detected (Albertini *et al.*, 1979).

Most of the studies on macromolecular syntheses during outgrowth have been made with aerobic spore-formers, in particular *B. subtilis* and *B. cereus*. Waites and Wyatt (1974) have investigated the outgrowth of *Cl. bifermentans*, which germinates rapidly and synchronously, and have found that increases in RNA and protein begin at 10–20 min and in DNA at about 30 min after inoculation of the medium with spores. These increases occur in a sequence that relates to morphological effects, the increase in DNA beginning simultaneously with elongation. DNA synthesis thus appears to take place at an earlier stage in this organism than in *Bacillus* spp. (Steinberg and Halvorson, 1968; Hansen *et al.*, 1970; Halvorson and Szulmajster, 1973).

Cell wall synthesis commences after RNA and protein, but before DNA, and coincides with swelling of the germinated spore (Halvorson and Szulmajster, 1973). Vinter (1965c, 1970) has shown that enzymes involved in cell wall synthesis are themselves formed within 20–40 min after the commencement of germination. Further information on this aspect is provided in Chapter 6.

V. *References*

Albertini, A. M., Baldi, M. L., Ferrari, E., Isnenghi, E., Zambelli, M. T. and Galizzi, A. (1979). *Journal of General Microbiology* **110**, 351–363.

Aronson, A. I. (1981). *Journal of Bacteriology* **145**, 541–547.

Aronson, A. I. and Fitz-James, P. C. (1968). *Journal of Molecular Biology* **33**, 199–212.

Aronson, A. I. and Fitz-James, P. C. (1971). *Journal of Bacteriology* **108**, 571–578.

Aronson, A. I. and Fitz-James, P. C. (1975). *Journal of Bacteriology* **123**, 354–365.

Aronson, A. I. and Fitz-James, P. C. (1976). *Bacteriological Reviews* **40**, 360–402.

Attwell, R. W., Cross, T. and Gould, G. W. (1972). *Journal of General Microbiology* **73**, 471–481.

Balassa, G. (1971). *Current Topics in Microbiology and Immunology* **56**, 99–192.

Barker, A. N., Gould, G. W. and Wolf, J. (1971) (Eds). "Spore Research 1971". Academic Press, London and New York.

Barker, A. N., Gould, G. W. and Wolf, J. (1974) (Eds). "Spore Research 1973". Academic Press, London and New York.

Barker, A. N., Wolf, J., Ellar, D. J., Dring, G. J. and Gould, G. W. (1977) (Eds). "Spore Research 1976". Academic Press, London and New York.

Beaman, T. C., Pankratz, H. S. and Gerhardt, P. (1972). *Journal of Bacteriology* **109**, 1198–1209.

Brown, M. R. W., Brown, M. W. and Porter, G. S. (1968). *Journal of Pharmacy and Pharmacology* **20**, 80.

Campbell, L. L. (1969) (Ed.). "Spores IV". American Society for Microbiology, Washington D.C.

Campbell, L. L. and Halvorson, H. O. (1965) (Eds). "Spores III". American Society for Microbiology, Ann Arbor, Michigan, U.S.A.

Chambliss, G. and Vary, J. C. (1978) (Eds). "Spores VII". American Society for Microbiology, Washington, D.C.

Cooney, P. H. and Freese, E. (1976). *Journal of General Microbiology* **95**, 381–390.

Coote, J. G. (1972). *Journal of General Microbiology* **71**, 1–15.

Crafts-Lighty, A. and Ellar, D. J. (1980). *Journal of Applied Bacteriology* **48**, 135–145.

Cross, T., Walker, P. D. and Gould, G. W. (1968). *Nature, London* **220**, 352–354.

Curran, H. R. and Evans, F. R. (1944). *Journal of Bacteriology* **47**, 437.

Curran, H. R. and Evans, F. R. (1945). *Journal of Bacteriology* **49**, 335–346.

Dancer, B. N. (1979). *Journal of Bacteriology* **140**, 786–797.

Dancer, B. N. and Mandelstam, J. (1975). *Journal of Bacteriology* **121**, 411–415.

Dion, P., Kay, D. and Mandelstam, J. (1978). *Journal of General Microbiology* **107**, 203–210.

Downing, R. G. and Dawes, I. W. (1977). *In* "Spore Research 1976" (A. N. Barker, J. Wolf, D. J. Ellar, G. J. Dring and G. W. Gould, eds), pp. 711–719. Academic Press, London and New York.

Dring, G. J. and Gould, G. W. (1975). *In* "Spores VI" (P. Gerhardt, R. N. Costilow and H. L. Sadoff, eds), pp. 488–494. American Society for Microbiology, Washington D.C.

Dunn, G., Torgersen, D. M. and Mandelstam, J. (1976). *Journal of Bacteriology* **125**, 776–779.

Dunn, G., Jeffs, P., Mann, N. H., Torgersen, D. M. and Young, M. (1978). *Journal of General Microbiology* **108**, 189–195.

Ellar, D. J. (1978). *In* "Relations between Structure and Function in the Prokaryotic Cell" (R. Y. Stanier, H. J. Rogers and J. B. Ward, eds), pp. 295–325. 28th

Symposium of the Society for General Microbiology. Cambridge University Press, Cambridge.

Ellar, D. J. and Lundgren, D. G. (1966). *Journal of Bacteriology* **92**, 1748–1764.

Evans, F. R. and Curran, H. R. (1943). *Journal of Bacteriology* **46**, 513–523.

Fitz-James, P. C. (1971). *Journal of Bacteriology* **105**, 1119–1136.

Fitz-James, P. C. and Young, I. E. (1969). *In* "The Bacterial Spore" (G. W. Gould and A. Hurst, eds), pp. 39–72. Academic Press, London and New York.

Foster, J. W. (1956). *Quarterly Reviews of Biology* **31**, 102–118.

Freese, E. (1977). *In* "Spore Research 1976" (A. N. Barker, J. Wolf, D. J. Ellar, G. J. Dring and G. W. Gould, eds), pp. 1–32. Academic Press, London and New York.

Freese, E. B., Vasantha, N. and Freese, E. (1979). *Molecular and General Genetics* **170**, 67–74.

Gerhardt, P., Costilow, R. N. and Sadoff, H. L. (1975) (Eds). "Spores VI". American Society for Microbiology, Washington D.C., U.S.A.

Germaine, G. R. and Murrell, W. G. (1973). *Photochemistry and Photobiology* **17**, 145–154.

Germaine, G. R. and Murrell, W. G. (1974). *Journal of Bacteriology* **118**, 202–208.

Gibbs, P. A. (1964). *Journal of General Microbiology* **37**, 41–48.

Gould, G. W. (1962). *Journal of Applied Bacteriology* **5**, 35–41.

Gould, G. W. (1969). *In* "The Bacterial Spore" (G. W. Gould and A. Hurst, eds), pp. 397–444. Academic Press, London and New York.

Gould, G. W. and Dring, G. J. (1972). *In* "Spores V" (H. O. Halvorson, R. Hanson and L. L. Campbell, eds), pp. 401–408. American Society for Microbiology, Washington D.C.

Greene, R. A. and Slepecky, R. A. (1972). *Journal of Bacteriology* **111**, 557–565.

Grelet, N. (1957). *Journal of Applied Bacteriology* **20**, 315.

Halmann, M. and Keynan, A. (1962). *Journal of Bacteriology* **84**, 1187–1193.

Halvorson, H. O. (1957a) (Ed.). "Spores I". American Institute of Biological Sciences, Washington D.C.

Halvorson, H. O. (1957b). *Journal of Applied Bacteriology* **20**, 305–314.

Halvorson, H. O. (1959). *Bacteriological Reviews* **23**, 267–272.

Halvorson, H. O. (1961) (Ed.) "Spores II". Burgess Publishing Co., Minneapolis, U.S.A.

Halvorson, H. O. (1962). *In* "The Bacteria" Vol. 4 (I. C. Gunsalus and R. Y. Stanier, eds), pp. 223–264. Academic Press, London and New York.

Halvorson, H. O. and Szulmajster, J. (1973). *In* "Biochemistry of Bacterial Growth" (J. Mandelstam and K. McQuillen, eds), 2nd edn, pp. 494–516. Blackwell Scientific Publications, Oxford.

Halvorson, H. O., Hanson, R. and Campbell, L. L. (1972) (Eds). "Spores V". American Society for Microbiology, Washington D.C.

Handley, P. S. (1977). *In* "Spore Research 1976" (A. N. Barker, J. Wolf, D. J. Ellar, G. J. Dring and G. W. Gould, eds), pp. 735–751. Academic Press, London and New York.

Hansen, J. N., Spiegelman, G. and Halvorson, H. O. (1970). *Science, New York* **168**, 1291–1298.

Hanson, R. S., Peterson, J. A. and Youssen, A. A. (1970). *Annual Review of Microbiology* **24**, 53–90.

Hashimoto, T. and Conti, S. F. (1971). *Journal of Bacteriology* **105**, 361–368.

Hashimoto, T., Freiben, W. R. and Conti, S. F. (1969). *Journal of Bacteriology* **98**, 1011–1020.

Hashimoto, T., Frieben, W. R. and Conti, S. F. (1972). *In* "Spores V" (H. O. Halvorson, R. Hanson and L. L. Campbell, eds), pp. 409–415. American Society for Microbiology, Washington D.C.

Hausenbauer, J. M., Waites, W. M. and Setlow, P. (1977). *Journal of Bacteriology* **129**, 1148–1150.

Harrell, W. K. and Halvorson, H. O. (1954). *Bacteriological Proceedings*, p. 30.

Hills, G. M. (1949a). *Biochemical Journal* **45**, 353–362.

Hills, G. M. (1949b). *Biochemical Journal* **45**, 363–370.

Hiragi, Y. (1972). *Journal of General Microbiology* **72**, 87–99.

Hitchins, A. D. and Slepecky, R. A. (1969). *Nature, London* **223**, 804–807.

Hitchins, A. D., Gould, G. W. and Hurst, A. (1963). *Journal of General Microbiology* **30**, 445–463.

Hobbs, B. and Gilbert, R. J. (1978). "Food Poisoning and Food Hygiene", 4th edn. Edward Arnold, London.

Hobbs, G. (1976). *Advances in Food Research* **22**, 135–185.

Hodgkiss, W., Ordal, Z. J. and Cann, D. C. (1967). *Journal of General Microbiology* **47**, 213–225.

Holmes, P. K. and Levinson, H. S. (1967). *Current Topics in Modern Biology* **1**, 256–258.

Holt, S. C., Gauthier, J. J. and Tipper, D. J. (1975). *Journal of Bacteriology* **122**, 1322–1338.

Howie, J. W. (1961). *Pharmaceutical Journal* **187**, 557–560.

Hutchinson, K. W. and Hanson, R. S. (1974). *Journal of Bacteriology* **119**, 70–75.

Hyatt, M. T. and Levinson, H. S. (1961). *Journal of Bacteriology* **81**, 204–211.

Hyatt, M. T. and Levinson, H. S. (1964). *Journal of Bacteriology* **88**, 1403–1415.

Hyatt, M. T. and Levinson, H. S. (1968). *Journal of Bacteriology* **95**, 2090–2101.

Hyatt, M. T., Holmes, P. K. and Levinson, H. S. (1966). *Biochemical and Biophysical Research Communications* **24**, 701–704.

Imae, Y. and Strominger, J. L. (1976). *Journal of Bacteriology* **126**, 907–913.

Imae, Y., Strominger, M. B. and Strominger, J. L. (1976). *Journal of Bacteriology* **127**, 1568–1570.

Issaharry, G., Hertman, I. and Evenchick, Z. (1974). *Journal of General Microbiology* **85**, 368–371.

Jeng, Y.-H. and Doi, R. H. (1974). *Journal of Bacteriology* **119**, 514–521.

Johnstone, K. and Holland, C. T. (1977). *Journal of General Microbiology* **100**, 217–220.

Johnstone, K., Ellar, D. J. and Appleton, T. C. (1980). *FEMS Microbiology Letters* **7**, 97–101.

Keynan, A. (1973). *In* "Microbial Differentiation" (J. M. Ashworth and J. E. Smith, eds), pp. 85–123. 23rd Symposium of the Society of General Microbiology. Cambridge University Press, Cambridge.

Keynan, A. and Evenchik, E. (1969). *In* "The Bacterial Spore" (G. W. Gould and A. Hurst, eds), pp. 359–396. Academic Press, London and New York.

Keynan, A. and Halvorson, H. (1965). *In* "Spores III" (L. L. Campbell and H. O. Halvorson, eds), pp. 174–179. American Society for Microbiology, Washington D. C.

Keynan, A., Evenchik, Z., Halvorson, H. O. and Hastings, J. W. (1964). *Journal of Bacteriology* **88**, 313–318.

Keynan, A., Issaharry-Brand, G. and Evenchik, Z. (1965). *In* "Spores III" (L. L.

Campbell and H. O. Halvorson, eds), pp. 180–187. American Society for Microbiology, Washington D. C.

Keynan, A., Berns, A. A., Dunn, G., Young, M. and Mandelstam, J. (1976). *Journal of Bacteriology* **128**, 8–14.

Korch, C. T. and Doi, R. H. (1971). *Journal of Bacteriology* **105**, 1110–1118.

Kornberg, A., Spudich, J. A., Nelson, D. L. and Deutscher, M. P. (1968). *Annual Review of Biochemistry* **37**, 51–78.

Labbe, R. G. and Duncan, C. L. (1976). *Journal of Bacteriology* **125**, 444–452.

Labbe, R. G. and Duncan, C. L. (1977). *Journal of Bacteriology* **129**, 843–849.

Leanz, G. and Gilvarg, C. (1973). *Journal of Bacteriology* **114**, 455–456.

Lee, W. H. and Ordal, Z. J. (1963). *Journal of Bacteriology* **85**, 207–217.

Levinson, H. S. and Hyatt, M. T. (1955). *Journal of Bacteriology* **70**, 368–374.

Levinson, H. S. and Hyatt, M. T. (1956). *Journal of Bacteriology* **72**, 176–183.

Levinson, H. S. and Hyatt, M. T. (1966). *Journal of Bacteriology* **91**, 1811–1818.

Levinson, H. S., Feeherry, F. E. and Mandels, G. R. (1978). *In* "Spores VII" (G. Chambliss and J. C. Vary, eds), pp. 3–15. American Society for Microbiology, Washington D.C.

Linnett, P. E. and Tipper, D. J. (1976). *Journal of Bacteriology* **125**, 565–574.

Lund, B. M., Gee, J. M., King, N. R., Horne, R. W. and Harnden, J. M. (1978). *Journal of General Microbiology* **105**, 165–174.

Mackey, B. M. and Morris, J. G. (1972a). *Journal of General Microbiology* **73**, 315–324.

Mackey, B. M. and Morris, J. G. (1972b). *Journal of General Microbiology* **73**, 325–338.

Mandels, G. R., Levinson, H. S. and Hyatt, M. T. (1956). *Journal of General Physiology* **39**, 301–309.

Mandelstam, J. (1969). *In* "Microbial Growth" (P. M. Meadow and S. J. Pirt, eds), pp. 377–402. 19th Symposium of the Society for General Microbiology. Cambridge University Press, Cambridge.

Mandelstam, J. (1976). *Proceedings of the Royal Society of London* **B 193**, 89–106.

Matz, L. L., Beaman, T. E. and Gerhardt, P. (1970). *Journal of Bacteriology* **101**, 196–201.

Millet, J. (1970). *Journal of Applied Bacteriology* **33**, 207–219.

Murrell, W. G. (1961). *Symposium of the Society for General Microbiology* **11**, 100–150.

Murrell, W. G. (1967). *Advances in Microbial Physiology* **1**, 133–251.

Murrell, W. G. (1969). *In* "The Bacterial Spore" (G. W. Gould and A. Hurst, eds), pp. 215–273. Academic Press, London and New York.

Mychajlonka, M. and Slepecky, R. A. (1974). *Journal of Bacteriology* **120**, 1331–1338.

Nakata, H. M. (1963). *Journal of Bacteriology* **86**, 577–581.

Ohye, D. F. and Murrell, W. G. (1973). *Journal of General Microbiology* **115**, 1179–1190.

Ordal, Z. J. (1961). *In* "Spores II" (H. O. Halvorson, ed.). Burgess Publishing Co., Ann Arbor, Minneapolis, U.S.A.

Orrego, C., Kerjan, P., de Nadra, M.C.M. and Szulmajster, J. (1973). *Journal of Bacteriology* **116**, 636–647.

Pandey, N. K. and Gollakota, K. G. (1977). *Applied and Environmental Microbiology* **33**, 1105–1111.

Pandey, N. K. and Gollakota, K. G. (1978). *Journal of Applied Bacteriology* **45**, 365–372.

Piggot, P. J. and Coote, J. G. (1976). *Bacteriological Reviews* **40**, 908–962.

Powell, E. O. (1957). *Journal of Applied Bacteriology* **20**, 342–348.

Powell, J. F. (1953). *Biochemical Journal* **54**, 210–211.
Powell, J. F. (1957). *Journal of Applied Bacteriology* **20**, 349–358.
Powell, J. F. and Hunter, J. R. (1955). *Journal of General Microbiology* **13**, 59–67.
Powell, J. F. and Strange, R. E. (1953). *Biochemical Journal* **54**, 205–209.
Rana, R. S. and Halvorson, H. O. (1972a). *Journal of Bacteriology* **109**, 599–605.
Rana, R. S. and Halvorson, H. O. (1972b). *Journal of Bacteriology* **109**, 606–615.
Riemann, H. (1961). *In* "Spores II" (H. O. Halvorson, ed.), pp. 24–48. Burgess Publishing Company, Minneapolis.
Riemann, H. and Ordal, Z. J. (1961). *Science, New York* **133**, 1703–1704.
Roberts, T. A. (1967). *Journal of Applied Bacteriology* **30**, 430–443.
Roberts, T. A. and Derrick, C. M. (1978). *Journal of Food Technology* **13**, 349–353.
Roberts, T. A. and Gibson, A. M. (1979). *Journal of Food Technology* **14**, 211–226.
Robinow, C. F. (1960). *In* "The Bacteria", Vol. 1 (I. C. Gunsalus and R. Y. Stanier, eds), pp. 207–248. Academic Press, London and New York.
Rode, L. J. and Foster, J. W. (1961). *Zeitschrift für Allgemeine Mikrobiologie* **1**, 307–322.
Rode, L. J. and Foster, J. W. (1962a). *Archiv für Mikrobiologie* **43**, 183–200.
Rode, L. J. and Foster, J. W. (1962b). *Archiv für Mikrobiologie* **43**, 201–212.
Rode, L. J., Lewis, C. W. and Foster, J. W. (1962). *Journal of Cell Biology* **13**, 423–435.
Rogers, H. J. (1977). *In* "Spore Research 1976" (A. N. Barker, J. Wolf, D. J. Ellar, G. J. Dring and G. W. Gould, eds), pp. 33–54. Academic Press, London and New York.
Rowley, D. B. and Feeherry, F. (1970). *Journal of Bacteriology* **104**, 1151–1157.
Ryter, A. (1965). *Annales de l'Institut Pasteur* (Paris) **108**, 40–60.
Sacks, L. E. and Thompson, P. A. (1971). *Journal of Bacteriology* **105**, 739–746.
Santo, L. Y. and Doi, R. H. (1974). *Journal of Bacteriology* **120**, 475–481.
Santo, L., Leighton, T. J. and Doi, R. H. (1972). *Journal of Bacteriology* **111**, 248–253.
Santo, L., Leighton, T. J. and Doi, R. H. (1973). *Journal of Bacteriology* **115**, 703–706.
Schaeffer, P. (1969). *Bacteriological Reviews* **33**, 48–71.
Scherrer, R. and Gerhardt, P. (1972). *Journal of Bacteriology* **112**, 559–568.
Setlow, P. (1975). *Journal of Biological Chemistry* **250**, 8168–8173.
Setlow, P. (1977). *In* "Spore Research 1976" (A. N. Barker, J. Wolf, D. J. Ellar, G. J. Dring and G. W. Gould, eds), pp. 661–682. Academic Press, London and New York.
Setlow, B. and Setlow, P. (1979). *Journal of Bacteriology* **139**, 486–494.
Setlow, P. and Waites, W. M. (1976). *Journal of Bacteriology* **127**, 1015–1017.
Shaw, M. V. and Armstrong, R. L. (1972). *Journal of Bacteriology* **109**, 276–284.
Singh, R. P., Setlow, B. and Setlow, P. (1977). *Journal of Bacteriology* **130**, 1130–1138.
Slepecky, R. (1978). *In* "Essays in Microbiology" (J. R. Norris and M. H. Richmond, eds), Chapter 14, pp. 1–31. John Wiley and Sons, Chichester.
Sofos, J. N. Busta, F. F. and Allen, C. E. (1979). *Journal of Food Protection* **42**, 739–770.
Steinberg, W. and Halvorson, H. O. (1968). *Journal of Bacteriology* **95**, 469–478.
Sterlini, J. M. and Mandelstam, J. (1969). *Biochemical Journal* **118**, 29–37.
Stevenson, K. E. and Vaughan, R. H. (1972). *Journal of Bacteriology* **112**, 618–621.
Stewart, G. S. A. B., Johnstone, K., Hazelberg, E. and Ellar, D. J. (1981). *Biochemical Journal* **198**, 101–106.
Strange, R. E. and Hunter, J. R. (1969). *In* "The Bacterial Spore" (G. W. Gould and A. Hurst, eds), pp. 445–483. Academic Press, London and New York.

Sussman, A. J. and Halvorson, H. O. (1966). "Spores: Their Dormancy and Germination". Harper and Row, London and New York.

Szulmajster, J. (1973). *In* "Microbial Differentiation" (J. M. Ashworth and J. E. Smith, eds), pp. 45–83. 23rd Symposium of the Society for General Microbiology, Cambridge University Press, Cambridge.

Thompson, P. J. and Thames, O. A. (1967). *Applied Microbiology* **15**, 975–979.

Ting, M. N. and Fung, D. Y. C. (1972). *Applied Microbiology* **24**, 755–759.

Tipper, D. J. and Gauthier, J. J. (1972). *In* "Spores V" (H. O. Halvorson, R. Hanson and L. L. Campbell, eds), pp. 3–12. American Society for Microbiology, Washington D.C.

Tipper, D. J. and Linnett, P. E. (1976). *Journal of Bacteriology* **126**, 213–221.

Torriani, A. and Levinthal, C. (1967). *Journal of Bacteriology* **94**, 176–183.

Umeda, A. and Amako, K. (1980). *Journal of General Microbiology* **118**, 215–221.

Van Iterson, W. and Aten, J. A. (1976). *Journal of Bacteriology* **26**, 384–399.

Vary, J. C. (1972). *Journal of Bacteriology* **112**, 640–642.

Vinter, V. (1958). *Folia Microbiologica* **4**, 216–221.

Vinter, V. (1965a). *Folia Microbiologica* **10**, 280–287.

Vinter, V. (1965b). *Folia Microbiologica* **10**, 288–298.

Vinter, V. (1965c). *In* "Spores III" (L. L. Campbell and H. O. Halvorson, eds), pp. 25–37. American Society for Microbiology, Washington D.C.

Vinter, V. (1967). *Folia Microbiologica* **9**, 238–248.

Vinter, V. (1969). *In* "The Bacterial Spore" (G. W. Gould and A. Hurst, eds), pp. 73–123. Academic Press, London and New York.

Vinter, V. (1970). *Journal of Applied Bacteriology* **33**, 50–59.

Waites, W. M. and Wyatt, L. R. (1974). *Journal of General Microbiology* **84**, 235–244.

Waites, W. M., Kay, D., Dawes, I. W., Wood, D. A., Warren, S. C. and Mandelstam, J. (1970). *Biochemical Journal* **118**, 667–676.

Walker, P. D. (1970). *Journal of Applied Bacteriology* **33**, 1–12.

Walker, P. D., Short, J. A., Roper, G. and Hodgkiss, W. (1976). *In* "Microbial Ultrastructure: The Use of the Electron Microscope" (R. Fuller and D. W. Lovelock, eds), pp. 117–146. Society for Applied Bacteriology Technical Series No. 11. Academic Press, London and New York.

Warth, A. D. (1978). *Advances in Microbial Physiology* **17**, 1–45.

Warth, A. D. and Strominger, J. L. (1969). *Proceedings of the National Academy of Sciences, U.S.A.* **64**, 528–535.

Warth, A. D. and Strominger, J. L. (1972). *Biochemistry* **11**, 1389–1395.

Warth, A. D., Ohye, D. F. and Murrell, W. G. (1963). *Journal of Cell Biology* **16**, 579–592.

Weinberg, E. D. (1964). *Applied Microbiology* **12**, 436–441.

Weinberger, S., Evenchik, Z. and Hertman, I. (1980). *Journal of General Microbiology* **118**, 223–228.

White, P. J. and Lotay, H. K. (1980). *Journal of General Microbiology* **118**, 13–19.

Wickus, G. G., Warth, A. D. and Strominger, J. L. (1972). *Journal of Bacteriology* **111**, 625–627.

Widdowson, J. P. (1967). *Nature, London* **214**, 812–813.

Wilkinson, B. J., Deans, J. A. and Ellar, D. J. (1975). *Biochemical Journal* **152**, 561–569.

Wolf, J. and Mahmoud, S. A. Z. (1957). *Journal of Applied Bacteriology* **20**, 124–136.

Yao, M. and Walker, H. W. (1967). *Applied Microbiology* **15**, 455.

Young, M. (1976). *Journal of Bacteriology* **126**, 928–936.

2

Inactivation of Bacterial Spores by Thermal Processes (Moist Heat)

I. *Introduction*

The thermal inactivation of bacterial spores has been studied for many years. Early investigations were made by Koch (1881), Bigelow and Esty (1920), Esty and Meyer (1922), Esty and Williams (1924), Dickinson *et al.* (1925), Magoon (1926) and Sommer (1930). Much of this work has been confirmed and extended, and in particular the studies of Bigelow and Esty (1922) and Esty and Meyer (1922) form the basis of the modern-day z-value approaching in the canning industry and in the sterilization of medical and pharmaceutical products.

The types of heating processes used in destroying bacteria involve moist heat (usually at temperatures above 100°C, although some spores are highly sensitive at temperatures below 100°C) and dry heat. These processes appear to kill bacteria and their spores by completely different mechanisms, and will thus be considered separately. Thermal processing is highly important in the sterilization of many foods and medical and pharmaceutical products (Vas, 1970; Halleck, 1977). Organisms such as *Clostridium perfringens* and *Bacillus cereus* may be implicated as food poisoning agents (Hobbs, 1973; Davies and Wilkinson, 1973) and heat-labile toxins of *Cl. botulinum* types A, B (Riemann, 1969a) and E. (Sakaguchi, 1969) are responsible for the highly lethal food poisoning, botulism. *Clostridium botulinum* type F has also caused a small number of outbreaks of botulism (Lynt *et al.*, 1979).

II. *Heat Activation*

Curran and Evans (1944, 1945) were the first to show that sublethal heat could induce dormant spores to germinate, and this phenomenon was referred to as heat activation. It has since been observed by several other workers, although not all spores are capable of being heat activated.

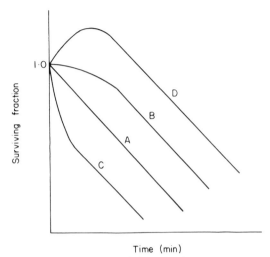

Time (min)

Fig. 2.1 Types of time-survivor curves.

Shull and Ernst (1962) found that the thermal death curves of *B. stearothermophilus* spores in saturated steam showed three phases: a sharp initial rise in viable count, due to heat activation of dormant spores, was followed by a slow rate of death which gradually increased leading to a final phase of logarithmic death at maximal rate (see Fig. 2.1, curve D). Other strains, after an initial activation, are inactivated in an exponential manner (Cook and Brown, 1965a).

Examples of the conditions (time at a particular temperature) required for the heat activation of spores of some bacilli are given in Table 2.1; this shows that the period of heating depends on the temperature and on the particular strain of organism used. With *Clostridium* spp., there is evidence of increased viable counts due to heat activation (see later in this section, also), for Roberts *et al.* (1966a) observed that *Cl. sordellii* and *Cl. aureofoetidum* spores give slightly higher counts after 30 min and 1 h, respectively, at 70°C than in unheated samples, as does *Cl. subterminale* after 1 h at 70°C or 30 min at 75°C; "food-poisoning" but not "classical" strains of *Cl. perfringens* require heat activation (Roberts, 1968).

Various authors have shown that a heat-shocking treatment alters the germination requirements of some bacterial spores. Hyatt and Levinson (1964) found that heat-shock at 60°C for 10 min increases the germination and decreases the concentration of certain hexose sugars required for germination of *B. megaterium* spores, strain QM B1551; 25 mM of D-glucose, D-mannose, 2-deoxy-D-glucose, D-glucosamine and N-acetyl-D-glucosamine supported appreciable germination (*ca.*

Table 2.1. Examples of heat activation of some bacterial spores[a]

Organism	Strain	Activation Conditions Temp. (°C)	Time (min)	Reference
B. stearothermophilus	NCA 1518	110	7–10	Finley and Fields (1962)
		110	7	Fields and Finley (1962, 1963)
	M	110	9	Fields and Finley (1962, 1963)
	NCIB 8919	115 121 100	15 1–2 13 h	Cook and Brown (1964)
	(in water) (in yeast suspension)	115 116	8 12	Cook and Gilbert (1965)
B. megaterium		60 70 80	50 17 8	Powell and Hunter (1955)
	QM B1551	50–60	10	Levinson and Hyatt (1964)
		65	10	Levinson and Hyatt (1960)
		60	60	Rode and Foster (1961, 1962a)
	Texas	60	60	Rode and Foster (1962b)
B. cereus	Laboratory	55–60	60	Powell and Hunter (1955)
	NCTC	70	30	Hitchins *et al.* (1963)
B. subtilis	M3	70	30	Hitchins *et al.* (1966)
B. pantothenticus	NCCT 8162	60	80	Widdowson (1967)
Various *Bacillus* spp.	—	70	30	Gould (1962)

[a] See also the more recent paper by Levinson and Fleeherry (1978).

25%) of unheated spores, whereas a 40–60% germination resulted with heat-shocked spores incubated in these compounds at a concentration of 2·5 mM. With *B. megaterium* Texas, pre-heating of the spores for 1 h at 60°C is essential for rapid germination by a mixture of L-alanine and

inosine (Rode and Foster, 1961). Freshly-harvested spores of a laboratory strain of *B. cereus* require either inosine or a mixture of alanine,
tyrosine and adenosine for optimal germination, whereas after a short
heat treatment, adenosine alone stimulates rapid and complete germination (Powell and Hunter, 1955).

It is also known that changes in the sporulation medium can change
the heat-activation requirements of *B. megaterium* spores for germination on D-glucose and L-alanine (Holmes *et al.*, 1965). After incubation
for 2 h in either substance, "basal spores" (i.e. those produced from the
basal medium) germinate to an extent dependent upon the temperature
of activation, whereas "glucose spores", produced from the basal
medium containing 0·05M glucose, are heat-activated only for germination on glucose, their germination on L-alanine being suppressed by
heat "activation".

Some spores are adversely affected by an initial heat-shocking process; Favero (1967) has shown that viable counts of spores of *B. subtilis*
var. *niger* (*B. globigii*) are consistently reduced 2–3 times after such a
treatment, and Finley and Fields (1962) observed heat-induced dormancy, again a reduction in viable counts, which they termed "deactivation", when spores of two strains of *B. stearothermophilus* were
exposed to sublethal temperature of 100°C or less. This is, however,
merely a transient phenomenon, for when the spores are subjected to a
more drastic heat treatment, at 105 or 115°C, true activation results.

Shull *et al.* (1963) derived equations to describe the interaction of
activation and inactivation on the thermal treatment of heat-resistant
dormant spores of *B. stearothermophilus*. Both heat activation and
inactivation obeyed first order kinetics, in combination and in that
order; as soon as a spore became activated, it was subject to the
inactivation law. The equations derived by Shull *et al.* (1963) were:

$$A_t = A_0 e^{-kt} + \frac{\alpha N_0}{k - \alpha} \cdot (e^{-\alpha t} - e^{-kt}) \tag{1}$$

$$L_t = N_t + A_t \tag{2}$$

in which k is the inactivation rate constant; L_0 and L_t the total numbers
of viable spores at times zero and t, respectively; A_0 and A_t the numbers
of activated spores at times zero and t; N_0 and N_t the numbers of spores
not activated at times zero and t (i.e. $N_0 + A_0 = L_0$); and α the activation rate constant.

The demonstration of heat activation may depend markedly on the
nature of the recovery medium used for enumerating viable organisms
(Cook and Gilbert, 1968a,b,c).

Recently, some important research has been carried out on the kinetics of heat activation of spores of *Cl. perfringens* (Levinson and Feeherry, 1978), heat activation being measured by an increase in the numbers of colony forming units (CFU) and by the germination rate (% decrease in optical density, OD, which does not therefore take into account outgrowth that is a necessary factor in determining CFU). Heat activation increases with the period, and with the temperature, of heating. Sporulation and spore heat resistance in *Cl. perfringens* can be affected by phage (Stewart and Johnson, 1977) and conceivably phage could also influence heat activation kinetics.

III. *Time–Survival Curves*

When bacterial spores are exposed to high temperatures, and the surviving fraction is plotted against time, various types of responses may be obtained (Fig. 2.1, curves A–D). Curve A follows an exponential law, so that a constant fraction of the spore population is dying off per unit time. This type of curve appears to be shown by *B. megaterium* spores in water at 100°C (Ley and Tallentire, 1964), although there may be a slight initial shoulder. However, deviations from the straight line response are constantly being observed, and destruction rate curves of either increasing death rate (Fig. 2.1, curve B) or of decreasing death rate (Fig. 2.1, curve C) have been obtained (Anand, 1961). In addition, in at least some species, there is an initial increase in colony-forming units (caused by heat activation: see the preceding section), followed by an exponential rate of death (Fig. 2.1, Curve D).

Dickinson *et al.* (1925), working with *Cl. botulinum* spores, stated that the majority of spores in a culture were destroyed relatively quickly by relatively low degrees of heat; however, a very small number of spores could be so highly resistant that they would survive prolonged exposure to degrees of heat which promptly destroyed the great majority of the spores. A minute, and fairly constant, fraction (1 in $10^7 - 10^8$) of *B. cereus* spores at 90°C may possess extreme heat resistance (Vas and Proszt, 1957). This fraction consists of cells which form part of the natural distribution of resistance and not of cells arising by mutation; cultures from such cells are not more heat resistant than the parent culture (Sommer, 1930; Vas and Proszt, 1957), in contrast to the process of selection described by Magoon (1926). The heat destruction curves described by Vas and Proszt (1957) are not linear, as a "tailing-off" portion occurs, which is responsible for the apparent increase in *D*-values (considered in Section IV, B). Similar resistant "tails" have been observed for *Cl. botulinum* type E (Roberts and Ingram, 1965), some other *Clostridium* spp. (Roberts *et al.*, 1966a), Putrefactive Anaerobe (PA) 3679 (Reynolds and Lichenstein, 1952), *B. subtilis* type C (Ridgeway, 1958), and *B. polymyxa* IA39 (Walker *et al.*, 1961), and for an unidentified *Bacillus* sp. probably *B. subtilis* (Tong *et al.*, 1962). The importance of considering the presence of injured cells (see Chapter 10) is discussed by Moats (1971).

Three phases of death have been observed with PA 3679 heated in phosphate buffer, pH 7, at 115°C: an initial phase, during which there is an accelerated death rate when about 50% or more of the spores become non-viable; an exponential death phase; and finally a decreasing death rate as the last few spores are inactivated (Reynolds and Lichenstein, 1952). Some strains of *B. subtilis* appear to exhibit a similar triphasic response (Ridgeway, 1958).

Exponential death of spores forms the basis of calculations used in the food industry and, despite the papers cited above, Stumbo (1973) believes that the available evidence supports a logarithmic order of death of heated spores (see also Charm, 1958), with non-logarithmic survivor curves the possible result of experimental artefacts. There is, however, a substantial body of evidence to indicate the non-logarithmic order of death of thermally treated spores, and Cerf (1977) has discussed experimental artefacts (such as heterogeneity of treatment, clumping, variations in the enumeration of survivors and composition of the recovery medium) and of ways of overcoming them. Possible interpretations of non-linear survival curves include a multisite hypothesis of thermal death of non-sporing organisms (Moats *et al.*, 1971) (and thus of spores, also?) and the heterogeneity of spore heat resistance, which envisages an initially homogeneously heat resistant, spore population followed by the development of heterogeneity, as a result of heat adaptation, during the heating process (Han, 1975; Han *et al.*, 1976). This theory does not however, distinguish between innate heterogeneity and acquired heat resistance (Sharpe and Bektash, 1977). Probit methods may be useful in interpreting thermal inactivation of spores (Fernelius *et al.*, 1958).

The Arrhenius rate theory may be employed in estimating an activation energy for the lethal reaction (Davies and Hobbs, 1980); this involves determining the temperature dependence of a specific death rate constant, k. If k is plotted against $1/T$ (where T is the absolute temperature, °K) a straight line is obtained of slope $\Delta E/R$, where ΔE is the activation energy (kJ mole^{-1}) of the lethal reaction and R is the gas constant (Prokop and Humphrey, 1970). For further information, the interested reader is referred to the papers by Richards (1965), Jones

(1968), Brannen (1968), Pflug (1973), Jonsson *et al.* (1977), and Reichart (1979).

However, the same strain can, under different conditions, give different time–survivor curves. This is clearly shown by Roberts and Ingram (1965) with *Cl. botulinum* type E, for when open tubes are used for heating the spores, curves with a resistant "tail" are produced, whereas this tail is eliminated when the spores are heated by total immersion of sealed ampoules. Walker and Matches (1966) found that the shape of the time–survivor curves for certain bacteria heated in buffer solutions at 100°C depends on the composition of the buffer and on its pH. The shape of time-survival curves may be influenced by the temperature of heating (Fox and Eder, 1969).

The temperature at which spore crops are produced may also influence the subsequent shape of the survival curve when the spores are exposed to high temperatures; *B. subtilis* strain L spores produced at 30°C show exponential death when heated at 98·5°C in M/40 phosphate buffer, whereas spores produced at 45°C show an initial shoulder, followed by exponential death, at 98·5°C (Lechowich and Ordal, 1962). A further factor which may influence the graphical response concerns the composition of the sporulation medium; with *B. megaterium* QM B1551, spores produced on calcium chloride-supplemented media exhibit an initial shoulder when heated in aqueous suspension at 90°C, whereas spores of this organism produced from other media give a decreasing death rate response (Levinson and Hyatt, 1964).

Pflug and Schmidt (1968) and Pflug and Holcombe (1977) have stated that there is a need for a realistic approach for reporting thermal destruction data, particularly in the development of nomenclature for semi-logarithmic (log survivor-time) curves which are not straight lines passing through N_0, i.e. the number of viable cells at zero time, when plotted on semi-logarithmic paper. For example, in Fig. 2.1, curve B, if the straight portion of the curve were extrapolated to cut the Y-axis, the *D*-value (see later), N_0 and the intercept, Y_0, would be given. Similarly, values could likewise be obtained for the other types of time–survivor curves. As pointed out by these authors, such additional data would be of much use. This is discussed further in Section IV, F (see also Fig. 2.3).

IV. *Mathematical Aspects*

Several terms are used in expressing the susceptibility or otherwise of bacterial spores to heat. These are considered below.

A. Thermal Death Time (TDT)

This is defined as the time, in minutes, required to kill all the spores in a given suspension at a given temperature. This time is, therefore highly dependent on the number of spores present in a suspension, and for this reason TDT is of rather doubtful value. Moreover, with some organisms, such as *Cl. perfringens* (*Cl. welchii*), there are widely differing opinions as to its TDT at 100°C: Rubbo and Gardner (1965) state that its TDT is 5 min, Sykes (1965) 5–10 min, Headlee (1931) 5 min or less for spores heated in 0·85% w/v sodium chloride, whereas Hobbs *et al.* (1953) and Barnes *et al.* (1963) give figures of *ca.* 5 h. Hobbs (1965) stated that, in general, *Cl. perfringens* was resistant to at least 90 min at 100°C. A possible reason for this discrepancy is the fact that only the food-poisoning strains are heat-resistant (Brooks *et al.*, 1957) and these seem to be in a minority (McKillop, 1959). One of the three heat-resistant strains isolated from foods by McKillop (1959) retained its resistance in culture, surviving boiling for 1 h, whereas cultures of the other two strains were killed after a 5 min exposure to 100°C.

The possible presence of injured spores, or of theoretically viable spores, of course alters the actual concept of TDT by establishing an arbitrarily chosen end-point on the time–survivor curve which represents spore destruction to a level which overcomes the possibility of any growth in, for example, food (Ball and Olsen, 1955). Plotting of survivor levels on a logarithmic basis against time on an arithmetic basis means that, theoretically, the number of survivors will never be zero. On the assumption that organisms below the minimum experimentally determined level are killed at the same rate, it is possible to extrapolate the death curve to determine the probability of survivors (see Section VIII, dealing with Biological Indicators, for explanation).

With this reservation in mind, additional examples of TDTs for various spores (based mainly on the data of Rubbo and Gardner, 1965; Kelsey, 1958; Sykes, 1966) are presented in Table 2.2.

B. *D*-Value

D-value (D_{10}-value, decimal reduction time, DRT) is the time, in minutes, required to bring about one decimal reduction in the viable spore population, i.e. to reduce the original number by 90% (or to 10%) at a given temperature. The term is also widely used in heat studies on non-sporing bacteria: see Hansen and Riemann (1963). Matsuyama *et al.* (1964) recommended the use of the term "D_{10}-value", and this was used in the previous review (Russell, 1971). It is more

Table 2.2. Thermal death times (TDT values) of some bacterial spores exposed to moist heat[a]

Organism	Temperature	TDT (min)	Reference[b]
B. subtilis	100	15–60	(1)
	100	Many hours	(2)
	115	<2–5	(1)
	115	40	(2)
B. anthracis	100	10	(3)
	100	2–15	(2)
	105	5–10	(2)
	121	3	(3)
B. stearothermophilus	100	300	(3)
	121	12	(1) (3)
	110	110	(4)
	121	11·8	(4)
B. megaterium	100	*ca.* 7	(5)
Cl. tetani	100	60	(3)
	100	90	(1)
	100	5–15	(2)
	121	5	(3)
Cl. perfringens	100	5	(3)
	100	5–10	(2)
	105	27	(1)
	105	5	(2)
Cl. botulinum	100	300–350	(2)
	100	300	(3)
	120	4–20	(2)
	121	12	(3)

[a] Note the wide differences in TDTs sometimes given by different authors for a particular organism. However, it must be remembered (a) that the figures quoted are obtained, not from one strain, but from several strains of a particular spore-former, (b) that differences in the initial numbers of spores, etc. will influence to a marked extent the TDT.

[b] Reference: (1) Kelsey (1958); (2) Sykes (1966); (3) Rubbo and Gardner (1965); (4) Whitbourne *et al.* (1977); (5) Ley and Tallentire (1964).

usual, however, to employ "*D*-value" as such or with a subscript to denote the temperature to which the *D*-value refers, e.g. $D_{90°C}$.

The *D*-value can be calculated in several ways. The usual method is to plot the number (or fraction) of surviving cells, on a logarithmic scale, against time, on an arithmetic scale, as shown in Fig. 2.1 in the previous section. When a straight line response (Fig. 2.1, curve A) is obtained, the *D*-value can be read quite easily from the graph. With an initial shoulder response (Fig. 2.1, curve B) or when a decreasing death rate curve (curve C) is produced, the *D*-value is obtained from the straight portion of the graph. This is satisfactory, provided that it is clearly stated and that due attention is given to the extent of the shoulder (curve B) or the extent of the decreasing death-rate (curve C), for example by citing the Y_0/N_0 value (see Part F of this section).

Alternatively, as described by Stumbo (1948, 1973), Esselen and Pflug (1956) and Hermier *et al.* (1975):

$$D\text{-value} = \frac{\text{duration of heat treatment (min)}}{\log_{10} \text{ initial no.} - \log_{10} \text{ final no. of spores}}$$

$$= \frac{U}{\log N_0 - \log N_u} \tag{3}$$

Another method of determining the *D*-value, when a straight-line response is obtained, is to calculate the velocity constant, k, which is the slope of the exponential curve; *D*-value is the reciprocal of k.

In some instances, notably in the food industry, *D*-values are calculated by using a replicate unit method. In this method, involving fractional-unit-negative (FN) data, several units are heated for a certain time, and the number spoiled and the number sterile are determined.

Details of the method of calculating *D*-values from FN data have been provided by Pflug and Schmidt (1968) and Pflug and Holcombe (1977) as follows.

If r represents the number of replicate units, p the number spoiled, q the number sterile (i.e. $r = p + q$), U the time in minutes, N_0 the initial number of viable spores per multiple replicate unit, N_u the number of viable spores per multiple replicate unit after time U, then:

$$N_u = \ln(r/q) = 2 \cdot 303 \log_{10} (r/q) \tag{4}$$

and

$$D\text{-value} = U/\log N_0 - \log N_u \text{ (as shown in equation (3)).}$$

A digital computer programme for calculating D, F, z and Q_{10} values has been described by Navani *et al.* (1970).

The *D*-value response of a spore to a heating process thus gives a useful indication of its susceptibility or resistance to that process. Consequently, a detailed list of *D*-values of both aerobic and anaerobic spores is given in Table 2.3. These values have either been quoted by

Table 2.3. *D*-values of some bacterial spores exposed to moist heat.

Organism and strain	Suspending medium	Temperature (°C)	D-value (min)	References
B. stearothermophilus				
NCIB 8919	Water	100	3000[a]	Briggs (1966)
	Water	115	ca. 25	Cook and Gilbert (1965)
	Water	115	24	Briggs (1966)
	Yeast	115	ca. 34	Cook and Gilbert (1965)
NCIB 8157	Water	121	4	Briggs (1966)
	Water	115	11	Ley and Tallentire (1964)
NCA 1518		115·6	7·03	Thorpe (1960)
	Skim milk	127	8 s	Busta (1967)
NCA 1518	Phosphate buffer	110	64·9 ⎫	
		115	14·7 ⎬	Wallace *et al.* (1978)
		121	5·1 ⎭	
NCIB 8224		115·6	5·24	Thorpe (1960)
—	Phosphate buffer pH 7	121·1	14·0	Murrell (1964)
ATCC 7953	Various concns of phosphate buffer $(0,0·31–9·3 \times 10^{-3}M)$	121	3·12, 5·37–4·9	Gauthier *et al.* (1978)
ATCC 7953	0·1 M phosphate buffer	120	4·1	Härnulv *et al.* (1977)
Strain?	Filter paper strips:			
	Freezer storage, 0 months ⎫		2·2	
	24 months ⎬ 121		1·5	Reich *et al.* (1979)
	Ambient storage, 24 months ⎭		0·99	
NCIB 8919 ⎫			3·5 ⎫	
NCIB 8157 ⎱	M/15 phosphate buffer,	121	2·48 ⎱	
NCIB 8923 ⎰	pH 7		2·84 ⎰	Navani *et al.* (1970)
NCIB 8924 ⎭			3·77 ⎭	
TH24	Water	120	16·7 ⎱	Davies *et al.* (1977)
	Milk	120	7·8 ⎰	
NCTC 10003	Acetate buffer, pH 5·0	110	50–92[b]	Friesen and Anderson (1974)
B. subtilis				
NCT 8236	Water	100	11·3	Briggs (1966)
	Water	105	2–2·5	Briggs (1966)
Bac 1–11	M/40 Phosphate buffer, pH 6·8	107·5	14 ⎫	
		110	6·9	
		112·5	4·3 ⎱	
		115	2·2	Put and Aalbersberg (1967)
		117·5	1·3 ⎰	
		121	0·57	
	Fried rice, pH 6·4	112·5	4·5	
		121	0·76 ⎭	
Bac 1–12	M/40 Phosphate buffer, pH 6·8	107·5	16·6 ⎫	
		110	9·1	
		112·5	4·9 ⎱	Put and Aalbersberg (1967)
		115	2·75	
		117·5	1·55 ⎰	
		121	0·71 ⎭	

Table 2.3. (*contd.*)

Organism and strain	Suspending medium	Tempera-ture (°C)	D-value (min)	References
	Evaporated milk, pH 6·4	112·5	6·7 ⎱	Put and Aalbersberg
5230(15u)		121	1·45 ⎰	(1967)
	M/16 Phosphate Buffer, pH 7	121·1	0·48	Pheil *et al.* (1967)
—	Phosphate Buffer, pH 7	121·1	0·08	Murrell (1964)
—		121	0·35	Pflug (1960)
NCIB 8054	Phosphate Buffer	85	71 ⎱	
		95	7·3 ⎬	Senhaji and Loncin
		105	0·58 ⎰	(1975)
189	?	110	8	Ordonez and Burgos (1976)
NCIB 8054	Solutions of different a_w values:			
	1·00		4·8 ⎱	
	0·93	95	9·1 ⎬	Härnulv and Snygg
	0·77		76 ⎰	(1972)
	0·48		4800 ⎰	
B. cereus	0·067 Phosphate Buffer (pH 7)	121 ⎱	0·03 (culture 1)	Bradshaw *et al.* (1975)
		⎬	2·37 (culture 2)	
B. megaterium Strain?	Aqueous		0·15	Gibriel and
	Orange juice, pH 3·7 ⎰	110	0·025	Abd-El Al (1973)
	Aqueous	120	0·02	
Lab. strain	Aqueous, produced from various media	95	0·86–1·39	Hodges and Brown (1974)
ATCC 8245	Water	100	50 s	Ley and Tallentire (1964)
NCTC 7581	Water	100	1·0 ⎱	Briggs (1966)
		115	0·025 ⎰	
—	Phosphate Buffer, pH 7	121·1	0·04	Murrell (1964)
B. coagulans Sp 33		106	6·3–7·3 ⎱	
		108	4·2–4·6 ⎬	Put and Wybinga
		110	2·2–2·5 ⎰	(1963)
		112	1·2–1·8 ⎰	
—	Phosphate Buffer, pH 7	121·1	3·0	Murrell (1964)
B. coagulans var. thermoacidurans				
ATCC 8038	M/40 Phosphate Buffer pH 7	89	32·05	
		93	18·8	El-Bisi and Ordal
		96	8·31	(1956a)
ATCC 8038	M/15 Phosphate Buffer pH 7	86	71·14	
		89	11·57	El-Bisi and Ordal
		93	6·06	(1956a)

Table 2.3. (contd.)

Organism and strain	Suspending medium	Tempera-ture (°C)	D-value (min)	References
B. cereus				
NCTC 5893	Phosphate Buffer, pH 7	100	5·5	Briggs (1966)
—		121·1	0·0065	Murrell (1964)
B. licheniformis				
NCTC 7589		100	13·5	Briggs (1966)
B. pantothenticus				
NCTC 8162		100	7·3	Briggs (1966)
Cl. sporogenes				
PA 3679	M/15 Phosphate Buffer pH 7	107 111 115	13·4–16·1 } 5·84–8·04 } 2·77–3·63 }	Reynolds and Lichenstein (1952)
	Phosphate Buffer, pH 7	90	>1000	Licciardello and Nickerson (1962, 1963)
	Phosphate Buffer, pH7	121	0·84	Pheil et al. (1967)
	Phosphate Buffer	121·1[a] 12·1[c]	0·48–1·4 0·18–0·35	Augustin and Pflug (1967)
	Phosphate Buffer	110 115 121	10·9 } 2·9 } 1·3 }	Wallace et al. (1978)
Lab. strain	Phosphate Buffer	115	2·7 (pH 4·8) } 3·2 (pH 5·4) } 5 (pH 6·5) }	Lowick and Anema (1972)
NCTC 532	Water	70 80 90 121[d]	1170 } 245·8 } 34·2 } 0·15 }	Roberts et al. (1966a)
BC₂	Various glucose concns. (% w/v): 0 (pH 6·6–7·3) } 0·2 (pH 6·4–7·3) } 0·2 (pH 7) } 0·5 (pH 5·9–6·6) } 0·5 (pH 7) } 1·0 (pH 5·7–5·8) } 1·0 (pH 7) }	110	<5 } 4 } 14 } 80 } 13 } <1? } 13 }	Anema and Geers (1973)
Cl. perfringens				
ATCC 3624		100	0·31–0·39 }	Weiss and Strong (1967a)
IU-1168		100	1·0–1·5 }	
T-65		100	5·2–6·6 }	
NCTC 8238		100	13·0–17·6 }	
Cl. botulinum				
Type E		77	1·8	Perkins (1965)

Table 2.3. (cont.)

Organism and strain	Suspending medium	Temperature (°C)	D-value (min)	References
62A	Buffer	112·8	1·23	
12885A	Buffer	112·8	1·09	
213B	Buffer	112·8	1·32	
32B	Buffer	112·8	0·15	Ito *et al.* (1967)
Saratago E	Buffer	77	1·95	
Minneapolis E	Buffer	77	1·55	
1304E	Buffer	77	1·23	
8E	Buffer	77	0·77	
Type A (A16037)	Tomato juice (pH 4·2)	115·6	0·39	
		110	1·55	Odlaug and Pflug (1977)
		104·4	6·00	
62A	Tomato juice	110	0·95	
	Buffer (pH 7)	110	2·8	Odlaug and Pflug
B15580	Tomato juice	110	0·74	(1977)
	Buffer (pH 7)	110	1·36	
Type F strains	Buffer (pH 7)	71	31·08–42·41	
		77	1·66–6·64	
		82	0·25–0·84	Lynt *et al.* (1979)
Type F (strain 202)	Crabmeat	77	9·5	
		82	1·16	
Cl. butyricum				
555	Phosphate Buffer, pH 6·5	85	23	
	Phosphate Buffer, pH 7	85	23	
	Milk	85	14	Cerf *et al.* (1967)
556	Phosphate Buffer, pH 6·5	85	18	
	Phosphate Buffer, pH 7	85	12	
	Milk	85	21	
Cl. tyrobutyricum				
500	Phosphate Buffer, pH 6·5	90	6·5	
	Phosphate Buffer, pH 7	90	13	
	Phosphate Buffer, pH 7·5	90	13	
	Milk	90	9	
	Phosphate Buffer, pH 7	121	0·012	
	Milk	121	0·006	
514	Phosphate Buffer, pH 6·5	90	15	
	Phosphate Buffer, pH 7	90	20·9	
	Phosphate Buffer, pH 7·5	90	18	
	Milk	90	14·1	Cerf *et al.* (1967)
	Phosphate Buffer, pH 7	121	0·012	
	Milk	121	0·008	
518	Phosphate Buffer, pH 6·5	90	11	
	Phosphate Buffer, pH 7	90	18	
	Phosphate Buffer, pH 7·5	90	21	
	Milk	90	10	
	Phosphate Buffer, pH 7	121	0·003	
	Milk	121	0·007	

Table 2.3. (*contd.*)

Organism and strain	Suspending medium	Tempera- ture (°C)	*D*-value (min)	References
Cl. aurofoetideum				
NCTC 505	Water	80	4205	Roberts *et al.*
		90	139·1	(1966a)
		95	27·2	
		121^d	0·0041	
Cl. histolyticum				
NCIB 503	Water	70	1097	Roberts *et al.*
		80	243·1	(1966a)
		85	40·5	
		90	11·5	
		121^d	0·011	

^{a} Sporulation medium was beef heart infusion. The *D*-value depended on the recovery medium used.
^{b} *D*-value depended on sporulation temperature.
^{c} Sporulation medium contained trypticase. The *D*-value depended on the recovery medium used.
^{d} Calculated from the other values.

the respective author(s) or have been calculated by the present writer from the results cited. Since the composition of the suspending medium during the heating process would be expected to influence the death rate of the spores (Section V, H), this aspect has been included in this table.

The following conclusions, with regard to *D*-values, may be obtained from Table 2.3:

(i) for a given spore, as would be expected, the *D*-value decreases as the temperature of heating increases;

(ii) among *Bacillus* spp., *B. stearothermophilus* is the most heat-resistant spore-forming organism whereas *B. megaterium* is highly sensitive to heat. *Bacillus subtilis* strains Bac 1–11 and Bac 1–12 possess a resistance greater than other members of this species;

(iii) among *Clostridium* spp., there is a considerable variation in sensitivity. *Clostridium botulinum* type E is far more sensitive to heat than are types A and B or C. *Clostridium putrefaciens* spores show an intermediate resistance (Roberts and Derrick, 1975). Marine strains of *Cl. botulinum* type C are more sensitive than terrestrial strains (Segner and Schmidt, 1971; Segner *et al.*, 1971a,b);

(iv) the suspending medium in which the cells are heated can influence to a considerable extent the *D*-values obtained. This is exemplified by *B. stearothermophilus* and *B. subtilis*. Furthermore, a difference of lethality of as much as three D-values occurs when *B. stearother-mophilus* is heated in saline at 121°C instead of water (Bühlmann *et al.*, 1973).

C. Inactivation Factor (IF)

This represents the degree of reduction in the number of viable spores, and is obtained by dividing the initial viable count (N_0) by the final viable count (N_u), i.e.:

$$IF = N_0/N_u \qquad (5)$$

An alternative method of calculating the IF is to use the D-value approach. In this, the number of log cycles is first obtained from the fraction: treatment dose/D-value. If this is put equal to x, then the IF is 10^x. This method is satisfactory providing that an exponential death curve is obtained, i.e. with the straight line going through the origin. In cases where there is an initial shoulder on the curve (Fig. 2.1, curve B) the D-value approach markedly overestimates the IF (Russell, 1965); the true IF may be less by a factor of about 10^2.

A knowledge of the IF of the process against an organism at a particular temperature, and of the number of organisms originally present, can be of importance in assessing the probability of survivors. This is of particular value when articles are being subjected to a sterilization process, since the probability of obtaining unsterile articles can be determined. An example of this has been provided by Rubbo and Gardner (1965) who state that the degree of sterility is the chance of failure in sterilization, and is expressed as the number of articles that can be processed before one unsterile article is likely to occur. It is calculated as follows:

Degree of sterility = IF/average number of organisms per article   (6)

For example, assuming that the IF for a heat process is 10^8, and that there are ten organisms per article initially, then the degree of sterility is $10^8/10 = 10^7$, i.e. there is a risk of one unsterile article occurring in every 10 000 000 processed, which is acceptable.

Examples of IF values of various spores have been given by Ley and Tallentire (1964) and Cook and Brown (1964). Thus, for *B. stearother-mophilus* after 30 min at 115°C, an IF of 10^3, based on the D-value approach, is to be found, whereas after 15 min at 121°C, an IF of *ca.* 10^8 is obtained, the latter value being based both on a D-value and on the more correct procedure. In contrast, with *B. megaterium*, there is an IF of *ca.* 10^7 after approximately 7 min at 100°C (Ley and Tallentire,

1964). These figures demonstrate the high thermoresistance and, in comparison, the high heat sensitivity, respectively, of these two spore-formers.

In the food industry, a 12 log reduction forms the basis of calculation for thermal processes.

D. z-Value

This is obtained from the slope of an exponential curve in which temperature (°C) on an arithmetic scale is plotted against TDT or *D*-value on a logarithmic scale (Fig. 2.2). It is thus defined as the number of degrees Celsius to bring about a ten-fold reduction in TDT or *D*-value. Unfortunately, several authors still quote *z*-value in °F and although in the examples given below for alternative methods of calculation, *z*-value is given in both notations, it will subsequently be referred to as °C only. Degrees F can be converted to °C by multiplying the former by 5/9. *z*-Values obtained from TDT curves are not always the same as those calculated from D curves (Lynt *et al.*, 1977).

Alternative methods of calculating the *z*-value are based on a knowledge of the Q_{10} (or θ^{10}) value, which is the temperature coefficient per ten-fold rise in temperature, and have been described by Wilkinson and Baker (1964), Pflug (1973) and Pflug and Holcombe (1977). For spores, these Q_{10}-values are between 8 and 10 at temperatures between 100 and 135°C (Rahn, 1945).

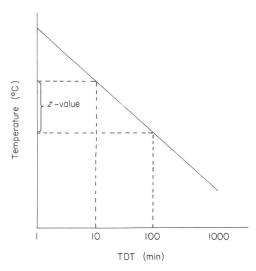

Fig. 2.2   Determination of *z*-value.

In Pflug and Schmidt's method:

$$Q_{10} = 10^{10/z} {}^\circ C$$

from which $\log Q_{10} = 10/z \log 10$, or $z(^\circ C) = 10/\log Q_{10}$ \hfill (7)

Similarly, $Q_{10} = 10^{18/z} {}^\circ F$

from which: \hfill $z(^\circ F) = 18/\log Q_{10}$ \hfill (8)

A list of the z-values for various bacterial spores is given in Table 2.4. These figures are based in part on those of Kelsey (1958), as presented by Russell (1971), and have been modernized to take into account developments in recent years. Generally, there is good agreement between different workers for a particular organism. Table 2.4 also demonstrates that, in at least one instance, the composition of the sporulation medium, and the composition of the recovery medium used for enumerating survivors, may influence the z-value obtained.

Another term which makes use of z is the sterilizing ratio, which is defined as the temperature difference between the thermal centre of the can and the heating (or cooling) medium divided by the slope (z) of the TDT curve. Sterilizing ratio has no dimension, and the method is claimed to be an improved one of process calculations (Steele and Board, 1979).

E. F and F_0-values

The F-value is defined as the time in minutes to destroy an organism in a specified medium at 121°C (250°F). Obviously, the F-value will vary with the organism, the number of spores present and the suspending medium. Many of the more resistant spore-formers have z-values of 10°C (18°F), and thus another symbol, F_0, is used in the canning industry when food processing times are being calculated (Frazier, 1958; Shapton *et al.*, 1970; Pflug, 1973; Stumbo, 1973; Stumbo *et al.*, 1975). F_0 is the F-value when z is 10°C (18°F), i.e. the F value of a process in terms of equivalent time (minutes) at 121°C, when z is 10°C. Another term that is sometimes employed is the F_c value, or "centre F value", which is the F-value of the process at the centre of the can. Integrated sterilizing value (I.S.) is the equivalence in minutes at 121°C (250°F) for the *entire* product volume (Houtzer and Hill, 1977; Yawger, 1978).

Calculations employing F_0 values are utilized in validating thermal sterilization processes. Although modern autoclaves rapidly attain the sterilizing temperature (e.g. 121°C), the temperature of the items being

Table 2.4. z-Values of some spores exposed to moist heat

Organism	z-value (°C)	References
"Thermophiles"	10	Bigelow and Esty (1920)[a] (see also Pflug, 1973)
B. stearothermophilus	7	Briggs (1966)
	8·3	Wang *et al.* (1964)
	8·5	Johnsson *et al.* (1977)
B. subtilis	13	Williams (1929)[a]
	5·6	Ordonez and Burgos (1976)
	8·2	Pflug (1960)
	9·4	Pheil *et al.* (1967)
	7·4	Briggs (1966)
	9·5	Senhaji and Loncin (1975)
Psychrotrophic *Bacillus* strains	(a) 6·8, 8·4, 6·9, 6·4, 7·3 (b) 7·1, 8·8, 7·3, 7·6	Davies (1975)
B. cereus	9·7, 9·9, 7·9	Briggs (1966)
B. licheniformis	6	Bradshaw *et al.* (1975) Briggs (1966)
B. megaterium	8·8	Briggs (1966)
B. pantothenticus	10·6	Briggs (1966)
Cl. tyrobutyricum	8·4–10	Cerf *et al.* (1967)
Cl. perfringens	10	Headlee (1931)[a]
"Food-poisoning" strains	8·8–17·2	Roberts (1968)
"Classical" strains	6–7·7	
Cl. botulinum		
Type E	8·3, 8·4, 7	Lynt *et al.* (1977)
Type A	9·43–9·93	Odlaug and Pflug (1977)
Cl. tetani	9	Esty and Meyer (1922)[a]
	12	Murray and Headlee (1931)[a]
Cl. aureofoetidum	6·8	Roberts *et al.* (1966a)
Cl. histolyticum	10	
Cl. sporogenes	13	
Cl. sporogenes PA 3679	10·6	Pheil *et al.* (1967)
	9·6–10·9[b]	Augustin and Pflug (1967)
	8·7–9·4[c]	
Cl. putrefaciens	4–6	Roberts and Derrick (1975)

[a] Value calculated by Kelsey (1958). (a), (b) Sporulation temperature 20°C and 2°C, respectively.

[b] Sporulation medium was beef heart infusion. The z-value depended on the recovery medium used.

[c] Sporulation medium contained trypticase. The z-value depended on the recovery medium used.

processed will usually show a lag in heat transfer; likewise, at the end of the sterilizing process, the temperature of the objects will gradually decrease. Allowances for the contribution to lethality by the heating-up and cooling-down processes are taken into account in F_0 calculations.

F_0 value can be calculated from the following equation:

$$F_0 = \Delta t \, \Sigma 10^{T-121/z} \tag{9}$$

in which Δt is the time intervals between F_0 measurements, T is the product temperature at time t, and z is 10°C. F_0 is thus an additive value (Akers *et al.*, 1979).

F-value is related to D-value by the equation:

$$F = D \times \log_{10} \text{ reduction in numbers of spores} \tag{10}$$

and it has been proposed that an F-value of at least 8 min is necessary for large volume parenterals (Korczynski *et al.*, 1974).

Thus, although the F-value is a relative value, it does provide a means of comparing steam sterilization processes (Whitbourne *et al.*, 1977). Modern autoclaves can issue printed information that a given load has received sufficient heat treatment to guarantee a given F_0 value (Bean, 1980).

A straight-line relationship generally holds when F-value is plotted against the square of the process time (th) divided by 100 (i.e. $th^2 10^{-2}$) (Shiga, 1976).

An F_0-value equivalent to 3 min at 121°C results in a probability of survival of *Cl. botulinum* spores of <1 in 10^{12}, and this—accepted in the canning industry—represents the so-called "botulinum cook" (Lovelock, 1980). This F_0 value is, in fact, derived from an F_0-value of 2·45 as the heat treatment necessary to reduce 10^{12} mesophilic *Cl. botulinum* spores to one at $a_w > 0.95$ and pH > 4·5, with a safety margin of 20% (thus giving a final value of 3·0) to allow for differences in the composition of the heating menstruum (Smelt and Mossel, 1982). F_0 values much less than 3·0 are required for many cured meats (Rieman, 1963). For recent information on F and F_0 values, the papers by Pflug and Christensen (1980), Smelt and Mossel (1982), Pflug *et al.* (1980) and Mossel (1982) should be consulted.

F. Y-intercept and Y_0/N_0 values

Exponential death curves of heated spores are the easiest to handle mathematically although, as pointed out in Section III, deviations from these occur frequently. With convex or concave type curves, extrapolation of the straight line portion of the curve to cut the Y-axis gives the

Y-intercept value (Y_0). If N_0 represents the initial number of cells, then:

(i) when $Y_0 = N_0$ a straight line response results;
(ii) when $Y_0 > N_0$, an initial shoulder is apparent (Fig. 2.3);
(iii) when $Y_0 < N_0$, a decreasing death rate is obtained (Fig. 2.3).

It must be pointed out that both Y_0 and N_0 are expressed as $\log_{10}$, giving rise to what has been termed the intercept ratio (IR: Pflug, 1973), where:

$$\text{IR} = \log Y_0/\log N_0 \qquad (11).$$

The IR value is thus useful in characterizing time survival curves, and involves the same type of principle as that used in calculating extrapolation numbers for convex survivor curves in irradiation (Chapter 4). IR, or Y_0/N_0 values, are also employed in studying time-survival curves of spores exposed to dry heat (Chapter 3).

V. *Factors Influencing the Heat Resistance of Spores*

Various factors are known to influence the thermal resistance of bacterial spores (Wilson, 1968). These can broadly be divided into pretreatment influences, the conditions prevailing during the actual treat-

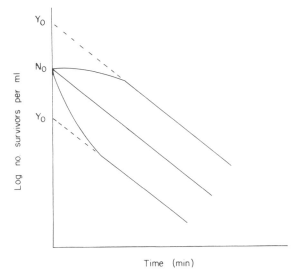

Fig. 2.3 Determination of Y_o/N_o values with different types of time-survivor curves.

ment, and post-treatment recovery. Of these, the chemical composition of the spores and the permeability of the spore wall at the heating temperature, together with recovery, have been suggested as being the most important (Put and Aalbersberg, 1967). It is unfortunate that, in many cases, authors have been content to report changes in heat sensitivity by altering, for example, the suspending medium without attempting to elucidate the reasons for the changes.

Any assessment of the thermal resistance of bacterial spores should involve a consideration of the factors discussed below.

A. Inoculum Size

Whilst the number of spores present would be expected to have an influence upon the time taken to sterilize a given suspension, there is evidence to suggest that the shape of time–survivor curves is unaffected by the initial spore population (Gilbert, 1966). The time necessary to sterilize a suspension of *B. subtilis* spores increases with increasing spore numbers, whereas with uniform numbers of spores, the time decreases as the temperature increases (Bigelow and Esty, 1920; Williams, 1929).

Thus, the size of the inoculum will influence the TDT value but not, assuming the same rate of death, the *D*-value. The higher the initial number of organisms, the greater the probability of isolating survivors after a given degree of heating. This is an important consideration in planning thermal sterilization processes and also in devising means of testing the efficiency of such processes (see Section VIII of this chapter).

B. Type of Organism

Spores of *Clostridium* species are relatively heat-sensitive (Roberts *et al.*, 1966a), although there is considerable variation between types and between strains, e.g. the heat resistance of strains of *Cl. botulinum* Type E spores is about one-thousandth that of spores of Types A, B and C (Ohye and Scott, 1957; Riemann, 1969b; Sakaguchi, 1969; Roberts and Gibson, 1979; see also Cockey and Tatro, 1974). Whereas spores of *Cl. botulinum* Types A and B have *D*-values at 112·8°C of 0·15–1·32 min, those of Type E have *D*-values at 77°C of 0·77 to 1·95 min (Ito *et al.*, 1967; see also Sakaguchi, 1969). Spores of non-proteolytic *Cl. botulinum* type F have a similar thermal resistance to type E spores (Lynt *et al.*, 1979).

Clostridium species are sometimes implicated in food poisoning, the food-poisoning strains of *Cl. perfringens* being heat-resistant (Brooks *et al.*, 1957; McKillop, 1959; Hobbs *et al.*, 1953; Hobbs, 1965; Barnes *et al.*, 1963; see also Willardsen *et al.*, 1978; Thompson *et al.*, 1979). A definite relationship between thermal resistance and toxigenicity (as measured by lecithinase activity) has been found in some strains of this organism (Weiss and Strong, 1967a) and in *Cl. botulinum* type A, the heat resistance of spore toxin parallels that of parent spores (Grecz and Lin, 1967). The destruction of *Cl. botulinum* by various means is well described by Hobbs (1976).

Some food-poisoning strains of *Cl. perfringens* recovered from samples pre-heated at 100°C are heat-resistant but sporulate poorly, whereas unheated samples or samples heated at 70°C sporulate well, but are poorly heat-resistant (Nishida *et al.*, 1969a, b; see also Hall *et al.*, 1963). Goodenough and Solberg (1972) have described a sonic treatment for producing *Cl. perfringens* spores of unaltered heat resistance.

Spores of *Baccilus* spp. also show considerable variation in their heat resistance. This is clearly demonstrated in Table 2.3. *Bacillus licheniformis* is the most common spore-former found in bulk milk, with the more heat-resistant *B. subtilis* the dominant spore-former in commercial sterilized milk (Ridgeway, 1958). Heat-resistant *B. subtilis* has been implicated as an aetiological agent in food poisoning traced to roast turkey (Long *et al.*, 1962). The heat resistance of spores of thermophilic strains of *Bacillus* is generally higher than that of mesophilic strains (Humbert *et al.*, 1972). The spores of psychrotrophic *Bacillus* spp. have a thermoresistance that depends on the temperature of sporulation (Davies, 1975; see part D of this Section). z-Values of approximately 10°C have been recorded for various psychrophilic strains of bacilli (Shehata and Collins, 1972). Spores of psychrotrophic and psychrophilic *Bacillus* spp. generally have low heat resistance (Michels and Visser, 1976; Michels, 1979).

Bacillus cereus spores have been associated with food-borne illness (Goepfert *et al.*, 1972). Whilst most strains are not particularly heat resistant, one strain has been described which possesses unusual thermal resistance (Bradshaw *et al.*, 1975).

C. Composition of the Sporulation Medium

The composium of the medium on which cells sporulate has a distinct influence on the subsequent heat resistance of bacterial spores. In particular, the pH, divalent cation content and phosphate concentration can affect the heat resistance of spores, although major differences in thermal resistance of various *Cl. sporogenes* strains are considered as

c

being genetically determined rather than reflecting the composition of different sporulation media (Duncan and Strong, 1968). Spores produced on different media may have different structures and show varying responses to heat or chemicals (Waites *et al.*, 1979; Bayliss *et al.*, 1981).

1. *Divalent metallic cations*

The divalent cation content of sporulation media is known to affect the heat resistance of bacterial spores (Sugiyama, 1951; Amaha and Ordal, 1957; Black *et al.*, 1960). The supplementation of growth media with calcium chloride allows the development of *B. megaterium* spores with increased heat resistance (Levinson and Hyatt, 1964). One possible reason for this, viz. the higher Ca:DPA molar ratio in such spores, is discussed in Section VIIA. Spore suspensions of *B. subtilis* having a high homogeneity with regard to heat resistance may be obtained by the addition of various divalent cations (expressed as parts/10^6: Ca 10–50, Mn 1–10 and Fe 1–5) to the sporulation medium (Slepecky and Foster, 1959).

In experiments with *B. megaterium*, Tallentire and Chiori (1963) used a sporulation medium containing Mg^{2+} and Fe^{2+} as sole divalent metallic cations; spores were also produced on this medium to which Mn^+ or Ca^{2+} or both had been added, or in which Mn^+ and/or Ca^{2+} had replaced the Fe^{2+}. It was found that spores produced in the medium containing Mg^{2+} and Fe^{2+} were the least resistant to heat; the addition of Ca^{2+} to the medium had no effect on the heat resistance of spores; the addition of Mn^{2+} or of ($Ca^{2+} + Mn^+$) to the sporulation medium produced spores of intermediate heat resistance. The most heat-resistant spores were produced when Fe^{2+} was replaced by ($Ca^{2+} + Mn^{2+}$).

Except at high concentrations (*ca.* 0·1%), the addition of manganese sulphate to media for the production of *B. stearothermophilus* spores has little effect on their subsequent heat resistance (Gilbert, 1960; Cook and Gilbert, 1968a; cf. Friesen and Anderson, 1974). This is in contrast to spores of *B. fastidiosus* (Aoki and Slepecky, 1973) and *B. megaterium* (Aoki and Slepecky, 1974), where Mn^{2+} at low concentrations in the sporulation medium is necessary for the development of heat-resistant spores.

There is obviously variation not only between spores of different species but also strain differences between spores of the same species.

Complex culture media show a considerable variation in their cation content (Bovallius and Zacharias, 1971), and consequently chemically defined media should be useful in preparing spores of controlled heat resistance. Chemically defined media have been employed for producing heat-resistant *B. stearothermophilus* spores (de Guzman *et al.*, 1972) and such spores possess a reproducible and stable thermal resistance (Friesen and Anderson, 1974). Spores of *B. megaterium* produced under different conditions of nutrient depletion in defined media vary in their heat resistance (Brown and Hodges, 1974).

2. *Phosphate concentration*

There is conflicting evidence about the effect of phosphate in the sporulation medium and the heat resistance of spores. Early work (Williams, 1929; Sommer, 1930) claimed that the cultivation of *B. subtilis* and *Cl. sporogenes* in media containing a suitable concentration of phosphate produced spores with an increased heat resistance. More recent studies have, however, shown that an increase in phosphate concentration in the sporulation medium gives rise to spores of *B. coagulans* var. *thermoacidurans* (El-Bisi and Ordal, 1956a, b; Amaha and Ordal, 1957) and of *B. megaterium* (Levinson and Hyatt, 1964) that possess reduced heat resistance.

3. *Other additives*

The dipicolinic acid (DPA) content of spores of *B. cereus* var. *terminalis* is drastically reduced by reducing the level of yeast extract in the sporulation medium, which in turn lowers their heat resistance. The addition of L- or DL-phenylalanine to the medium raises the DPA content of the spores and hence their heat resistance (Church and Halvorson, 1959). The inclusion in the sporulation medium of L-glutamate or L-proline gives spores of *B. megaterium* with reduced heat resistance (Levinson and Hyatt, 1964).

A sporulation medium with a low protein content was found by Put and Aalbersberg (1967) to give spores of *B. subtilis* having a high homogeneity with regard to heat resistance. Tsuji and Perkins (1962) showed that the maximal thermostability of *Cl. botulinum* spores was produced in a commercial mixture of dehydrated enzymatic hydrolysates of casein and animal tissues.

The heat resistance of *Cl. botulinum* spores grown in broth media supplemented with various fatty acids was studied by Sugiyama (1951), who found that the addition of acetate, propionate, butyrate, and, to some variable extent, caprylate, gave spores of slightly greater thermostability, whereas the addition of palmitate, stearate and oleate gave spores with a marked increase in heat resistance.

In contrast to the above findings, however, El-Bisi and Ordal (1956a) noted that the type of nutrient medium had no effect on the thermal death rate of spores of *B. coagulans* var. *thermoacidurans*.

The effect of glucose is considered in sub-section C.4 (pH), below.

4. *pH*

Comparatively few studies have been made on the effect of the pH of the sporulation medium on heat resistance. It seems that this pH plays no significant role (Williams, 1929; El-Bisi and Ordal, 1956a). However, the pH during growth of cells will fall, and consequently the final pH of the medium may bear little resemblance to the initial value. This is clearly shown in the studies of Anema and Geers (1973), who found that the presence of different glucose concentrations produced *Cl. sporogenes* spores of differing heat resistance. When, however, the pH value of the medium was kept constant at 7, the spores had a *D*-value that was independent of the glucose concentration.

D. **Temperature of Sporulation**

Williams (1929) observed that the higher the temperature at which *B. subtilis* spores were formed, the greater their heat resistance. A similar finding has been made for another *B. subtilis* strain (Lechowich and Ordal, 1962), *B. coagulans* (Lechowich and Ordal, 1962) and *B. stearothermophilus* (Gilbert, 1966; Cook and Gilbert, 1968a). In contrast, the heat resistance of spores of *Cl. perfringens* strains is not modified by the sporulation temperature (Rey *et al.*, 1975). As maximum growth temperature for *Bacillus* spp. increases, so does the spore death temperature (Warth, 1978a).

With an increase in sporulation temperature, there may be an increase in the cation/DPA ratio of the spore and this could be of some significance in heat resistance (discussed in Section VII; see also Table 2.6).

E. **Effect of Pre-irradiation**

It has been shown that spores of *Clostridium* and *Bacillus* spp. are generally more sensitive to heat following exposure of the spores to sublethal doses of ionizing radiation or of ultraviolet radiation. Although the exact reason for this has yet to be fully elucidated, there is some evidence that prior irradiation reduces the ability of spores to maintain the dehydrated state of the cortex. This is considered in more detail in Chapter 9 (Section IVB).

F. Development of Spores and Heat Resistance

During the process of spore development, there is an increase in the heat resistance of the organism. This is clearly shown from the studies of Vinter (1957, 1959, 1960), Hashimoto *et al.* (1960), Cash and Collee (1962), Ellar and Postgate (1974) and La Nauze *et al.* (1974). In contrast, during germination, heat resistance is lost (Wilkinson and Davies, 1973).

In *Cl. perfringens* type A, for example, refractile acid-fast forms precede by about 6 h the development of heat resistance (Cash and Collee, 1962). In synchronously sporulating cells of *Cl. roseum*, the formation of spores has been found to precede the synthesis of DPA and heat resistance (Halvorson, 1957).

The cystine-containing structure is formed in the prespore stage in *B. cereus* shortly before formation of the refractile spore. During the process of sporulation, the formation of refractile forespores is followed by Ca^{2+} uptake, which is closely connected with DPA synthesis, the development of heat resistance following some time later (Vinter 1959, 1960). In general (Murrell, 1967) the times for these events to take place from the end of exponential growth are 2, 2·5 and 2·5 h, and development of thermal resistance 3–4·5 h. The sequence of events, as described by Vinter (1960) is summarized in Fig. 2.4 and Table 2.5.

Decadent sporulation mutants, in which cells reach only a certain

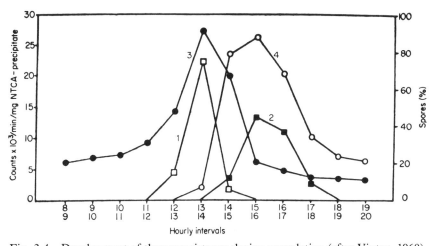

Fig. 2.4   Development of thermoresistance during sporulation (after Vinter, 1960). Curve 1: increase in percentage of refractile spores. Curve 2: increase in thermoresistant spores in chains. Curve 3: incorporation of ^{35}S-cysteine. Curve 4: incorporation of [45]Ca.

Table 2.5. Heat resistance and the sporulation process[a]

Stage of development	Refractility	Stainability	DPA (%)	Thermoresistance (%)
Filamentous vegetative cell	None	Full	0	0
Granular sporangium	None	Full	0	0
Forespore	None	Full	0	0
Early transitional spore	Rapidly increasing	Decreasing	0–40	0
Late transitional spore	High	Low	40–100	0–100
Mature spore	Full	None	100 (Maximum)	100 (Maximum)

[a] Based on the data of Hashimoto *et al.* (1960).

stage of development with decreasing frequencies, have been described (Balassa *et al.*, 1979a, b). In one of these mutants, DB16, of *B. subtilis* the majority of the cells reach only stage III or IV but rare cells reach octanol resistance and even chloroform or heat resistance (Balassa *et al.*, 1979b).

During germination, spores lose their heat resistance. A possible application of this is therefore to determine whether germination can be stimulated so that the germinated spores can be destroyed by pasteurization. Such a procedure has been shown to be of potential value in skim-milk (Martin and Blackwood, 1972), although the problem of "superdormant" spores (Gould *et al.*, 1968) remains.

G. Water Activity (a_w)

Water activity (a_w) may be defined as the equilibrium relative humidity (ERH) divided by 100. Thus, a_w values can vary from 0·00 to 1·00. Spores can remain viable for long periods in systems of low moisture contents (oils, fats and liquid paraffin: Bullock and Keepe, 1951) and dried spores stored at an a_w of 0·32 are more heat resistant than those stored over phosphorus pentoxide (Bullock and Lightbown, 1947). When powders containing *B. subtilis* spores are exposed to increasing humidities a definite sequence of events occurs: below a certain moisture content, the spores remain viable and heat resistant; over a certain range of moisture uptake, the spores retain their viability but not their heat resistance; and at a still higher moisture content both viability and heat resistance are lost (Bullock and Tallentire, 1952).

Studies on the relationship between a_w and thermoresistance have generally been examined from two aspects, viz. pre-heating adjustment of a_w values, and a_w adjustment during heating. Both aspects are considered below; see also Pace *et al.* (1972).

1. *Preheating adjustment of* a$_w$

Drying increases the heat resistance of thermosensitive spores in dilute buffer solution, the resistance of *Cl. botulinum* type A spores increasing about 30 000 times by equilibration at 25°C to an a_w of 0·8 (Murrell and Scott, 1957). The resistance of *B. megaterium* and *B. stearothermophilus* spores following the same treatment is increased by factors of approximately 3000 and 10, respectively (Murrell and Scott, 1957; Marshall *et al.*, 1963). In general terms, the greatest heat resistance occurs with spores equilibrated at an a_w of *ca.* 0·8–0·9, the maximum resistance being about 10–100 times that of very dry spores.

2. *Adjustment of* a$_w$ *during heating*

Clostridium botulinum type E spores are some 10^5 times as resistant at a_w 0·2–0·3 as compared to an a_w of 1·00, whereas *B. stearothermophilus* spores show only a 20-fold increase in heat resistance as the a_w decreases, reaching a maximum thermoresistance at an a_w of *ca.* 0·2 (Murrell and Scott, 1966). The maximum heat resistance of *B. subtilis* or *B. stearothermophilus* in water vapour or in glycerol solutions is likewise shown at low, but not zero, a_w values (Härnulv and Snygg, 1972; Härnulv *et al.*, 1977).

These findings are of particular interest since they indicate that bacterial spores are most heat-resistant when almost, but not completely, dry. Indeed, as a_w values approach zero, spores of different species become more thermolabile. Murrell and Scott (1966) postulate that water hydrates some component(s) of the spore to produce marked stabilization against the adverse changes caused by high temperatures and that it seems likely that protein or protein-containing complexes are involved in this stabilization. A similar conclusion may be reached by an examination of the findings of Kooiman and Jacobs (1977). Thus, changes can readily occur in the equilibrium water status of bacterial spores with consequent alterations in thermoresistance (Gould, 1977; Gould and Measures, 1977).

The water content of spores is, in fact, a most important aspect of the theories of their inactivation by moist heat (this chapter, Section VII) and by dry heat (Chapter 3, Section V.B).

H. Suspending Medium During Heat Treatment

The thermal death of bacterial spores is markedly dependent on the composition and pH of the suspending medium and also on the presence of any antibacterial agent during the heating process.

1. *Composition of suspending menstruum*

It has been repeatedly observed that the composition of a buffer used as suspending medium influences the thermal death rate of spores. Spores of *B. megaterium*, strain QM B1551, are more resistant when heated in phosphate buffer than in water or cacodylate (Levinson and Hyatt, 1960) whereas spores of *B. megaterium*, strain 1A–48, and of *B. polymyxa* strain 1A–39 are less resistant in phosphate buffer than in citrate, phthalate or ammonium buffers (Walker, 1964). *Bacillus stearothermophilus* and *Cl. sporogenes* spores are more resistant in phosphate buffer than in parenteral solutions (Pflug and Smith, 1977), and the addition of this buffer to a parenteral solution may produce changes in spore sensitivity to heat (Gauthier *et al.*, 1978). The concentration of phosphate buffer (Williams and Hennessee, 1956) and the type of phosphate buffer (Pflug and Smith, 1977) may be important factors. Thus, the heat resistance of *B. coagulans* spores is higher in M/40 than in M/15 phosphate buffer (Amaha and Ordal, 1957; Put and Wybinga, 1963). *Clostridium botulinum* spores are more resistant in phosphate buffer than in tomato juice (Odlang and Pflug, 1977) although this may reflect the difference in pH of the suspending fluid.

Apparent *D*-values obtained in phosphate buffer may, in fact, depend upon the subsequent procedure. With *Cl. perfringens* type A spores, for example, treatment with EDTA and recovery in plating medium containing lysozyme increases the *D*-values (Bradshaw *et al.*, 1977).

The presence of sodium chloride as suspending fluid may also cause changes in the thermal death rate of spores. Esty and Mayer (1922) found that certain aerobic spores heated in 6% w/v sodium chloride solutions showed no decrease in heat resistance, whereas when heated in 0·5–1% there was an enhanced resistance and in 8, 10 or 20% a decreased resistance. The thermal death of *B. anthracis* likewise decreases with increasing salt concentration (Murray, 1931), *Clostridium tetani* shows greatest heat resistance at 2% NaCl (Murray and

Headlee, 1931) and *Cl. perfringens* at 3% NaCl (Headlee, 1931). *Bacillus stearothermophilus* spores suspended in physiological (0·9% w/v) saline display a much higher heat resistance than those in water (Bühlmann *et al.*, 1973; compare the effect of high salt concentrations: Cook and Gilbert, 1968d). Roberts *et al.* (1966b), however, could find no effect of sodium chloride on the heat resistance of PA3679 spores but only investigated two concentrations, 3 and 6%, of salt.

The presence of yeast cells during the heat process increases the heat resistance of *B. stearothermophilus* spores (Cook and Gilbert, 1965) and yeast extract reduces thermally-induced damage in *Escherichia coli* (Russell and Harries, 1968). A possible reason for this is a reduction in the amount of leakage of intracellular material (Demain, 1966).

Put and Aalsberberg (1967) described the occurrence of *B. subtilis* strains Bac 1–11 (isolated from processed fried rice) and Bac 1–12 (isolated from processed evaporated milk) with high heat resistance. The *D*-value of spores of Bac 1–11 at 112·5°C in M/40 phosphate buffer, pH 6·8, was 4·2 min with a *z*-value of 18°C, and in fried rice, pH 6·4, was 4·5 min with *z* of 20°C. For Bac 1–12, the D_{10}-value at 112·5°C in the buffer was 5 min, with *z* of 18°C, and in evaporated milk, pH 6·4, was 6·7 min, with *z* of 23°C.

With *Cl. perfringens*, Canada *et al.* (1964) found that peptone water as heating medium confers slight protection on the spores. Considerably greater protection of these spores occurs in cooked meat broth than in water (Collee *et al.*, 1961).

Molin and Snygg (1967) studied the apparent heat resistance of spores of various *Bacillus* spp. and of *Cl. botulinum* type E in lipids, and compared this with the resistance of spores in phosphate buffer solution. It was found that the most pronounced increase occurs with *B. subtilis* and *Cl. botulinum*, that the increase varies with the type of lipid, and that a high water content of the lipids used as heating menstruum lowers the heat resistance. It is thus unlikely that the protection conferred by lipid can be explained solely in terms of a poor heat conductivity: see also Senheji and Loncin (1975) and Senhaji *et al.* (1976).

2. *pH of suspending medium*

There are conflicting reports on the effect of pH on thermal inactivation of bacterial spores. Bigelow and Esty (1920) found that as the pH increased, the time for complete destruction of a spore suspension at a given temperature decreased. Williams (1929), however, reported that over the pH range 4·4 to 7·6, *B. subtilis* spores were more sensitive at the lowest pH. *Clostridium tetani* spores are more thermosensitive at acid than at alkaline pH (Murray, 1931) whereas *Cl. perfringens* spores are claimed to be more tolerant of acid than of alkali, with a maximum resistance at pH 5 (Headlee, 1931). *Bacillus stearothermophilus* and other spores are more heat-sensitive at acid than alkaline pH values (Cook and Gilbert, 1968a; see also Gibriel and Abd-El Al, 1973). Increased acidity is accompanied by a decreased heat resistance of *Cl. sporogenes* spores (Cameron *et al.*, 1980).

A possible reason for the discrepancy is the use of different buffer systems by different authors, since the same spores can show maximum heat sensitivity at different pHs which depend on the buffer (Levinson and Hyatt, 1960). A point that is frequently overlooked, also, is the "carry-over" into the recovery medium of phosphate (Williams and Hennessee, 1956; Cook and Gilbert, 1968a).

Bacterial spores show a base exchange behaviour which will reduce, restore or enhance the heat resistance of mature spores (Alderton and Snell, 1963, 1969a, b, 1970). Gould (1978) has recently shown that sucrose will osmotically protect spores of *B. cereus* T from heat inactivation (80°C) at low pH values. The combined influence of pH and a_w on heat resistance is described by Smelt *et al.* (1977).

Clostridium botulinum 62A spores produce a toxin that shows maximal stability at pH 5 in beef broth at 80°C (Losikoff, 1978).

I. Recovery Conditions

Spores that are injured but not killed can pose a problem in estimating the efficacy of any sterilizing procedure. Such spores may be highly sensitive to the presence of inhibitory agents in the recovery media, or may become increasingly sensitive to their nutritional environment. Alternatively, spores may require the presence of non-nutrient germination stimulants before they can germinate and outgrow. Recent studies have indicated a requirement for the presence of sucrose (or similar substance) in the recovery media (Busta *et al.*, 1976, 1977).

Other factors that influence recovery and revival of heat-damaged spores include pH of the recovery medium and the temperature of incubation. These, together with those listed above, are considered more fully in Chapter 10, and will thus not be discussed further here.

VI. *Biochemical Changes in Heated Spores*

During spontaneous heat-activated germination, calcium dipicolinate accounts for about 50–60% of the exudate (J. F. Powell, 1957). When spores are lethally heated, also, intracellular constituents are released and there is a progressive loss of DPA and calcium from such spores (Rode and Foster, 1960; Hunnell and Ordal, 1961), the rate of release being temperature-dependent (Rode and Foster, 1960; Brown and Melling, 1973). Woese (1958, 1959) found that the ultraviolet absorption spectra of substance(s) released from autoclaved suspensions of spores of *B. megaterium*, *B. cereus* and *B. mesentericus* showed a peak at 270 nm and that the spectra were those of chelated DNA.

The total amount and rate of release of DPA is known to vary not only between species but also between strains of the same species, with the most resistant strains releasing the least (Walker and Matches, 1966; Rotman and Fields, 1969a, b; Grecz and Tang, 1970). The pH and constitution of the heating medium can have a profound effect on the loss of DPA. With *B. megaterium* spores, only small amounts of DPA are exuded at pH 8 and the loss at pH 7, but not at pH 5, can largely be prevented by the addition of phosphate or of ethylenediamine tetraacetic acid (Levinson and Hyatt, 1960). Some species release the least amount of DPA at pH 7 (Walker and Matches, 1966), and smooth and rough strains of *B. stearothermophilus* at pH 8 (Rotman and Fields, 1969a).

In selected strains of *Cl. botulinum*, differing widely in heat resistance, thermal destruction is closely paralleled by release of DPA (Tang and Grecz, 1965). An important finding in this study is the discovery that free DPA can be readsorbed by the heat-inactivated spore until a point is reached where no DPA can be detected in the heating medium.

This close relationship between loss of viability and DPA release inevitably leads to a consideration of whether the leakage of DPA is a cause or a consequence of thermal inactivation of spores. In some spores, there is evidence of DPA loss before viability decrease (Walker and Matches, 1966), and in *Cl. botulinum* 33A spores at 100°C DPA loss is more rapid than the fall in viability and much faster than calcium loss (Grecz *et al.*, 1970). However, in *B. megaterium* and *B. polymyxa* the percentage of spores killed in a given time is greater than the percentage of total DPA, carbohydrate or nitrogen-containing compounds released in the same period (Walker and Matches, 1966). A loss of viability precedes leakage of DPA in heated spores of *B. megaterium* (Rode and Foster, 1960; Levinson and Hyatt, 1971) and *Cl. roseum* (Wooley and Collier, 1965). DPA loss from heated *B. cereus* spores is initially slower than enzyme inactivation, but increases rapidly as heating proceeds; nevertheless, it does not occur as rapidly as loss of viability (Warth, 1980). It thus seems likely that, as with non-sporulating bacteria (Allwood and Russell, 1968, 1970) leakage occurs as a result of damage to a "permeability barrier" and cannot, therefore, be considered a primary effect.

Thermally-inactivated spores contain little or no DPA and remain refractile (Rode and Foster, 1960; Lund, 1962). This is, however, an over-simplification, as the use of the electron microscope has revealed cytological changes occurring in lethally heated spores. Several stages of breakdown have been noted in such spores (Hunnell and Ordal, 1961; Sousa *et al.*, 1978), with a progressive loss of internal material. There may be a loss of integrity of the outer spore coat on prolonged heating, with an apparent loss of stainability of plasma membrane and coagulation of the protoplast (Prokop and Humphrey, 1972). The composition of the sporulation medium can influence the structure and thermal resistance of spores (Waites *et al.*, 1979; Warburg and Moir, 1981).

VII. *Possible Mechanisms of Thermal Resistance and Inactivation of Spores*

The mechanism whereby bacterial spores are killed on exposure to moist heat is still unknown, although several theories are available. Savage (1959) asked the question "What kills a spore?" and went on to state that it was the toxic properties of water at high temperatures which hydrolyzed proteins and denatured them, etc., and that superheated steam was an inferior sterilizing agent because it did not allow the water content of the spore to increase.

Two broad theories will be considered here, one involving the possible role of DPA in heat resistance, and the other the role of the cortex (either in an expanded or contractile form).

A. The Role of DPA

Several studies have been carried out in an attempt to demonstrate a relationship between DPA content of spores and heat resistance. Higher growth temperatures markedly enhance the thermal resistance of spores of *B. coagulans* var. *thermoacidurans* and *B. subtilis*, but whereas the DPA content of the former organism increases, that of the latter decreases (El-Bisi and Ordal, 1956a, b; Lechowich and Ordal, 1962). However, the ratio of the total cation content (Ca^{2+}, Mg^{2+}, Mn^{2+}) to DPA content increases in both strains (Table 2.6). Analyses of spores of *Bacillus* species for nitrogen, carbohydrate, DPA and phosphorus shows little correlation with heat resistance (Walker *et al.*, 1961) and there appears to be no simple quantitative relationship between

Table 2.6. Cation: DPA ratios for spores of *B. subtilis* and *B. coagulans* produced at different temperatures[a]

Organism	Sporulation temperature (°C)	Cation:DPA ratio
B. subtilis	30	1·1
	45	1·38
B. coagulans	30	0·81
	45	1·32
	52	1·96

[a] Based on the data of Lechowich and Ordal (1962).

Table 2.7. Calcium, DPA and heat resistance of *Bacillus* spores

Organism	Molar ratio Ca:DPA	Survival of spores[b]
B. subtilis	1·42	27·8
B. megaterium	1·22	0·27
B. cereus	1·04	0·002
B. mycoides	0·85	0·0007

Based on the data of Levinson *et al.* (1961).
[b] % Survival after heating at 90°C for 20 min.

heat resistance and DPA content (Byrne *et al.*, 1960). As the molar concentration of Mg increases in relation to DPA and Ca, the heat resistance generally, but not invariably, decreases (Walker *et al.*, 1961). Levinson *et al.* (1961) have found that as the molar ratio of spore Ca:DPA decreases, the heat resistance likewise decreases (Table 2.7), and that by altering the Ca and DPA content, *B. megaterium* spores of differing susceptibility can be obtained.

Murrell and Warth (1965) found that the heat resistance of spores was directly related to their Ca, and inversely to their Mg, content. The Mg:Ca ratio was very significantly related to thermal resistance, varying from 0·3 in the least resistant, to 0·05 in the most resistant, spores. In species with more than a 700-fold range in heat resistance, there was only a small range in DPA content, which led the authors to state that "DPA may be involved in a mechanism producing the heat resistant state, but perhaps is not involved directly in determining the efficiency with which that state resists damage."

Heat-sensitive spores are produced when sporulation occurs in a Ca^{2+}-deficient medium. Replacement of Ca^{2+} in part by other cations gives spores which are less thermoresistant than those possessing a normal Ca^{2+} content (Slepecky and Foster, 1959), and with spores formed endotrophically in water, DPA accumulation depends on Ca concentration in the sporulation medium, and heat resistance increases with increasing DPA.

Church and Halvorson (1959) found that the rate of thermal inactivation at 80°C of spores of *B. cereus* showed a biphasic dependence on DPA content, and concluded that DNA protected at least two sites of the spore against heat activation. Powell (1957) considered that calcium dipicolinate was incorporated throughout the spore through further linkages of calcium with protein, such an arrangement contributing to heat-resistant properties. Young (1959) suggested that DPA and Ca^{2+} could act together in stabilizing essential proteins and nucleic acids. An interesting finding in this context has been made by Mishiro and Ochi (1966), who studied the heat treatment of proteins in the presence of sodium or calcium dipicolinate. It was found that human serum albumin solution became turbid at 60–95°C; however, this occurrence of turbidity was completely prevented in the presence of 0·05% solutions of DPA, which thus had a preventive effect on the heat denaturation of proteins, which in turn could be connected with the heat resistance of spores. This has yet to be shown conclusively as occurring in the bacterial spore, although the resistance of spores could be determined by the nature of DPA-metal-protein bonds, the rupture of which results in the breaking of dormancy (Brown and Melling, 1967; see also Grecz *et al.*, 1970; Rajan and Grecz, 1977). DPA has been shown to be located in the spore protoplast and not in the cortex (Leanz and Gilvarg, 1973). Almost all of the spore calcium, magnesium and manganese is located in the core region (Stewart *et al.*, 1980).

Nevertheless, the role of DPA in heat resistance remains the subject of conjecture. DPA-less mutants of *B. cereus*, *B. subtilis* and *B. megaterium* have been described (Wise *et al.*, 1971; Hanson *et al.*, 1972; Zytkovicz and Halvorson, 1972) and of these a DPA-less mutant of *B. cereus* T is very heat-sensitive, although a thermoresistant revertant of this DPA mutant has been isolated (Hanson *et al.*, 1972). The DPA-less mutant of *B. subtilis* strain 168 is as thermoresistant as the wild-type strain. DPA mutants of *B. cereus* T, but not wild-type, show germination-like changes when suspended in sodium bicarbonate (Frank and Tonaki, 1971). Holland and Taylor (1974) have proposed that DPA is required at a threshold value for the breaking of dormancy, and Hanson *et al.* (1972) that Ca and DPA are not required for the acquisition of thermoresistance but for its maintenance in the spore.

Other workers have, however, shown that mutants of *Cl. histolyticum* (Sebald, 1968) and *B. megaterium* (Fukuda and Gilvarg, 1968) that are unable to synthesize DPA produce heat-sensitive spores, and that heat resistance only becomes apparent when DPA is added to the medium. More recently, studies with a *B. subtilis* mutant which produces heat-sensitive but chloroform-resistant spores (Balassa and Yamamoto, 1970) have demonstrated that:

(i)   the mutant is unable to synthesize DPA,
(ii)   the strain can incorporate DPA from the external environment,
(iii) heat resistance of spores depends directly on the incorporation of added DPA which in turn depends on the concentration of external DPA,
(iv)   non-saturating DPA concentrations results in the production of spores with intermediate heat resistance (Balassa *et al.*, 1979a).

Unfortunately, the picture is again clouded by studies involving the effects of osmotic stabilizers on the heat resistance of heat-sensitive DPA⁻ spores of *B. cereus* Ht-8 (Bhothipaksa and Busta, 1978). This investigation shows that increased osmotic pressure enhances the heat resistance, probably as a result of dehydration of the spore protoplast in accordance with the expanded cortex theory (see next part of this section). The demonstration of muramic lactam as a unique spore constituent in cortical peptidoglycan (Warth and Strominger, 1969, 1972) means that the detection of muramic lactam can be used as a specific procedure for the presence of spore cortex (Wickus *et al.*, 1972; Imae and Strominger, 1976a, b, c; Imae *et al.*, 1978). Several conditional spore cortex-less mutants of *B. sphaericus* 9602 have been isolated and the synthesis of cortex, DPA accumulation and heat resistance studied. The existence of spore cortex is essential for DPA accumulation, refractility and shape (Imae and Strominger, 1976c); for heat resistance, both cortex and DPA accumulation are required (Imae and Strominger, 1976c) although this appears to be more closely related to the amount of cortex than to the DPA content of the spore (Imae and Strominger, 1976a). Stewart and Johnson (1977) have been unable to detect differences in DPA in sporulated suspensions that would account for their variations in heat resistance.

B. The Role of the Cortex

Virtannen and Pulkki (1933) could find no difference between spores and vegetative bacteria as regards moisture affinity in the range of humidities which they studied, and Savage (1959) has repudiated the suggestion that the cell wall of a spore could offer a resistance to the penetration of heat. Friedman and Henry (1938) found that spores contained about twice as much bound water as vegetative cells, and Wadham and Halvorson (1954) showed that spores exhibited a low affinity for water, so that the polar groups necessary to attract water molecules were masked; they further proposed that heat resistance was a result of "bound protein" rather than "bound water". Powell and Strange (1953) had earlier suggested that the resting spore contained little or no water, and that during germination there was an exchange of solids for water from the suspending medium.

The likelihood that the heat resistance of spores in the wet state is due to their impermeability to water is no longer acceptable, for Black and Gerhardt (1962) have found with *B. cereus* var. *terminalis* that the internal and external water are in virtually complete equilibrium. They proposed an "insoluble gel" theory, in which the protoplast was envisaged as an insoluble gel with cross-linking between macromolecules through stable but chemically reversible bonds, so that a high polymer matrix with entrapped free water could be formed.

In the contractile cortex theory, first put forward by Lewis *et al.* (1960), it is proposed that the water content of the protoplast is reduced by a mechanical contraction of the cortex about the protoplast. This theory does not suggest an entirely anhydrous "core", and this is an important point when it is realized that proteins are more thermolabile under extremely dry conditions. Warth *et al.* (1963a, b) stated that the cortex could be visualized as a structural matrix which carried free carboxyl and amino groups; its contraction and swelling would be controlled by calcium or calcium dipicolinate concentration. They also found that spore peptidoglycan was located mainly in the cortex and cortical membrane. The findings in the paper by Murrell and Warth (1965) of the very significant relationship between the Mg:Ca ratio and heat resistance and the interrelationships of Ca, Mg and hexosamine and DAP and heat resistance suggest that these constituents may be involved in the contractile mechanism. Differences in heat resistance from one type of spore to another could then be ascribed to variations in the actual chemical composition of the peptidoglycan, leading to different degrees of contraction of the cortex and consequent differences in the final water content of the protoplast (Murrell, 1967). In this context, the studies (see Section V, part G) on the effect of a_w on spore resistance take on an added significance. The overall result of the contractile cortex theory would consequently be a dehydration of the protoplasm and a maintenance of this state, the degree of dehydration depending on the species of spore. The importance of the cortex peptidoglycan which responds to the ionic strength of the environment has been stressed by Baillie and Murrell (1974).

An alternative theory to a *contractile* cortex is that involving an *expanded* cortex (Alderton and Snell, 1963; Gould and Dring, 1975a, b; Dring and Gould, 1975a, b). These authors found that germinating spore suspensions of *B. cereus* suspended in water were highly sensitive to moist heat whereas when heated in concentrations of sucrose > 1·5 M the germinated spores regained thermoresistance. Replacement of the non-penetrating sucrose with glycerol, which readily penetrates membranes, did not result in restoration of heat resistance. These findings led Gould (1977, 1978) to propose an osmoregulatory hypothesis which predicts that when there is a reduction in the osmotic pressure in the cortex compartment or an increase in the osmotic pressure in the core compartment, the consequence would be an increase in core water content and a decrease in resistance to heat (and to ultraviolet and ionizing radiations). This theory also assumes a low water content of the spore core brought about initially during the sporulation process by osmotic dehydration by the mother cell, and then maintained in the mature spore by means of the electronegative peptidoglycan and positively charged counterions in the cortex (Lewis, 1975). Acid-treatment of spores renders them heat-sensitive (Section H in present chapter; see also Chapter 9, Section II, E) and this could occur through protonation of peptidoglycan with a resultant fall in its osmotic effectiveness (Gould, 1977). Peptidoglycan hydrolysis is part of a sequence of losses in heat resistance, DPA, absorbance and refractility during germination (Hsieh and Vary, 1975).

The heat resistance of non-sporulating microorganisms is also increased when they are treated in the presence of high concentrations of non-permeating solutes (Corry, 1974, 1976a, b).

Pre-irradiation of spores renders them sensitive to subsequent heat treatment (see Chapter 9). If, however, the pre-irradiated spores are heated in the presence of high concentration of sucrose they do not become heat sensitive, possibly because of the reimposed dehydration of the spore core (Gomez *et al.*, 1980).

Radiobiological evidence for a dehydrated, but not entirely dry, core comes from the recent findings of Tallentire *et al.* (1977).

Ljunger (1970) suggested that the thermal stability of thermophilic bacteria, such as *B. stearothermophilus*, could be attributed to an active transport of Ca^{2+} ions from the environment into the cells, other cations being unable to replace Ca^{2+}. Spores of *Cl. perfringens* and *B. cereus* T become thermosensitive when heated in high concentrations of cross-linking divalent and trivalent (but not monovalent) cations, although for this to be achieved either spore mutants possessing defective coats, spores in which the coats have been chemically modified or normal spores in the presence of a divalent cation ionophore have to be used (Gould and Dring, 1975a, b). These findings suggest that in "normal" spores, the cortex is protected from the collapsing effect of cations by virtue of the presence of the spore coat and that the cortex peptidoglycan restricts the expansion of the core, which is thus maintained in a dehydrated state (Gould and Dring, 1975a, b). Spores of *B. subtilis* NCDO 2130 produced on different media have differing heat resistances; those with the smallest protoplasts and the largest cortices are most resistant to heat (Bayliss *et al.*, 1981). Further support for the expanded cortex theory comes from Waites *et al.* (1979).

Another theory which deals with the involvement of the spore cortex is that put forward by Warth (1978b). This anisotropic theory also envisages an expanding cortex with the expansion taking place in a radial direction as a consequence of the removal of peptide cross-links in the peptidoglycan with the formation of muramic lactam.

An even more recent theory is that propounded by Algie (1980) who proposes reverse osmosis as a mechanism for dehydrating the spore protoplast. This is conceived as resulting from the cortex, as it grows at its inner surface, pushing upon the protoplast so that water is expelled from both the protoplast and the cortex.

Whatever the actual means of removing water from the spore core, there appears to be general agreement that a lowering of the water content is associated with heat resistance. Rajan and Grecz (1977), however, refute the concept of a relationship between increased water content and increased heat sensitivity.

C. Conclusions

Despite extensive research, the mechanism underlying the high resistance of bacterial spores to moist heat remains unsolved. Indeed, it might well be erroneous to imply that there is a single reason for this resistance; rather, it might be correct to infer that various factors contribute. Spore coats do not appear to be implicated (Gould *et al.*, 1970; Aronson and Fitz-James, 1975; Gould, 1977, 1978), and whatever the actual reason(s), it seems clear that the state of hydration (or dehydration) of the core is a predominating factor. In this context, the recent studies on conditional cortex-less mutants in which heat resistance depends, to a considerable extent, on the amount of cortex present indicates the importance of the cortex as a controlling influence (see also Gerhardt and Murrell, 1978; Keynan, 1978).

This still leaves unexplained the role of DPA in heat resistance. DPA appears to reside in the inner forespore membrane and in the spore protoplast (Germaine and Murrell, 1974). DPA can reduce, *in vitro*, the thermal denaturation of proteins. This, in turn, assumes that protein coagulation is itself responsible for spore inactivation at high temperatures. In vegetative bacteria, events other than protein coagulation at least contribute to thermal injury and death, including RNA degradation, DNA strand breakage and membrane damage (Allwood and Russell, 1970; Tomlins and Ordal, 1976), although protein coagulation has also been proposed as being responsible for the lethal effect (Rosenberg *et al.*, 1971), as has DNA denaturation (Brannen, 1970).

Finally, questions that remain unanswered concern the differing sensitivities of different spores. Why is *B. stearothermophilus* so much more resistant than other spores? Is the nature and resistance of spore enzymes a contributory factor (see review by Sadoff, 1970)? Enzymes in thermophilic species are generally more heat-stable than those in mesophiles (Singleton and Ameluxen, 1973; see also Warth, 1980). Why are spores of *Cl. botulinum* type E and non-proteolytic type F thermosensitive? Is the reason for resistance simply the state of hydration of the spore core (implying a more efficient expanded or contractile cortex system) in resistant spores? Are the most resistant spores those that have the highest cortex content of carboxyl groups, as predicted by Gould (1977)? It would be instructive to examine Gould's osmoregulatory hypothesis with such spores as test organisms. Or, after all, do heat-resistant spores merely possess a more efficient repair system which enables them to repair sublethal injury and hence be revived? Answers to at least some of these questions could well shed light on the present mystery.

VIII. *Testing of Sterilizers*

The above-average resistance of certain types of bacterial spores to thermal sterilization processes can be put to practical use by employing such spores to monitor the efficacy of these procedures. The spores, usually impregnated on filter paper, are exposed to the sterilization process and are then transferred to an appropriate recovery medium. If, after incubation, no growth occurs the sterilization process is considered satisfactory, although it must be added that growth itself could result from one surviving spore or from many survivors. A homogenization technique for the quantitative recovery of spores from spore papers, followed by a viable counting procedure, may be of value in overcoming this criticism (Everall and Morris, 1978).

It is important to use standardized suspensions of bacterial spores (Day, 1971) and to place them strategically in the sterilizer (Howie, 1961). The use of an unnamed, unstandardized aerobic spore-former of insufficient heat resistance, such as the one used by Howie and Timbury (1956), is to be deplored. Kelsey (1958, 1959) showed in his studies on the z-values of bacterial spores (Section IV.D, Table 2.4) that, in the absence of other information, spores to be considered for testing autoclaves should have a survival time of *ca.* 10 h at 100°C. This effectively eliminates mesophilic spore-formers and soil may be considered as unsuitable because of its variable spore composition and therefore heat resistance. Swabs contaminated by exposure to hospital dust have also been recommended (Howie and Timbury, 1956). Hospital dust is also likely, however, to be of variable composition and it is far more logical to use standardized spore suspensions.

Filter paper strips impregnated with *B. stearothermophilus* spores have been widely employed as sterilization indicators (Nuffield Provincial Hospitals Trust, 1958; Kelsey, 1961; Cook and Brown, 1964, 1965b, c; Myers and Chrai, 1980). Kelsey (1961) stated that each batch of spore papers should be calibrated by plotting dose-response curves for exposure to steam, and postulated that it was reasonable to assume that the slope of this curve was characteristic of the strain and that it would remain reasonably constant for some months. A shelf life of at least 6 months was proposed. The LD_{50} (time, in minutes, to kill 50% of the organisms) could be used to characterize a batch of spore papers, and an LD_{50} of 4·5–6·5 min at 121°C appeared to be the recommended resistance. However, the recovery medium used by Kelsey, which was dextrose tryptone broth (Oxoid), contained 0·004% w/v bromocresol purple, and this medium has been shown to give significantly less recovery of *B. stearothermophilus* spore strips exposed to steam than the same medium made from the individual components without the dye (Cook and Brown, 1960). The pH of the recovery broth also effects recovery from heated spore papers, and a pH of 7·4 is optimum, with 6·3 the worst of those tested (Cook and Brown, 1965c). No reasons were given for this pH effect.

The number of spores per filter paper disc would be expected to be important, but significant differences have been found to occur between spore papers produced by different manufacturers (Mayernik, 1972). Shelf storage is also dependent, in part, on the spore content with filter papers containing more than 10^6 (but not those with 10^4) spores of

B. stearothermophilus retaining their heat resistance over long periods (Cook and Brown, 1965b). The maintenance of a stable level of resistance is important. A loss of heat resistance may result from a fall in spore viability together with progressive spore germination, and these may be delayed by storing the strips at $-20°C$ (Reich *et al.*, 1979). Statements that *B. stearothermophilus* spores are killed without details of the strain, method of testing or recovery (Wells and Whitwell, 1960) are of little value.

Thus, *B. stearothermophilus* spores appear to be a suitable indicator of moist heat sterilization (Selkon *et al.*, 1979) particularly at a temperature of 121°C (Anderson and Rae, 1979). *Bacillus coagulens* strains FRR B666 has also been suggested as a potential indicator organism (Jones and Pflug, 1981). In the United Kingdom, Oxoid spore strips of *B.*

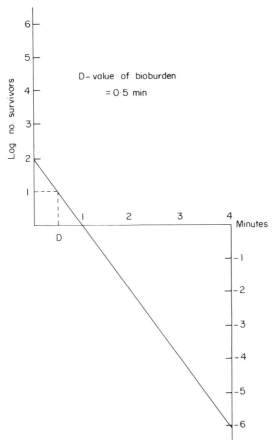

Fig. 2.5   Fractional exposure validation studies of moist heat sterilization processes.

stearothermophilus are stated to resist 5 min, but not 12 min, at 121°C, but the recommended recovery medium, notwithstanding the above, is dextrose-tryptone agar. Biological indicators employing spores of this organism are also used in the United States (see Green, 1982 for a review). The number of spores per filter strip may be of the order of 10^5-10^6 which is far in excess of what would be expected to occur on relatively clean hospital supplies and thus would be expected to provide a wide safety margin. In recent years, some new terminology has been introduced into the monitoring of heat sterilization processes; since absolute sterility cannot be guaranteed, it is usual to consider the *validation* (ratification) of such a process by means of the probability of survival. The initial number of test spores is referred to as the *bioburden*, and in an "overkill" situation there should be at least a 10^{-6} probability of microbial survival based on a *D*-value of 1 min (or more) and sufficient lethality to achieve a 12-log reduction in viable numbers. Thus, for a bioburden of 10^6 spores, there should be 10^{-6} survivors (see also Korczynski *et al.*, 1974; Kereluk, 1975).

Fractional exposure validation studies (see Fig. 2.5) require determination of the population and resistance of the bioburden in the production cycle, the cycle exposure time necessary to reduce the bioburden population to a 10^{-6} probability of a survivor, determination of the resistance of the biological indicator organism in the production cycle and determination of the equivalency between the 10^{-6} assurance of sterility of the bioburden and biological indicator challenge level (Owen, 1978). Thus, this type of cycle is designed to provide an assurance of non-sterility of one in a million; this is considered to be acceptable in the moist heat sterilization of parenteral products where initial contamination levels before sterilization are likely to be low.

IX. *Applications of Moist Heat Sterilization*

Moist heat has long been a very important method of sterilization, with wide application in foods and pharmaceutical properties. A full consideration of its uses is beyond the scope of this chapter, and the following will merely serve as a summary.

A. Ultrahigh Temperature (UHT)

UHT processes are used to ensure spore inactivation in processing equipment by direct steam injection. The holding period at the desired temperature is very short, being of the order of seconds (see Perkin *et al.*, 1980, for practical information).

Williams *et al.* (1957) described a method of assessing the sporicidal activity of a UHT milk sterilizing plant operating on water. Water, heavily contaminated with spores of *B. subtilis* strain 786 was filtered, after treatment in the plant, through membrane filters and the survivors estimated by incubation of the membranes in nutrient agar. A satisfactory degree of destruction of the spores was obtained at *ca.* 135°C and a holding time of 2–4 s. It was subsequently found from the same laboratory (Franklin *et al.*, 1958a) that with *B. subtilis* spores in milk, a temperature of 130·5°C was necessary to give a destruction of 99·99999% (IF = 10^7), which was less than that required in water. It was considered that UHT milk was inhibitory to germination and/or outgrowth of heated spores. However, the results of Martin *et al.* (1966) would suggest that this reason is not valid. These authors studied the effects of UHT of 104·5, 121 and 137·8°C for *ca.* 1 s on various bacterial spores added to milk and showed, as would be expected, that, as the intensity of the UHT treatment increased, the number of surviving spores decreased. However, an interesting finding was that survivors of higher temperatures were capable of more rapid growth in the treated milk during subsequent incubation at 35°C, e.g. in the case of *B. megaterium*, the number of generations during a 6 h incubation period at this temperature following UHT treatment of 104·5, 121 and 137·8°C were 5·9, 10·8 and 15, respectively. One possible reason for this is the heat activation of at least some of the spores.

The kinetics of death of bacterial spores have been considered by Wang *et al.* (1964) and Burton (1958). Wang *et al.* (1964) heated *B. stearothermophilus* spores of strain FS 7954 in phosphate buffer, pH 7, at elevated temperatures in the range 127·2 to 143·8°C, with exposure times of 0·203 to 4·15 s. However, the heating conditions and procedures could not be extended to UHT treatment of spores in milk by direct steam injection (Busta, 1967). Busta (1967) studied the thermal inactivation of *B. stearothermophilus* strain 1518 and PA 3679 spores suspended in skim milk, after treatment in pilot plant UHT processing equipment. Temperature-survival curves indicated heat activation of the former, but not of the latter, organism, as well as inactivation at higher temperatures. With *B. subtilis* strain 786 spores in milk, a non-logarithmic order of death was generally observed (Franklin *et al.*, 1958b). Within the range of 110 to 120°C, the thermal death curves for spores suspended in milk gave Q_{10} values of approximately 30; other strains of *B. subtilis* also gave high Q_{10} values (Franklin *et al.*, 1958b). At 120–125°C, *D*-values of *B. stearothermophilus* strain NCDO 1096 are much higher for spores in water than in milk, whereas at higher temperatures there is little difference between the two (Davies *et al.*,

1977). Data obtained at lower temperatures must be very accurate before they can be extrapolated to provide thermal data at UHT (Perkin *et al.*, 1977; see also Adams, 1978; O'Connor, 1974), and temperature coefficients (Q_{10} values) are higher for spore inactivation in UHT plants than in capillary tubes. Agreement is closer when spores are suspended in water than in milk (Burton *et al.*, 1977).

Only the heating and holding sections of the UHT process contribute to the overall sporicidal effect, because of the rate of cooling of liquid in the plant immediately after the holding section; an increase in lethal effect has been found to be much more effectively obtained with an increase in temperature than by an increase in the holding time (Burton, 1958; Burton *et al.*, 1958a, b).

Edwards *et al.* (1965a, b) suggested that *B. subtilis* A spores were injured, but not completely inactivated, by UHT treatment. The basis of this conclusion was that:

(i)   higher survival counts were obtained when calcium chloride and sodium dipicolinate were added to the standard counting medium,
(ii) more survivors were enumerated with the standard medium after incubation at 32°C than at 45°C, in contrast to unheated spores,
(iii) there was an apparent increase in the number of survivors when suspensions were held at 3°C prior to using the standard counting medium at 45°C.

It is noteworthy that calcium chloride and sodium dipicolinate eliminate the requirement for heat activation by spores from certain strains of *B. subtilis* (Busta and Ordal, 1964a, b, c). The last point ((iii) above) would suggest that there is a repair of heat injury upon storage of the spores at temperatures below the growth range; a similar suggestion for thermally-injured non-sporing bacteria has been put forward by Hansen and Riemann (1963). Interestingly, bacterial spore injury may be much more extensive at UHT than at sub-UHT (Adams, 1978), with lysozyme required for the maximal revival of *Cl. perfringens* type A spores surviving extended, but not early, stages of heat treatment (Adams, 1973). Exposure of *B. subtilis* A spores to UHT for several seconds activates a low-temperature germination system (Adams and Busta, 1972).

UHT processing of milk is considered (Davies, 1975) to be of considerable importance in countries which have hot climates or which have distribution problems.

B. Foods

There are various methods available for preserving foods; these include high temperatures, low temperatures, chemical preservation and irradiation. Canning is one of the chief methods employed: it usually implies heat treatment as the principal factor in the prevention of spoilage (Frazier, 1958; Stumbo, 1973), the objective being to destroy spores of *Cl. botulinum* types A, B and, if necessary, type C (Roberts and Gibson, 1979) and spoilage organisms. Briefly, two methods are mainly used for heat-processing foods: either the food is heated in hermetically-sealed containers or it is heated in a heat-exchanger and then filled into containers.

Cameron (1940) divided canned foods into various groups, depending on their pH. These groups were:

(i)   Low acid foods, having a pH of more than 5·3;
(ii) Medium acid foods, having a pH between 5·3 and 4·5;
(iii) Acid foods, with a pH between 4·5 and 3·7;
(iv) High acid foods, with a pH of 3·7 and below.

It has been shown in an earlier section (V, H) that pH may influence the thermoresistance of bacterial spores, and thus the acidic nature of the food, based on Cameron's grouping, is an important factor. High acid foods do not, ordinarily, undergo spoilage by microorganisms. The importance of pH is considered again in the context of combined sporicidal treatments (Chapter 9).

Heating processes are thus most useful in treating canned foods. It must not be forgotten, however, that they can induce changes in foods.

C. Pharmaceutical and Medical Products

Moist heat has long been adopted as a process for sterilizing various types of pharmaceutical and medical products, although it is only recently that the kinetic approach to heat sterilization has been adopted (Bean, 1980) in contrast to the food industry. Reports published by the Medical Research Council (Report, 1959, 1978) should be consulted for full details of the correct manipulation and packing of sterilizers. Useful accounts of the applications of moist heat sterilization are provided by Allwood (1980, 1982) and the "Pharmaceutical Handbook" (Anon., 1980). Products and equipment which can be sterilized include surgical dressings, some parenteral products and some eye-drop products. Historical information on the design of sterilizers is given by Gaughran and Goudie (1975).

References

Adams, D. M. (1973). *Applied Microbiology* **26**, 282–287.
Adams, D. M. (1978). *In* "Spores VII" (G. Chambliss and J. C. Vary, eds), pp. 15–16. American Society for Microbiology, Washington D.C.

Adams, D. M. and Busta, F. F. (1972). *Applied Microbiology* **24**, 418–423.
Akers, M. J., Attia, I. A. and Avis, K. E. (1979). *Journal of the Parenteral Drug Association* **33**, 195–200.
Alderton, G. and Snell, N. S. (1963). *Biochemical and Biophysical Research Communications* **10**, 139–143.
Alderton, G. and Snell, N. S. (1969a). *Science, New York* **163**, 1212–1213.
Alderton, G. and Snell, N. S. (1969b). *Applied Microbiology* **17**, 745–749.
Alderton, G. and Snell, N. (1970). *Applied Microbiology* **19**, 565–572.
Algie, J. E. (1980). *Current Microbiology* **3**, 287–290.
Allwood, M. C. (1980). *In* "Pharmaceutical Microbiology" (W. B. Hugo and A. D. Russell, eds), 2nd edn, pp. 295–308. Blackwell Scientific Publishers, Oxford.
Allwood, M. C. (1982). *In* "Principles and Practice of Disinfection, Preservation and Sterilization" (A. D. Russell, W. B. Hugo and G. A. J. Ayliffe, eds), pp. 469–477. Blackwell Scientific Publications, Oxford.
Allwood, M. C. and Russell, A. D. (1968). *Applied Microbiology* **15**, 1266–1269.
Allwood, M. C. and Russell, A. D. (1970). *Advances in Applied Microbiology* **12**, 89–119.
Amaha, M. and Ordal, Z. J. (1957). *Journal of Bacteriology* **74**, 596–604.
Anand, J. C. (1961). *Journal of Scientific and Industrial Research* **20C**, 295–298.
Anderson, R. A. and Rae, W. A. (1979). *Australian Journal of Pharmaceutical Sciences* **8**, 55–56.
Anema, P. J. and Geers, J. M. (1973). *Journal of Applied Bacteriology* **36**, 553–558.
Anon. (1980). "Pharmaceutical Handbook", 2nd edn. Pharmaceutical Press, London.
Aoki, H. and Slepecky, R. (1973). *Journal of Bacteriology* **114**, 137–143.
Aoki, H. and Slepecky, R. (1974). *In* "Spore Research 1973" (A. N. Barker, G. W. Gould and J. Wolff, eds), pp. 93–102. Academic Press, London and New York.
Aronson, A. I. and Fitz-James, P. C. (1975). *Journal of Bacteriology* **123**, 354–365.
Augustin, J. A. L. and Pflug, I. J. (1967). *Applied Microbiology* **15**, 266–276.
Baillie, E. and Murrell, W. G. (1974). *Biochimica et Biophysica Acta* **372**, 23–31.
Balassa, G. and Yamamoto, T. (1970). *Microbios* **5**, 73–76.
Balassa, G., Milhaud, P., Raulet, E., Silva, M. T. and Sousa, J. C. F. (1979a). *Journal of General Microbiology* **110**, 365–379.
Balassa, G., Milhaud, P., Sousa, J. C. F. and Silva, M. T. (1979b). *Journal of General Microbiology* **110**, 381–392.
Ball, C. D. and Olson, F. C. W. (1955). *Food Research* **20**, 666–686.
Barnes, E. M., Despaul, J. E. and Ingram, M. (1963). *Journal of Applied Bacteriology* **26**, 415–427.
Bayliss, C. E., Waites, W. M. and King, N. R. (1981). *Journal of Applied Bacteriology* **50**, 379–390.
Bean, H. S. (1980). *Pharmaceutical Journal* **224**, 41–42.
Bhothiapaksa, K. and Busta, F. F. (1978). *Applied and Environmental Microbiology* **35**, 800–808.
Bigelow, W. D. and Esty, J. R. (1920). *Journal of Infectious Diseases* **27**, 602–617.
Black, S. H. and Gerhardt, P. (1962). *Journal of Bacteriology* **83**, 960–967.
Black, S. H., Hashimito, T. and Gerdardt, P. (1960). *Canadian Journal of Microbiology* **6**, 213–224.
Bovallius, A. and Zacharias, B. (1971). *Applied Microbiology* **22**, 260–262.
Bradshaw, J. G., Peeler, J. T. and Twedt, R. M. (1975). *Applied Microbiology* **30**, 943–945.

Bradshaw, J. G., Peeler, J. T. and Twedt, R. M. (1977). *Applied and Environmental Microbiology* **34**, 280–284.

Brannen, J. P. (1968). *Mathematical Biosciences* **2**, 165–179.

Brannen, J. P. (1970). *Journal of Theoretical Biology* **27**, 425–432.

Briggs, A. (1966). *Journal of Applied Bacteriology* **29**, 490–504.

Brooks, M. M., Sterne, M. and Warrack, G. H. (1957). *Journal of Pathology and Bacteriology* **74**, 185–195.

Brown, M. R. W. and Hodges, N. A. (1974). *Journal of Pharmacy and Pharmacology* **26**, 217–227.

Brown, M. R. W. and Melling, J. (1967). *Biochemical Journal* **106**, 44p.

Brown, M. R. W. and Melling, J. (1973). *Journal of Pharmacy and Pharmacology* **25**, 478–483.

Bühlmann, X., Gay, M. and Schiller, I. (1973). *Pharmaceutica Acta Helvetiae* **48**, 223–244.

Bullock, K. and Keepe, W. G. (1951). *Journal of Pharmacy and Pharmacology* **3**, 717–731.

Bullock, K. and Lightbown, J. W. (1947). *Quarterly Journal of Pharmacy and Pharmacology* **20**, 312–328.

Bullock, K. and Tallentire, A. (1952). *Journal of Pharmacy and Pharmacology* **4**, 917–931.

Burton, H. (1958). *Journal of Dairy Research* **25**, 75–84.

Burton, H., Franklin, J. G., Williams, D. J., Jean, A., Harrison, W. and Clegg, L. F. L. (1958a). *Journal of Dairy Research* **25**, 324–337.

Burton, H., Franklin, J. G., Williams, D. J., Jean, A., Harrison, W. and Clegg, L. F. L. (1958b). *Journal of Dairy Research* **25**, 338–343.

Burton, H., Perkin, A. G., Davies, F. L. and Underwood, H. M. (1977). *Journal of Food Technology* **12**, 149–161.

Busta, F. F. (1967). *Applied Microbiology* **15**, 640–645.

Busta, F. F. and Ordal, Z. J. (1964a). *Applied Microbiology* **12**, 106–110.

Busta, F. F. and Ordal, Z. J. (1964b). *Applied Microbiology* **12**, 111–114.

Busta, F. F. and Ordal, Z. J. (1964c). *Journal of Food Science* **29**, 345–353.

Busta, F. F., Baillie, E. and Murrell, W. G. (1976). *Applied and Environmental Microbiology* **32**, 312–314.

Busta, F. F., Baillie, E. and Murrell, W. G. (1977). *In* "Spore Research 1976" (A. N. Barker, J. Wolf, D. J. Ellar, G. J. Dring and G. W. Gould, eds), pp. 431–450. Academic Press, London and New York.

Byrne, A. F., Burton, T. H. and Koch, R. B. (1960). *Journal of Bacteriology* **80**, 139–140.

Cameron, E. J. (1940). *Journal of the Association of Official Agricultural Chemists* **23**, 607–608.

Cameron, M. S., Leonard, S. J. and Barrett, E. L. (1980). *Applied and Environmental Microbiology* **39**, 943–949.

Canada, J. C., Strong, D. H. and Scott, L. G. (1964). *Applied Microbiology* **12**, 273–276.

Cash, J. D. and Collee, J. G. (1962). *Journal of Applied Bacteriology* **25**, 225–231.

Cerf, O. (1977). *Journal of Applied Bacteriology* **42**, 1–19.

Cerf, O., Bergere, J. L. and Hermier, J. (1967). *Journal of Dairy Research* **34**, 221–229.

Charm, S. E. (1958). *Food Technology* **12**, 4–9.

Church, B. D. and Halvorson, H. O. (1959). *Nature, London* **188**, 124–125.

Cockey, R. R. and Tatro, M. C. (1974). *Applied Microbiology* **27**, 626—633.

Collee, J. G., Knowlden, J. A. and Hobbs, B. C. (1961). *Journal of Applied Bacteriology* **24**, 326–339.

Cook, A. M. and Brown, M. R. W. (1960). *Journal of Pharmacy and Pharmacology* **12**, 116T–118T.

Cook, A. M. and Brown, M. R. W. (1964). *Journal of Pharmacy and Pharmacology* **116**, 725–732.

Cook, A. M. and Brown, M. R. W. (1965a). *Journal of Applied Bacteriology* **28**, 361–364.

Cook, A. M. and Brown, M. R. W. (1965b). *Journal of Pharmacy and Pharmacology* **17**, 1S–6S.

Cook, A. M. and Brown, M. R. W. (1965c). *Journal of Pharmacy and Pharmacology* **17**, 7S–11S.

Cook, A. M. and Gilbert, R. J. (1965). *Journal of Pharmacy and Pharmacology* **17**, 20S–21S.

Cook, A. M. and Gilbert, R. J. (1968a). *Journal of Food Technology* **3**, 295–302.

Cook, A. M. and Gilbert, R. J. (1968b). *Journal of Pharmacy and Pharmacology* **20**, 626–629.

Cook, A. M. and Gilbert, R. J. (1968c). *Journal of Food Technology* **3**, 285–293.

Cook, A. M. and Gilbert, R. J. (1968d). *Journal of Applied Bacteriology* **32**, 96–102.

Corry, J. E. L. (1974). *Journal of Applied Bacteriology* **37**, 41–43.

Corry, J. E. L. (1976a). *Journal of Applied Bacteriology* **40**, 269–276.

Corry, J. E. L. (1976b). *Journal of Applied Bacteriology* **40**, 277–284.

Curran, H. R. and Evans, F. R. (1944). *Journal of Bacteriology* **47**, 437.

Curran, H. R. and Evans, F. R. (1945). *Journal of Bacteriology* **49**, 335–346.

Davies, D. J. G. and Hobbs, R. (1980). *In* "Pharmaceutical Microbiology" (W. B. Hugo and A. D. Russell, eds), 2nd edn, pp. 280–294. Blackwell Scientific Publications, Oxford.

Davies, F. L. (1975). *Journal of the Society of Dairy Technology* **28**, 69–78.

Davies, F. L. and Wilkinson, G. (1973). *In* "The Microbiological Safety of Food" (B. C. Hobbs and J. H. B. Christian, eds), pp. 57–67. Academic Press, London and New York.

Davies, F. L., Underwood, H. M., Perkin, A. G. and Burton, H. (1977). *Journal of Food Technology* **12**, 115–129.

Day, L. M. (1971). *Bulletin of the Parenteral Drug Association* **25**, 73–75.

de Guzman, A., Fields, M. L., Humbert, R. D. and Kazana, N. (1972). *Journal of Bacteriology* **110**, 775–776.

Demain, A. L. (1966). *Biochemical and Biophysical Research Communications* **24**, 39–43.

Dickinson, E. C., Burke, G. S., Beck, D. and Johnston, J. (1925). *Journal of Infectious Diseases* **36**, 472–483.

Dring, G. J. and Gould, G. W. (1975a). *In* "Spores VI" (P. Gerhardt, R N. Costilow and H. L. Sadoff, eds), pp. 488–494. American Society for Microbiology, Washington, D.C.

Dring, G. J. and Gould, G. W. (1975b). *Biochemical and Biophysical Research Communications* **66**, 202–208.

Duncan, C. L. and Strong, D. H. (1968). *Applied Microbiology* **16**, 82–89.

Duncan, C. L., Labbe, R. G. and Reich, R. R. (1972). *Journal of Bacteriology* **109**, 550–559.

Edwards, J. L., Busta, F. F. and Speck, M. L. (1965a). *Applied Microbiology* **13**, 851–857.

Edwards, J. L., Busta, F. F. and Speck, M. L. (1965b). *Applied Microbiology* 13, 858–864.

El-Bisi, H. M. and Ordal, Z. J. (1965a). *Journal of Bacteriology* 71, 1–9.

El-Bisi, H. M. and Ordal, Z. J. (1956b). *Journal of Bacteriology* 71, 10–16.

Ellar, D. J. and Postgate, J. A. (1974). *In* "Spore Research 1973" (A. N. Barker, G. W. Gould and J. Wolf, eds), pp. 21–40. Academic Press, London and New York.

Esselen, W. B. and Pflug, I. J. (1956). *Food Technology* 10, 557–560.

Esty, J. R. and Mayer, K. F. (1922). *Journal of Infectious Diseases* 31, 650–663.

Esty, J. R. and Williams, C. C. (1924). *Journal of Infectious Diseases* 34, 516–528.

Everall, P. H. and Morris, C. A. (1978). *Journal of Clinical Pathology* 31, 423–425.

Favero, M. S. (1967). *In* "Spore Newsletter" (W. G. Murrell, ed.), Vol. 2, No. 12, pp. 163–164.

Fernelius, A. L., Wilkes, C. E., Dearman, I. A. Jr., and Lincoln, R. E. (1958). *Journal of Bacteriology* 75, 300–304.

Fields, M. L. and Finley, N. (1962). *University of Missouri College of Agriculture Research Bulletin* No. 807.

Fields, M. L. and Finley, N. (1963). *Applied Microbiology* 11, 453–457.

Finley, N. and Fields, M. L. (1962). *Applied Microbiology* 10, 231–236.

Fox, K. and Eder, B. D. (1969). *Journal of Food Science* 34, 518–521.

Frank, H. A. and Tonaki, K. I. (1971). *Journal of Bacteriology* 106, 292–293.

Franklin, J. G., Williams, D. J., Chapman, H. R. and Clegg, L. F. L. (1958a). *Journal of Applied Bacteriology* 21, 47–50.

Franklin, J. G., Williams, D. J. and Clegg, L. F. L. (1958b). *Journal of Applied Bacteriology* 21, 51–57.

Frazier, W. C. (1958). "Food Microbiology". McGraw-Hill, New York.

Friedman, C. A. and Henry, B. S. (1938). *Journal of Bacteriology* 36, 99–105.

Friesen, W. T. and Anderson, R. A. (1974). *Canadian Journal of Pharmaceutical Sciences* 9, 50–53.

Fukuda, A. and Gilvarg, C. (1968). *Journal of Biological Chemistry* 243, 3871–3876.

Gaughran, E. R. L. and Goudie, A. J. (1975). *Acta Pharmaceutica Suecica* 12, Supplement, 15–25.

Gauthier, C. A., Smith, G. M. and Pflug, I. J. (1978). *Applied and Environmental Microbiology* 36, 457–464.

Gerhardt, P. and Murrell, W. G. (1978). *In* "Spores VII" (G. Chambliss and J. C. Vary, eds), pp. 18–20. American Society for Microbiology, Washington, D.C.

Germaine, G. R. and Murrell, W. G. (1974). *Journal of Bacteriology* 36, 321–327.

Gibriel, A. Y. and Abd-El Al, A.T.H. (1973). *Journal of Applied Bacteriology* 36, 321–327.

Gilbert, R. J. (1966). *Ph.D. Thesis*, University of London.

Goepfert, J. M., Spira, W. M. and Kim, H. U. (1972). *Journal of Milk and Food Technology* 35, 213–227.

Gomez, R. F., Gombas, D. E. and Herrero, A. (1980). *Applied and Environmental Microbiology* 39, 525–529.

Goodenough, E. R. and Solberg, M. (1972). *Applied Microbiology* 23, 429—430.

Gould, G. W. (1962). *Journal of Applied Bacteriology* 5, 35–41.

Gould, G. W. (1977). *Journal of Applied Bacteriology* 42, 297–309.

Gould, G. W. (1978). *In* "Spores VII" (G. Chambliss and J. C. Vary, eds), pp. 21–26. American Society for Microbiology, Washington, D.C.

Gould, G. W. and Dring, G. J. (1975a). *In* "Spores VI" (P. Gerhardt, R. N. Costilow and H. L. Sadoff, eds), pp. 541–546. American Society for Microbiology, Washington D.C.

Gould, G. W. and Dring, G. J. (1975b). *Nature, London* **285**, 402–405.

Gould, G. W. and Dring, G. J. (1977). *In* "Spore Research 1976" (A. N. Barker, J. Wolf, D. J. Ellar, G. J. Dring and G. W. Gould, eds), pp. 421–429. Academic Press, London and New York.

Gould, G. W. and Measures, J. C. (1977). *Philosophical Transactions of the Royal Society of London, Series B* **278**, 151–166.

Gould, G. W., Jones, A. and Wrighton, C. (1968). *Journal of Applied Bacteriology* **31**, 357–366.

Gould, G. W., Stubbs, J. M. and King, W. L. (1970). *Journal of General Microbiology* **60**, 347–355.

Grecz, N. and Lin, C. A. (1967). *In* "Botulism 1966" (M. Ingram and T. A. Roberts, eds), pp. 302–322. Chapman and Hall, London.

Grecz, N. and Tang, T. (1970). *Journal of General Microbiology* **63**, 303–310.

Grecz, N., Smith, R. F. and Hoffman, C. C. (1970). *Canadian Journal of Microbiology* **16**, 573–579.

Grecz, N., Tang, T. and Rajan, K. S. (1972). *In* "Spores V" (H. O. Halvorson, R. Hanson and L. L. Campbell, eds), pp. 53–60. American Society for Microbiology, Washington, D.C.

Greene, V. W. (1982). *In* "Principles and Practice of Disinfection, Preservation and Sterilization" (A. D. Russell, W. B. Hugo and G. A. J. Ayliffe, eds) Blackwell Scientific Publications, Oxford.

Hall, H. E., Angelotti, R., Lewis, K. H. and Foster, M. J. (1963). *Journal of Bacteriology* **85**, 1094–1103.

Halleck, F. E. (1977). *Developments in Industrial Microbiology* **18**, 335–351.

Halvorson, H. O. (1957) (Ed.). "Spores I". American Institute of Biological Sciences, Washington, U.S.A.

Han, Y. W. (1975). *Canadian Journal of Microbiology* **21**, 1464–1467.

Han, Y. W., Zhang, H. I. and Krochta, J. M. (1976). *Canadian Journal of Microbiology* **22**, 295–300.

Hansen, N. H. and Riemann, H. (1963). *Journal of Applied Bacteriology* **26**, 314–333.

Hanson, R. S., Curry, M. V., Garner, J. V. and Halvorson, H. D. (1972). *Canadian Journal of Microbiology* **18**, 1139–1143.

Härnulv, B. G. and Snygg, B. G. (1972). *Journal of Applied Bacteriology*, **35**, 615–624.

Härnulv, B. G., Johansson, M. and Snygg, B. G. (1977). *Journal of Food Science* **42**, 91–93.

Hashimoto, T., Black, S. H. and Gerhardt, P. (1960). *Canadian Journal of Microbiology* **6**, 203–212.

Headlee, M. R. (1931). *Journal of Infectious Diseases* **48**, 468–483.

Heiligman, F., Desrosier, N. W. and Broumand, H. (1956). *Food Research* **21**, 63–69.

Hermier, J., Begue, P. and Cerf, O. (1975). *Journal of Dairy Research* **42**, 437–444.

Hitchins, A. D., Gould, G. W. and Hurst, A. (1963). *Journal of General Microbiology* **30**, 445–453.

Hitchins, A. D., King, W. L. and Gould, G. W. (1966). *Journal of Applied Bacteriology* **29**, 505–511.

Hobbs, B. C. (1965). *Journal of Applied Bacteriology* **28**, 74–82.

Hobbs, B. C. (1973). *In* "The Microbiological Safety of Food" (B. C. Hobbs and J. H. B. Christian, eds), pp. 129–142. Academic Press, London and New York.

Hobbs, B. C., Smith, M. E., Oakley, C. L., Warrack, G. H. and Cruickshank, J. C. (1953). *Journal of Hygiene, Cambridge* 51, 75–80.

Hobbs, G. (1976). *Advances in Food Research* 22, 135–185.

Hodges, N. A. and Brown, M. R. W. (1975). *In* "Spores VI" (P. Gerhardt, R. N. Costilow and H. L. Sadoff, eds), pp. 550–555. American Society for Microbiology, Washington D.C.

Holland, K. T. and Taylor, C. E. (1974). *In* "Spore Research 1973" (A. N. Barker, G. W. Gould and J. Wolf, eds), pp. 185–198. Academic Press, London and New York.

Holmes, P. K., Nags, E. H. and Levinson, H. S. (1965). *Journal of Bacteriology* 90, 827–828.

Houtzer, R. L. and Hill, R. C. (1977). *Journal of Food Science* 42, 775–777.

Howie, J. W. (1961). *Journal of Clinical Pathology* 14, 49–54.

Howie, J. W. and Timbury, M. C. (1956). *Lancet* 2, 669–673.

Hsieh, K. K. and Vary, J. C. (1975). *In* "Spores VI" (P. Gerhardt, R. N. Costilow and H. L. Sadoff, eds), pp. 465–471. American Society for Microbiology, Washington D.C.

Humbert, R. D., de Guzman, A. and Fields, M. L. (1972). *Applied Microbiology* 23, 693–698.

Hunnell, J. W. and Ordal, Z. J. (1961). *In* "Spores II" (H. O. Halvorson, ed.), pp. 101–112. Burgess Publishing Company, Minneapolis.

Hyatt, M. T. and Levinson, H. S. (1964). *Journal of Bacteriology* 88, 1403–1415.

Imae, Y. and Strominger, J. L. (1976a). *Journal of Bacteriology* 126, 907–913.

Imae, Y. and Strominger, J. L. (1976b). *Journal of Bacteriology* 126, 914–918.

Imae, Y. and Strominger, J. L. (1976c). *Journal of Biological Chemistry* 251, 1493–1499.

Imae, Y., Strominger, M. B. and Strominger, J. L. (1978). *In* "Spores VII" (G. Chambliss and J. C. Vary, eds), pp. 62–66. American Society of Microbiology, Washington D. C.

Ito, K. A., Sesler, D. J. and Mercer, W. A. (1967). *In* "Botulism 1966" (M. Ingram and T. A. Roberts, eds), pp. 108–122. Chapman and Hall, London.

Jones, A. T. and Pflug, I. J. (1981). *Journal of Parenteral Science and Technology* 35(3), 82–87.

Jones, M. C. (1968). *Journal of Food Technology* 3, 31–38.

Jonsson, U., Snygg, B. G., Härnulv, B. G. and Zachrisson, T. (1977). *Journal of Food Science* 42, 1251–1263.

Kelsey, J. C. (1958). *Lancet* 1, 306–309.

Kelsey, J. C. (1959). *In* "The Operation of Sterilizing Autoclaves" pp. 22–28. Pharmaceutical Press, London.

Kelsey, J. C. (1961). *Journal of Clinical Pathology* 14, 313–319.

Kereluk, K. (1975). *In* "Quality Control in Microbiology" (J. E. Prier, J. Bartola, and H. Friedman, eds), pp. 21–39. University Park Press, Baltimore.

Keynan, A. (1978). *In* "Spores VII" (G. Chambliss and J. C. Vary, eds), pp. 43–53. American Society for Microbiology, Washington D.C.

Koch, R. (1881). *Arbeiten aus dem K. Gesundheitsamte* 1, 1–49.

Kooiman, W. J. and Jacobs, R. P. W. M. (1977). *In* "Spore Research 1976" (A. N. Barker, J. Wolf, D. J. Ellar, G. J. Dring and G. W. Gould, eds), pp. 477–485. Academic Press, London and New York.

Korczynski, M. S., Peterson, C. L. and Loshbaugh, C. C. (1974). *Bulletin of the Parenteral Drug Association* 28, 270–277.

La Nauze, J. M., Ellar, D. J., Denton, G. and Postgate, J. A. (1974). *In* "Spore Research 1973" (A. N. Barker, G. W. Gould and J. Wolf, eds), pp. 41–46. Academic Press, London and New York.

Leanz, G. and Gilvarg, C. (1973). *Journal of Bacteriology* **114**, 455–456.

Lechowich, R. V. and Ordal, Z. J. (1962). *Canadian Journal of Microbiology* **8**, 287–295.

Levinson, H. S. and Feeherry, E. E. (1978). *In* "Spores VII" (G. Chambliss and J. C. Vary, eds), pp. 34–40. American Society for Microbiology, Washington D.C.

Levinson, H. S. and Hyatt, M. T. (1960). *Journal of Bacteriology* **80**, 441–451.

Levinson, H. S. and Hyatt, M. T. (1964). *Journal of Bacteriology* **87**, 876–886.

Levinson, H. S. and Hyatt, M. T. (1971). *Journal of Bacteriology* **108**, 111–121.

Levinson, H. S., Hyatt, M. T. and Moore, F. E. (1961). *Biochemical and Biophysical Research Communications* **5**, 417–421.

Lewis, J. C. (1975). *In* "Spores VI" (P. Gerhardt, P. N. Costilow and H. L. Sadoff, eds), pp. 547–549. American Society for Microbiology, Washington D.C.

Lewis, J. C., Snell, N. S. and Burr, H. K. (1960). *Science, New York* **132**, 544–545.

Ley, F. J. and Tallentire, A. (1964). *Pharmaceutical Journal* **193**, 59–61.

Licciardello, J. T. and Nickerson, J. T. R. (1962). *Journal of Food Science* **27**, 211–218.

Licciardello, J. T. and Nickerson, J. T. R. (1963). *Applied Microbiology* **11**, 216–219.

Ljunger, C. (1970). *Physiologia Plantarum* **23**, 351–364.

Long, J. L., Engle, H. M., Cullyford, J. S. and Love, C. E. (1962). *American Journal of Public Health* **52**, 976–990.

Losikoff, M. E. (1978). *Applied and Environmental Microbiology* **36**, 386–388.

Lovelock, D. W. (1980). *In* "Microbial Growth and Survival in Extremes of Environment" (G. W. Gould and J. E. L. Corry, eds), pp. 159–172. Society for Applied Bacteriology Technical Series No. 15. Academic Press, London and New York.

Lowick, J. A. M. and Anema, P. J. (1972). *Journal of Applied Bacteriology* **35**, 119–121.

Lund, B. M. (1962). *Ph.D. Thesis*, University of London.

Lynt, R. K., Kautter, D. A. and Solomon, H. M. (1977). *Journal of Food Science* **44**, 108–111.

Lynt, R. K., Solomon, H. M., Lilly, T., Jr. and Kautter, D. A. (1979). *Journal of Food Science* **52**, 1022–1025.

Magoon, C. A. (1926). *Journal of Infectious Diseases* **38**, 429–439.

Marshall, B. J., Murrell, W. G. and Scott, W. J. (1963). *Journal of General Microbiology* **31**, 451–460.

Martin, J. H. and Blackwood, P. W. (1972). *Journal of Dairy Science* **55**, 577–580.

Martin J. H., Harper, W. J. and Gould, I. A. (1966). *Journal of Dairy Science* **49**, 1367–1370.

Matsuyama, A., Thornley, M. J. and Ingram, M. (1964). *Journal of Applied Bacteriology* **27**, 125–133.

Mayernik, J. J. (1972). *Bulletin of the Parenteral Drug Association* **26**, 205–211.

McKillop, E. J. (1959). *Journal of Hygiene, Cambridge* **57**, 31–46.

Michels, M. J. M. (1979). *In* "Cold-tolerant Micro-organisms in Spoilage and the Environment" (A. D. Russell and R. Fuller, eds), pp. 39–50. Society for Applied Bacteriology Technical Series No. 13. Academic Press, London and New York.

Michels, M. J. M. and Visser, F. M. W. (1976). *Journal of Applied Bacteriology* **41**, 1–11.

Mishiro, Y. and Ochi, M. (1966). *Nature, London* **211**, 1190.

Moats, W. A. (1971). *Journal of Bacteriology* **105**, 165–171.

Moats, W. A., Dabbah, R. and Edwards, V. M. (1971). *Journal of Food Science* **36**, 523–526.

Molin, N. and Snygg, B. G. (1967). *Applied Microbiology* **15**, 1422–1436.

Murray, T. J. (1931). *Journal of Infectious Diseases* **48**, 457–467.

Murray, T. J. and Headlee, M. R. (1931). *Journal of Infectious Diseases* **48**, 436–456.

Murrell, W. G. (1964). *Australian Journal of Pharmacy* S40–S46.

Murrell, W. G. (1967). *Advances in Microbial Physiology* **1**, 133–251.

Murrell, W. G. and Scott, W. J. (1957). *Nature, London* **179**, 481–482.

Murrell, W. G. and Scott, W. J. (1966). *Journal of General Microbiology* **43**, 411–425.

Murrell, W. G. and Warth, A. D. (1965). *In* "Spores III" (L. L. Campbell and H. O. Halvorson, eds), pp. 1–24. American Society for Microbiology, Washington D.C.

Myers, T. and Chrai, S. (1980). *Journal of the Parenteral Drug Association* **34**, 234–243.

Navani, S. K., Scholefield, J. and Kirby, M. R. (1970). *Journal of Applied Bacteriology* **33**, 609–620.

Nishida, S., Seo, N. and Nakagawa, M. (1969a). *Applied Microbiology* **17**, 303–309.

Nishida, S., Yamagishi, T., Tamai, K., Sanada, I. and Takahashi, K. (1969b). *Journal of Infectious Diseases* **120**, 507–516.

Nuffield Provincial Hospitals Trust (1958). "Present Sterilizing Practice in Six Hospitals".

O'Connor, F. (1974). *Irish Journal of Agricultural Research* **13**, 61–68.

Odlaug, T. E. and Pflug, I. J. (1977). *Applied and Environmental Microbiology* **34**, 23–29.

Ohye, D. F. and Scott, W. J. (1957). *Australian Journal of Biological Science* **10**, 85–94.

Ordonex, J. A. and Burgos, J. (1976). *Applied and Environmental Microbiology* **32**, 183–184.

Owen, J. (1978). *In* "Large Volume Parenterals": Seminar, Oslo, 1978, pp. 67–84. Published by Secretariat to the Convention for the Mutual Recognition of Inspections in Respect of the Manufacture of Pharmaceutical Products, Geneva.

Pace, P. J., Krumbiegel, E. R. and Wisniewski, H. J. (1972). *Applied Microbiology* **23**, 750–757.

Perkin, A. G., Burton, H., Underwood, H. M. and Davies, F. L. (1977). *Journal of Food Technology* **12**, 131–148.

Perkin, A. G., Davies, F. L., Neaves, P., Jarvis, B., Ayres, C. A., Brown, K. L., Falloon, W. C., Dallyn, H. and Bean, P. G. (1980). *In* "Microbial Growth and Survival in Extremes of Environment" (G. W. Gould and J. E. L. Corry, eds.), pp. 173–188. Society for Applied Bacteriology Technical Series No. 15. Academic Press, London and New York.

Perkins, W. E. (1965). *Journal of Applied Bacteriology* **28**, 1–16.

Pflug, I. J. (1960). *Food Technology* **14**, 483–487.

Pflug, I. J. (1973). *In* "Industrial Sterilization" (G. B. Phillips and W. S. Miller, eds), pp. 239–282. Duke University Press, Durham, North Carolina.

Pflug, I. J. and Christensen, R. (1980). *Journal of Food Science* **45**, 35–40.

Pflug, I. J. and Holcombe, R. G. (1977). *In* "Disinfection, Sterilization and Preservation" (S. S. Block, ed.), 2nd edn, pp. 933–994. Lea and Febiger, Philadelphia.

Pflug, I. J. and Schmidt, C. F. (1968). *In* "Disinfection, Sterilization and Preservation" (C. A. Lawrence and S. S. Block, eds), pp. 63–105. Lea and Febiger, Philadelphia.

Pflug, I. J. and Smith, G. M. (1977). *In* "Spore Research 1976" (A. N. Barker, J. Wolf, D. J. Ellar, G. J. Dring and G. W. Gould, eds), pp. 501–525. Academic Press, London and New York.

Pflug, I. J., Jones, A. T. and Blanchett, R. (1980). *Journal of Food Science* **45**, 940–945.

D

Pheil, C. G., Pflug, I. J., Nicholas, R. C. and Augustin, J. A. L. (1967). *Applied Microbiology* **15**, 120–124.

Powell, J. F. (1957). *Journal of Applied Bacteriology* **20**, 349–358.

Powell, J. F. and Hunter, J. R. (1955). *Journal of General Microbiology* **13**, 59–67.

Powell, J. F. and Strange, R. E. (1953). *Biochemical Journal* **54**, 205–209.

Prokop, A. and Humphrey, A. E. (1970). *In* "Disinfection" (M. A. Benarde, ed.), pp. 61–83. Marcell Dekker, New York.

Prokop, A. and Humphrey, A. E. (1972). *Folia Microbiologica* **17**, 437–445.

Put, H. M. C. and Aalsberberg, W. I. J. (1967). *Journal of Applied Bacteriology* **30**, 411–419.

Put, H. M. C. and Wybinga, S. J. (1963). *Journal of Applied Bacteriology* **26**, 428–434.

Rahn, O. (1945). *Bacteriological Reviews* **9**, 1–47.

Rajan, K. S. and Grecz, N. (1977). *In* "Spore Research 1976". (A. N. Barker, J. Wolf, D. J. Ellar, G. J. Dring and G. W. Gould, eds), pp. 527–543. Academic Press, London and New York.

Reich, R. R., Whitbourne, J. E. and McDaniel, A. W. (1979). *Journal of the Parenteral Drug Association* **33**, 228–234.

Reichart, O. (1979). *Acta Alimentaria* **8**, 131–155.

Report (1959). Medical Research Council: Report of a Working Party on Pressure Steam Sterilizers. *Lancet* **1**, 425–435.

Report (1978). Autoclaving practice in microbiology laboratories: report of a survey. *Journal of Clinical Pathology* **31**, 418–422.

Rey, C. R., Walker, H. W. and Rohrbaugh, P. L. (1975). *Journal of Milk and Food Technology* **38**, 461–465.

Reynolds, H. and Lichenstein, H. (1952). *Bacteriological Reviews* **16**, 126–135.

Richards, J. W. (1965). *British Chemical Engineering* **10**, 166–169.

Ridgeway, J. D. (1958). *Journal of Applied Bacteriology* **21**, 118–127.

Riemann, H. (1963). *Food Technology* **17**, 39–49.

Riemann, H. (1969a). *In* "Food-borne Infections and Intoxications" (H. Riemann, ed.), pp. 291–327. Academic Press, London and New York.

Riemann, H. (1969b). *In* "Food-borne Infections and Intoxications" (H. Riemann, ed.), pp. 489–541. Academic Press, London and New York.

Roberts, T. A. (1968). *Journal of Applied Bacteriology* **31**, 133–144.

Roberts, T. A. and Derrick, C. M. (1975). *Journal of Applied Bacteriology* **38**, 33–37.

Roberts, T. A. and Gibson, A. M. (1979). *Journal of Food Technology* **14**, 211–226.

Roberts, T. A. and Ingram, M. (1965). *Journal of Applied Bacteriology* **28**, 125–139.

Roberts, T. A., Gilbert, R. J. and Ingram, M. (1966a). *Journal of Food Technology* **1**, 227–235.

Roberts, T. A., Gilbert, R. J. and Ingram, M. (1966b). *Journal of Applied Bacteriology* **29**, 549–555.

Rode, L. J. and Foster, J. W. (1960). *Journal of Bacteriology* **79**, 650–656.

Rode, L. J. and Foster, J. W. (1961). *Zeitschrifte für Allgemeine Mikrobiologie* **1**, 307–322.

Rode, L. J. and Foster, J. W. (1962a). *Archiv für Mikrobiologie* **43**, 183–200.

Rode, L. J. and Foster, J. W. (1962b). *Archiv für Mikrobiologie* **43**, 201–212.

Rosenberg, B., Kemeny, G., Switzer, R. C. and Hamilton, T. C. (1971). *Nature, London* **232**, 471–473.

Rotman, Y. and Fields, M. L. (1969a). *Journal of Food Science* **34**, 343–344.

Rotman, Y. and Fields, M. L. (1969b). *Journal of Food Science* **34**, 345–346.

Rubbo, S. D. and Gardner, J. F. (1965). "A Review of Sterilization and Disinfection". Lloyd-Luke, London.

Russell, A. D. (1965). *Manufacturing Chemist and Aerosol News* **36**, 38–45.

Russell, A. D. (1971). *In* "Inhibition and Destruction of the Microbial Cell" (W. B. Hugo, ed.), pp. 451–612. Academic Press, London and New York.

Russell, A. D. and Harries, D. (1968). *Applied Microbiology* **16**, 335–339.

Sadoff, H. L. (1970). *Journal of Applied Bacteriology* **33**, 130–140.

Sakaguchi, G. (1969). *In* "Food-borne Infections and Intoxications" (H. Riemann, ed.), pp. 329–358. Academic Press, London and New York.

Savage, R. H. M. (1959). *In* "The Operation of Sterilizing Autoclaves", pp. 1–11. Pharmaceutical Press, London.

Sebald, M. (1968). *Annales de l'Institut Pasteur* **114**, 265–276.

Segner, W. P. and Schmidt, C. F. (1971). *Applied Microbiology* **22**, 1030–1033.

Segner, W. P., Schmidt, C. F. and Boltz, J. K. (1971a). *Applied Microbiology* **22**, 1017–1024.

Segner, W. P., Schmidt, C. F. and Boltz, J. K. (1971b). *Applied Microbiology* **22**, 1025–1029.

Selkon, J. B., Sisson, P. R. and Ingham, H. R. (1979). *Journal of Hygiene, Cambridge* **83**, 121–125.

Senhaji, A. F. and Loncin, M. (1975). *Industries Alimentaires et Agricoles* **92**, 611–617.

Senhaji, A. F., Bimbenet, J. J. and LeMaguer, M. (1976). *Industries Alimentaires et Agricoles* **93**, 13–20.

Shapton, D. A., Lovelock, D. W. and Laurita-Longo, R. (1971). *Journal of Applied Bacteriology* **34**, 491–500.

Sharpe, K. and Bektash, R. M. (1977). *Canadian Journal of Microbiology* **23**, 1501–1507.

Shehata, T. E. and Collins, E. B. (1972). *Journal of Dairy Science* **55**, 1405–1409.

Shiga, I. (1976). *Journal of Food Science* **41**, 461–462.

Shull, J. J. and Ernst, R. R. (1966). *Applied Microbiology* **10**, 452–457.

Shull, J. J., Cargo, G. T. and Ernst, R. R. (1963). *Applied Microbiology* **11**, 485–487.

Singleton, R. and Ameluxen, R. E. (1973). *Bacteriological Reviews* **37**, 320–342.

Slepecky, R. A. and Foster, J. W. (1959). *Journal of Bacteriology* **78**, 117–123.

Smelt, J. P. P. M. and Mossel, D. A. A. (1982). *In* "Principles and Practice of Disinfection, Preservation and Sterilization" (A. D. Russell, W. B. Hugo and G. A. J. Ayliffe, eds), 478–512. Blackwell Scientific Publications, Oxford.

Smelt, J. P. P. M., Santos da Silva, M. J. and Haas, H. (1977). *In* "Spore Research 1976" (A. N. Barker, J. Wolf, D. J. Ellar, G. J. Dring and G. W. Gould, eds), pp. 469–485. Academic Press, London and New York.

Sommer, E. W. (1930). *Journal of Infectious Diseases* **46**, 85–114.

Sousa, F., Silva, M. T. and Balassa, G. (1978). *Annales de Microbiologie (Institut Pasteur)* **129B**, 377–390.

Steele, R. J. and Board, P. W. (1979). *Journal of Food Technology* **14**, 227–235.

Steinbach, E. (1977). *In* "Spore Research 1976" (A. N. Barker, J. Wolf, D. J. Ellar, G. N. Dring and G. W. Gould, eds), pp. 451–468. Academic Press, London and New York.

Stewart, A. W. and Johnson, M. G. (1977). *Journal of General Microbiology* **103**, 45–50.

Stewart, M., Somlyo, A. P., Somlyo, A. V., Shuman, H., Lindsay, J. A. and Murrell, W. G. (1980). *Journal of Bacteriology* **143**, 481–491.

Stumbo, C. R. (1948). *Food Technology* **2**, 228–240.

Stumbo, C. R. (1973). "Thermobacteriology in Food Processing", 2nd edn. Academic Press, London and New York.

Stumbo, C. R., Purohit, K. S. and Ramakrishnan, T. V. (1975). *Journal of Food Science* **40**, 1316–1323.

Sugiyama, H. (1951). *Bacteriological Reviews* **16**, 125–126.

Sundberg, A. D. and Carlin, A. F. (1978). *Journal of Food Science* **43**, 285–288.

Sykes, G. (1965). "Disinfection and Sterilization", 2nd edn. Spon, London.

Sykes, G. (1966). *Process Biochemistry* August, pp. 1–5.

Tallentire, A. and Chiori, C. D. (1963). *Journal of Pharmacy and Pharmacology* **15**, 148T–149T.

Tallentire, A., Maughan, R. L., Michael, B. D. and Stratford, I. J. (1977). *In* "Spore Research 1976" (A. N. Barker, J. Wolf, D. J. Ellar, G. J. Dring and G. W. Gould, eds), pp. 649–659. Academic Press, London and New York.

Tang, T. C. and Grecz, N. (1965). *Bacteriological Proceedings* A37, p. 7.

Thompson, D. R., Willardsen, R. R., Busta, F. F. and Allen, C. E. (1979). *Journal of Food Science* **44**, 646–651.

Thorpe, R. H. (1960). *Journal of Applied Bacteriology* **23**, 136–145.

Toda, K. (1970). *Journal of Fermentation Technology* **48**, 811–818.

Tomlins, R. I. and Ordal, Z. J. (1976). *In* "Inhibition and Inactivation of Vegetative Microbes" (F. A. Skinner and W. B. Hugo, eds), pp. 153–190. Society for Applied Bacteriology Symposium Series No. 5. Academic Press, London and New York.

Tong, J. L., Engle, H. M., Cullyford, J. S. and Love, C. E. (1962). *American Journal of Public Health* **52**, 976–990.

Tsuji, K. and Perkins, W. E. (1962). *Journal of Bacteriology* **84**, 81–85.

Vas, K. (1970). *Journal of Applied Bacteriology* **33**, 157–166.

Vas, K. and Proszt, G. (1957). *Journal of Applied Bacteriology* **20**, 431–441.

Vinter, V. (1957). *Journal of Applied Bacteriology* **20**, 325–332.

Vinter, V. (1959). *Folia Microbiologica* **4**, 216–221.

Vinter, V. (1960). *Folia Microbiologica* **5**, 217–230.

Virtannen, A. I. and Pulkki, L. (1933). *Archiv für Mikrobiologie* **4**, 99–122.

Wadham, D. G. and Halvorson, H. O. (1954). *Applied Microbiology* **2**, 333–338.

Waites, W. M., Stansfield, R. and Bayliss, C. E. (1979). *FEMS Microbiology Letters* **5**, 365–368.

Walker, H. W. (1964). *Journal of Food Science* **29**, 360–365.

Walker, H. W. and Matches, J. R. (1966). *Journal of Food Science* **30**, 1029–1036.

Walker, H. W., Matches, J. R. and Ayres, J. C. (1961). *Journal of Bacteriology* **82**, 960–966.

Wallace, M. J., Nordsiden, K. L., Wolf, I. D., Thompson, D. R. and Zottola, E. A. (1978). *Journal of Food Science* **43**, 1738–1740.

Wang, D. I. C., Scherer, J. and Humphrey, A. E. (1964). *Applied Microbiology* **12**, 451–454.

Warburg, R. J. and Moir, A. (1981). *Journal of General Microbiology* **124**, 243–253.

Warth, A. D. (1978a). *Journal of Bacteriology* **134**, 699–705.

Warth, A. D. (1978b). *Advances in Microbial Physiology* **17**, 1–45.

Warth, A. D. (1980). *Journal of Bacteriology* **143**, 27–34.

Warth, A. D. and Strominger, J. L. (1969). *Proceedings of the National Academy of Sciences, U.S.* **64**, 528–535.

Warth, A. D. and Strominger, J. L. (1972). *Biochemistry* **11**, 1389–1396.

Warth, A. D., Ohye, D. F. and Murrell, W. G. (1963a). *Journal of Cellular Biology* **16**, 579–592.

Warth, A. D., Ohye, D. F. and Murrell, W. G. (1963b). *Journal of Cellular Biology* **16**, 593–609.

Weiss, K. F. and Strong, D. H. (1967a). *Journal of Bacteriology* **93**, 21–26.

Weiss, K. F. and Strong, D. H. (1967b). *Nature, London* **215**, 530.

Wells, C. and Whitwell, F. R. (1960). *Lancet* **2**, 643–644.

Whitbourne, J. E., Ferris, B. K. and Morien, L. L. (1977). *Developments in Industrial Microbiology* **18**, 353–362.

Wickus, G. G., Warth, A. D. and Strominger, J. L. (1972). *Journal of Bacteriology* **111**, 625–627.

Widdowson, J. P. (1967). *Nature, London* **214**, 812–813.

Wiksell, J. C., Pickett, M. S. and Hartman, P. A. (1973). *Applied Microbiology* **25**, 431–435.

Wilkinson, G. and Davies, F. L. (1973). *Journal of Applied Bacteriology* **36**, 485–496.

Wilkinson, G. R. and Baker, L. C. (1964). *Progress in Industrial Microbiology* **5**, 231–282.

Willardsen, R. R., Busta, F. F., Allen, C. E. and Smith, L. B. (1978). *Journal of Food Science* **43**, 470–475.

Williams, D. J., Franklin, J. G., Chapman, H. R. and Clegg, L. F. L. (1957). *Journal of Applied Bacteriology* **20**, 43–49.

Williams, O. B. (1929). *Journal of Infectious Diseases* **71**, 225–227.

Williams, O. B. and Hennessee, A. D. (1956). *Food Research* **21**, 112–116.

Wilson, D. A. (1968). *Journal of Medical and Laboratory Technology* **25**, 301–312.

Wise, J., Swanson, A. and Halvorson, H. O. (1971). *Journal of Bacteriology* **94**, 2075–2076.

Woese, C. (1958). *Journal of Bacteriology* **75**, 5–8.

Woese, C. (1959). *Journal of Bacteriology* **77**, 38–42.

Wooley, B. C. and Collier, R. E. (1965). *Canadian Journal of Microbiology* **11**, 279–285.

Yawger, E. S. (1978). *Food Technology* **32**(6), 59–62.

Young, I. E. (1959). *Canadian Journal of Microbiology* **5**, 197–202.

Zytkovicz, T. H. and Halvorson, H. O. (1972). *In* "Spores V" (H. O. Halvorson, R. Hanson and L. L. Campbell, eds), pp. 49–52. American Society for Microbiology, Washington, D.C.

3

Inactivation of Bacterial Spores by Thermal Processes (Dry Heat)

I. *Introduction*

There is less information available about the resistance of bacterial spores to dry heat than to moist heat, although it has been known for many years that dry heat is less effective in destroying bacteria than moist heat (see Richards, 1968). It has been shown that whereas vegetative cells were destroyed after 1½ h at 100°C, a temperature of 140°C for 3 h was required to destroy spores. More recently, the development of the United States space programme has of necessity meant that knowledge of sterilization processes has been improved. This applies particularly to dry heat sterilization, since many components of spacecraft are sterilized by such means. An important off-shoot has been a better understanding of dry heat, of the factors that influence its efficacy and of the nature of its lethal effects.

II. *Types of Dry Heat Processes*

Normally, dry heat sterilization processes are carried out in hot-air ovens, although a number of sterilizing temperature-time levels have been advocated by various authors (Darmady and Brock, 1954). Gas-heated ovens may have a wide variation of temperature, and electrically-heated ovens without a fan are also unsatisfactory, since heat is taken up slowly and temperature fluctuations are again a problem. Prompt absorption of heat and minimal temperature variations are advantages of the presence of a fan (Darmady and Brock, 1954; Darmady *et al.*, 1961; Patrick *et al.*, 1961).

Other types of dry heat sterilizer, apart from methods using super-heated steam, include the following:

(a) the conveyor oven (Darmady *et al.*, 1961), which consists of an insulated tunnel in which a series of infrared heaters has been placed at predetermined intervals, and in which a moving belt carries articles to be sterilized;

(b) a thermostatically-controlled hot plate (Darmady *et al.*, 1958, 1961), on to which an aluminium block has been fixed; instruments, etc., are heated by conducted heat;

(c) an infrared sterilizer, infrared rays having the property of rapidly raising the temperature of objects they strike (Darmady *et al.*, 1961; Molin and Ostlund, 1975, 1976; Molin, 1977a,b,c, 1982; Molin and Svensson, 1976);

(d) an automatic dry heat sterilizer operating at 200°C (Quesnel *et al.*, 1967).

It must be remembered, however, that hot air, hot inert gases, dry heat in a vacuum, and superheated steam (see Savage, 1959) should not be accepted as equivalent sources of dry heat sterilization (Bruch *et al.*, 1963). An apparatus for determining the resistance of bacterial spores to dry heat conditions at temperatures in the range 149–193°C has been designed and constructed by Pflug (1960). Willing (1979) has recently described a short-term, hot air laminar flow process.

The basis of dry heat sterilization is that the object to be sterilized is brought up to and maintained at the desired temperature for the requisite period of time. Thus, the packing of the sterilizer is very important, and details of this aspect have been published elsewhere (Darmady *et al.*, 1961; Knox, 1961; Report, 1962).

III. *Mathematical Aspects*

A. **Definitions**

Various terms employed in moist heat sterilization are also used here. These are:

(a) Thermal death time (TDT). This is the time in minutes at a particular dry heat temperature to kill all the spores in a given population.

(b) D-value. This is defined as the time in minutes at a particular temperature to reduce the original spore population by 90%, i.e. to 10%.

(c) F-value. This is the time in minutes at 350°F (176°C) to destroy the spores. (For further information on F and F_0-values, Chapter 2 should be consulted).

(d) z-value. This represents the slope of the straight line when D-value or TDT is plotted against temperature, and is expressed in °C (or occasionally in °F).

A more detailed consideration of these values was given in Chapter 2. D-values may be calculated from the equation:

$$D = U/\log N_0 - \log N_u \text{ (equation number (3) in Chapter 2)} \quad (1)$$

where N_0 represents the initial number of spores per replicate unit, and N_u is the number surviving after heating time U.

Equation (4), page 40, showed that $N_u = 2 \cdot 303 \log_{10}(r/q)$. Thus, when the fraction negative is 50%, N_u is 0·6932 and $\log_{10} N_u$ is 1·8408 which is approximately $-0·16$ (Pheil *et al.*, 1967).

When the fraction negative is 50%, the above equation ((1)) is simplified to:

$$D\text{-value} = \frac{U_{FN50}}{\log N_0 + 0.16} \qquad (2)$$

in which U_{FN50} denotes the time to give a 50% fraction-of-units (FN) negative.

A method of determining F-values from D-values was described by Bruch *et al.* (1963), both of equations (3) and (4) being applicable:

$$F = D\text{-value} (\log A + 2) \qquad (3)$$

in which A is the number of spores per replicate;

$$F = D\text{-value} (\log M + 1) \qquad (4)$$

where M is the number of spores per replicate multiplied by the number of replicates.

B. Graphical Responses

Results of the exposure of spores to dry heat are usually expressed as (a) the surviving fraction plotted against time, or (b) plots of D-value, TDT or U_{FN50} against temperature (°C or °F). Time–survivor curves are variable, either non-linear with decreasing death-rate of soil samples (Bond *et al.*, 1970); linear with pure cultures of *B. subtilis* var. *niger* (Bond *et al.*, 1970; Brannen and Garst, 1972; Gurney and Quesnel, 1980), *B. subtilis* (Put and Aalbersberg, 1967), *B. globigii* (Bruch *et al.*, 1963), *B. stearothermophilus* (Darmady *et al.*, 1961), *Cl. tetani* (Darmady *et al.*, 1961) and unoccluded but not crystal occluded spores of *B. globigii* (Doyle and Ernst, 1967), the actual slope depending on the recovery medium used (Gurney and Quesnel, 1980); or an initial shoulder followed by a linear response, as found with *B. subtilis* MD2 spores (Gurney and Quesnel, 1980). Naturally occurring spores obtained directly from soil show non-logarithmic inactivation (Bond *et al.*, 1970). The occurrence of two fractions of spores of *B. subtilis* ATCC 6633 with differing heat sensitivities has been described (Molin and Östlund, 1975) and an extremely dry heat resistant *Bacillus* sp. (ATCC 27380) has been shown to require either dry heat or moist heat for activation (Bond *et al.*, 1973). As would be expected, plots against temperature, °C or °F, of D-value (Pflug, 1960; Augustin and Pflug, 1967; Molin, 1977b; Gurney and Quesnel, 1980), TDT (Darmady *et al.*, 1958; Bruch *et al.*, 1963) or U_{FN50} (Pheil *et al.*, 1967) give a straight line response.

Table 3.1. Thermal death times (TDTs) of some bacterial spores exposed to dry heat

Organism	Temperature (°C)	TDT (min)	Reference
B. anthracis	120	40–45	Murray (1931)
	120	60	Oag (1940)
	125	25	Murray (1931)
	130	15–20	Murray (1931)
	135	5–10	Murray (1931)
	150	60–120	Sykes (1966)
	160	9	Oag (1940)
	160	9–90	Sykes (1966)
	185	3	Oag (1940)
B. licheniformis	140	30	
	150	20	
	160	10	
	170	5	Francis (1956)
	180	1	
	190	1	
	200	0·5	
Cl. tetani	125	20–40	Murray and Headlee (1931)
	130	20–40	Sykes (1966)
	135	5–25	Murray and Headlee (1931)
	140	5–15	Murray and Headlee (1931)
	140	5–15	Sykes (1966)
	150	30	
	160	12	Darmady et al. (1958)
	170	5	
	180	1	

C. Thermal Death Times

A summary of TDTS obtained for certain spores, and particularly for
B. anthracis and *Cl. tetani* is given in Table 3.1. In some cases there is a
reasonably close agreement between the results cited by different
authors, whereas in other cases there is a marked variation. Possibly,
the differences in spore strains used may be responsible for some of this
variation, and the fact that the lag in bringing spore samples up to a
particular temperature has not always been considered (Oag, 1940) is
undoubtedly responsible for some of the discrepancies. There has also
been a variation in the initial number of spores used by different
authors, and this important fact should always be borne in mind (see
Section IVA, also).

Table 3.2. D-values of some bacterial spores exposed to dry heat

Organism	Strain	Type of dry heat[a]	Temperature (°C)	D-value (min)	Reference
B. subtilis	—	Superheated steam	176	0·57	Pflug (1960)
	—	CO$_2$	160	1·40	
		Air	160	1·46	Pheil *et al.* (1967)
		Oxygen	160	1·47	
		Helium	160	1·63	
		Nitrogen	160	1·96	
	MD2[b]	Hot oil	140	2·19–4·2	Gurney and Quesnel (1980)
			150	0·51–1·31	
			160	0·2 – 0·41	
			170	0·08–0·11	
	NCIB 8054	Hot oil: Soybean	112	275	Molin and Snygg (1967)
			117	105	
			121	108	
		Triolein	112	65	
			117	13	
			121	8	
B. subtilis var. *niger*	—[b]	Hot oil	140	4·79–5·68	Gurney and Quesnel (1980)
			150	1·26–1·6	
			160	0·5 –0·65	
			170	0·17–0·23	
	ATCC 372	Infrared	100	528	Molin (1977b)
			120	30	
			190	1s	

Table 3.2. (contd.)

Organism	Strain	Type of dry heat[a]	Temperature (°C)	D-value (min)	Reference
	ATCC 9372	Resistometer			
		In oils	160	0·32–0·53 ⎫	
		Serum albumin	160	1·07 ⎬	Molin (1977)
		Sugars	160	0·1 –1 ⎭	
B. stearothermophilus	1518	Conducted	121	15 ⎫	Bruch *et al.* (1963
	1518		160	0·35 ⎬	Collier and Townsend (1956)
		Superheated steam	176	0·14	Molin and Snygg (1967)
	NCIB 8924	Hot oil (soybean)	121	8	
	—	Alumina-attached, oil bath	120	70 ⎫	Niepokajczycka and Zekrzewski (1972)
			140	20 ⎬	
			160	5 ⎭	
B. polymyxa	—	Superheated steam	176	0·13	Collier and Townsend (1956)
B. globigii	—	Conducted	121	52·7 ⎫	Bruch *et al.* (1963)
			160	1·8 ⎬	
Bacillus sp.	ATCC 27380	Hot air oven	125	139 h	Bond *et al.* (1973)

Table 3.2 (*contd.*).

Organism	Strain	Type of dry heat[a]	Temperature (°C)	D-value (min)	Reference
B. cereus	NCIB 5893	Hot oil: Soybean	112	46·5	
			121	30	
		Olive oil	121	17·4	Molin and
		Triolein	112	14	Syngg (1967)
			121	10	
		Liquid paraffin	112	21	
			121	8	
B. megaterium	NCIB 8508	Hot oil: Soybean	112	11·5	
			117	8	
			121	6	Molin and
		Olive oil	121	7	Snygg (1967)
		Triolein	112	15	
			117	9	
			121	6	
C. sporogenes	PA 3679	Superheated steam	176	0·125	Collier and Townsend (1956)
	PA 3679-45	CO_2	148·9	8	
		Air	148·9	6	
		Helium	148·9	8·8	Pheil *et al.* (1967)
		CO_2	160	2·4	
		Air	160	1·95	
		Helium	160	2·4	

[a] Nature of dry heat technique used, or of gas present.
[b] D-value depends on recovery medium used.

D. *D*-values

Examples of *D*-values of various spores at various temperatures, and under different heating conditions are given in Table 3.2. This table indicates that the type of dry heat employed, the presence of various gases and the temperature all influence the *D*-value. In addition, it is apparent that an organism such as *B. stearothermophilus* which is highly resistant to moist heat is not especially resistant to dry heat. In fact, the results in this table indicate that it is considerably more sensitive than *B. subtilis* or *B. globigii*. The effect of a_w values on the heat resistance of bacterial spores was considered in Chapter 2, where it was shown that maximum resistance of spores to heat occurred at an a_w value of *ca.* 0·2–0·3, and that under drier conditions, the resistance of the spore decreased (see also Table 3.6, which deals with the effects of humidity on dry heat sterilization).

Certain aspects of this table will be considered more fully in Section IV. Much higher *D*-values occur when spores are exposed to dry heat than to moist heat (Table 3.3).

E. *z*-values

Examples of *z*-values of various spores are given in Table 3.4, which indicates that they are much higher than those obtained with moist heat processes. As regards individual organisms, the *z*-value is of the order of 20°C for most of the *Bacillus* and *Clostridium* spp. listed, although it is to be noted that the results of Collier and Townsend (1956) attribute a

Table 3.3. Comparison[a] of *D*-values of *B. subtilis* (strain 5230) exposed to wet heat and dry heat

Temp. (°C)	D-value (min)	
	Wet heat	Dry heat
77	720	—
95	32	24 900
104	14	—
113	—	2268
121	0·5	—
129	—	270
152	—	10·5

[a] Data of Fox and Eder (1969).

Table 3.4. z-values of some spores[a] exposed to dry heat

Organism	z-value (°C)	Reference
B. stearothermophilus	14·4	Collier and Townsend (1956)
	24·4	Bruch *et al.* (1963)
	29[b]	Molin (1977b)
	40	Niepokojczycka and Zakrzewski (1972)
B. subtilis	23·3	Pflug (1960)
	18·3	Pheil *et al.* (1967)
	17	Fox and Eder (1969)
	23	Molin (1977c)
	18·25–18·75[d]	Gurney and Quesnel (1980)
B. subtilis var. *niger*	12·9–32[c]	Angelotti *et al.* (1968)
	22–25	Molin (1977a), Molin and Svensson (1976), Molin and Östlund (1976)
	21	Gurney and Quesnel (1980)
B. globigii	27·2	Bruch *et al.* (1963)
B. polymyxa	22	Molin (1977c)
	15·5	Collier and Townsend (1956)
B. cereus	22 ⎫	
B. coagulans	31 ⎬	Molin (1976)
B. megaterium	21 ⎪	
B. pumilus	25 ⎭	
Cl. tetani	25	Darmady *et al.* (1958)
Cl. sporogenes (PA 3679)	33	Collier and Townsend (1956)
	18·3–21·7[e]	Augustin and Pflug (1967)
	20–20[f]	Augustin and Pflug (1967)
	21·7	Pheil *et al.* (1967)

[a] Variations may in part be attributable to differences in strains and in techniques.

[b] Over range of 150–180°C: a decreasing z-value occurred at lower temperatures, and a z-value of 23°C was obtained if the spores were dried before heat treatment.

[c] z-value depended on actual carrier used.

[d] Only slight variations in z-value when different recovery media used.

[e] Sporulation medium was brain heart infusion. z-values depended on the recovery medium used.

[f] Sporulation medium contained trypticase. z-values were constant, irrespective of recovery medium used.

much lower z-value to *B. stearothermophilus* and a much higher z-value to *Cl. sporogenes* PA 3679 than do the findings of other authors.

F. Y-intercept and Y_0/N_0 values

A consideration of the usefulness of the Y-intercept and of calculating Y_0/N_0 values (both expressed as $\log_{10}$) was given in the previous Chapter (Section IV.F). It will be recalled that when Y_0/N_0 is < 1, then the shape of the time–survivor curve is one of decreasing death-rate,

Table 3.5. Y_0/N_0 values for some bacterial spores exposed to dry heat[a]

Organism	Strain	Temperature range (°C)	Range of Y_0/N_0 values [b]
B. cereus	NCIB 9373	140–160	1·0 –1·0
B. coagulans	NCIB 9365	140–170	0·83–0·7
B. megaterium	NCIB 9376	140–170	1·0 –1·0
B. polymyxa	NCIB 8158	140–170	0·99–1·0
B. pumilus	NCTC 10337	150–180	0·84–0·8
B. stearothermophilus	ATCC 7953	150–170	0·79–0·86
	NCTC 1033	150–180	0·98–0·86
B. subtilis	NCIB 8054	150–170	0·94–0·89
B. subtilis var. niger	ATCC 9372	120–190	1·1 –1·0

[a] Based on the data of Molin and Östlund (1976) and Molin (1977a).

[b] Values are those at lowest and highest temperatures in the range tested.

NCIB, National Collection of Industrial Bacteria; ATCC, American Type Culture Collection; NCTC, National Collection of Type Cultures.

whereas when Y_0/N_0 is >1, there is an initial shoulder followed by exponential death.

Values of Y_0/N_0 obtained from Molin (1977c), and Molin and Östlund (1976) for various types of spores are listed in Table 3.5. These values are calculated by determining the Y-intercept value (Y_0) and dividing by the $\log_{10}$ of the original number of spores (N_0). With some types of spores the Y_0/N_0 value is one, and does not change as the temperature rises, indicating an exponential order of death. With other spores, the Y_0/N_0 values change with temperature. Molin (1977a) has shown that the dry heat resistance of *B. subtilis* var. *niger* ATCC 9372 spores is influenced by the presence of serum albumin, carbohydrates and lipids and that the Y_0/N_0 values are affected also.

It is, however, pertinent to add that Y_0/N_0 values should not be considered in isolation but rather as part of the entire information available, embracing D-, z- and F-values.

IV. *Factors Influencing the Sensitivity of Spores to Dry Heat*

Several factors influence the response of spores to dry heat. Whereas it could at one time be stated that only a fairly small amount of information was available (Russell, 1971) this is no longer a valid conclusion. For example, acidification increases the dry heat sensitivity of spores (Heckly and Dimatteo, 1975).

A. Inoculum Size and Type of Organism

As with moist heat, the number of spores present initially will influence the period necessary to achieve a total kill. For this reason, it would be logical to expect a variation in TDT values from one laboratory to another where different inocula of the same organism are employed. TDT values are thus of little importance, whereas D-values and z-values, both of which are independent of the initial spore population, thus give a more accurate representation of the rate of death (*cf.* Molin and Östlund, 1975, 1976).

Bacillus subtilis var. *niger* spores are frequently used in studies of sterilization of spacecraft by dry heat. However, these spores have not been detected on spacecraft (Puleo *et al.*, 1975) and are less resistant to dry heat than naturally occuring bacterial spores (Bond *et al.*, 1970, 1973; Wardle *et al.*, 1971; Puleo *et al.*, 1975). An extremely dry heat-resistant *Bacillus* species is described by Bond and Favero (1975).

Clostridium perfringens spores are reduced in number, but not eliminated, when heated in rump roasts cooked in an oven or an electric crockery pot (Sundberg and Carlin, 1976).

B. Sporulation Medium

The composition of the medium in or on which spores are formed would be expected to influence their response to dry heat.

Few studies have, however, been made. Molin and Svensson (1976) investigated the composition of sporulation medium on the dry heat resistance of *B. subtilis* var. *niger* spores and observed that those obtained from synthetic media were more heat resistant than those from complex media, and that the concentrations of calcium, sucrose and glucose were criticial. Similar findings are reported by Wardle *et al.* (1971).

C. Type of Dry Heat

The type of dry heat is known to influence the degree of killing of bacterial spores. Microorganisms are more resistant to hot gases of low water content than to superheated steam (Collier and Townsend, 1956). The type of gas, also, can influence the degree of resistance, and *B. subtilis* spores heated in helium and particularly in nitrogen are more resistant to dry heat than those heated in oxygen, carbon dioxide or air where the D-values are of the same order (Table 3.6: Pheil *et al.*, 1967).

When spores at various flow rates of air or nitrogen are dry heated at

Table 3.6. Effect of carrier on the dry heat resistance at 120°C of some bacterial spores[a]

| Organism | Strain | D-value (min) of spores dried on carriers | | |
		Paper strip	Glass tube	Sand
B. globigii	—			
Spore crop A		54·6	66	108
Spore crop B		37·8	43·2	72
B. subtilis	5230			
Spore crop A		43·2	—	78
Spore crop B		28·8	30	66
B. subtilis	120	23·4	16·8	72
B. coagulans	WH.9	108	126	144
B. stearothermophilus	1518			
Spore crop A		18·6	16·2	25·2
Spore crop B		19·2	13·2	—
Cl. sporogenes	PA 3679	16·2	16·2	42
Cl. sporogenes	Vera	8·4	16·2	36
Cl. tetani	—	19·8	9	—
Cl. perfringens type A	—	10·8	6	—

[a]Data of Bruch *et al.* (1963).

various temperatures, the effect of temperature on the spore destruction rate decreases as the flow rates increase (Fox and Pflug, 1968). This may be the result of greater dehydration of the spores, since flowing gas is a more effective system than static gas, so that spore moisture loss could well be a major factor in determining the thermal death rate of spores exposed to dry heat (Angelotti, 1968; Angelotti *et al.*, 1968; Fox and Pflug, 1968; Pflug, 1973; Pflug and Schmidt, 1968; Pflug and Holcombe, 1977). The importance of a_w values in dry heat resistance or sensitivity will be considered below (Section V).

D. Effect of Spore Carrier

The response of bacterial spores to dry heat depends upon the spore carrier, and spore samples dried on sand are more resistant than those dried on to paper or glass (Bruch *et al.*, 1963; see Table 3.6). In fact, spores entrapped in various solids are more resistant than the same organisms on paper strips at all temperatures (Koesterer, 1965; Doyle and Ernst, 1967). Angelotti (1968) and Angelotti *et al.* (1968) have likewise shown that the dry heat resistance of *B. subtilis* var. *niger* spores varies with their location on or in various materials, *D*-values at 135°C varying from 114 min (epoxy plastic, spores encapsulated in rods) to 2·6 min (stainless steel strips, spores on the surface). Again the importance of water in dry heat processes is apparent, since these enormous variations may be related to differences in the water retention capacity of the carriers (Angelotti, 1968). This aspect is discussed in more detail in Section V.B.

The dry heat resistance of spores located between mated surfaces depends on the composition of the components of the surfaces (Simko *et al.*, 1971).

Aerosolized bacterial spores are killed rapidly in a hot-air sterilizer (Mullican *et al.*, 1971).

E. Recovery Conditions

Russell (1971) stated that there was little information then available as to the influence of recovery conditions (composition and pH of the recovery medium, incubation temperature, etc.) on bacterial spores. In the intervening years, the situation has improved to some extent, and recovery and revival will be discussed in more detail in Chapter 10 (Section II.A,B).

It must, nevertheless, be added that recovery conditions should always be considered as being of great importance in evaluating sterilization or disinfection processes as erroneous conclusions could well be reached.

V. *Possible Mechanisms of Spore Inactivation by Dry Heat*

Microbial destruction by dry heat has been considered as being primarily an oxidation process (Sykes, 1965; Ernst, 1968, 1977). In the dry state, vegetative cells are "probably inactivated by oxidative reactions, chemical combinations that inactivate essential constituents and free radical reactions" (Murrell, 1964). If, in fact, oxidation is of prime importance, it would be expected that spores heated in oxygen would be far more sensitive to dry heat than when exposed in other gases, which is not invariably so in practice (Pheil *et al.*, 1967: Table 3.2).

Thus, whereas oxidation may play some role in dry heat destruction, other possibilities should also be considered.

A. Induction of Mutants

The induction of mutants by exposing *B. subtilis* strain 168 ind spores to dry heat *in vacuo* at temperatures in excess of 105°C was reported by Zamenhof (1960) and Chiasson and Zamenhof (1966). At temperatures above 105°C the proportion of auxotrophs increased rapidly reaching a maximum at 115°C and then slowly declining. A study of the depurination of DNA *in vitro* when heated under similar conditions also revealed that this chemical injury to the genetic material was negligible at temperatures below 100°C. Mutants of *B. subtilis* strain Marburg resulting from depurination at elevated temperatures have also been described (Northrop and Slepecky, 1967).

According to Molin (1977c), sensitivity or resistance of spores to dry heat may result from genetically determined differences in water content or in water-retaining capacity of the spores. The importance of water is discussed in Section B below.

B. The Role of Water

The water content of spores is an important factor in inactivation by dry heat (Brannen, 1970, 1971). Spores pre-equilibrated to an a_w value of 0·8–0·9 are more resistant than spores equilibrated to higher or lower a_w values (Murrell and Scott, 1957). If spores are pre-equilibrated at a particular a_w and heated at the same a_w in closed vessels, the higher resistance occurs at 0·2–0·4 (Murrell and Scott, 1966; see also Angelotti *et al.*, 1968). Prado Filho (1975) found that spores pre-equilibrated at a_w of 1·0 are most resistant to dry heat, this being independent of the gas atmosphere; in contrast, with spores pre-equilibrated at a_w of 0·0, 0·3 or 0·6 the resistance depends on the spore moisture content, the gas phase and the treatment temperature.

There is an increasing removal of water from spores as the exposure time at a constant drying temperature rises, and also during a constant exposure time as the drying temperature increases (Soper and Davies, 1973). When spores are heated in a dry atmosphere, most of their moisture is rapidly lost (Hoffman *et al.*, 1968). Spores held at 116·5°C adsorb water to an equivalent extent to those held at room temperature for a_w up to 0·05, but beyond this a_w value a reduction in moisture content occurs with the former in comparison to the latter (Rowe and Silverman, 1970). At high temperatures, spores rapidly exchange water with their environment, and wet spores equilibrated to a_w of 0·8 quickly lose moisture at a high temperature. These findings led Rowe and Silverman (1970) to postulate that only a relatively small amount of water is needed to protect the heat-sensitive site in spores and that dry heat resistance depends mainly on the location of water, rather than the amount, in the spore together with the nature of its association with other molecules. In fact, water is considered to exert a protective action against inactivation of spores by dry heat (Prado Filho, 1975). There is no significant difference between dry heat-inactivated or viable spores in terms of adsorption or desorption of water (Rowe and Silverman, 1970). The rate of spore desiccation during heating is important as is the water-retaining capacity of the material on or in which the spores are placed. Closed systems retard or prevent spore moisture loss and such spores are more resistant than when heated in open systems, where rapid loss of moisture takes place (Angelotti *et al.*, 1968).

Thus, in addition to those factors discussed in Section IV, it is obvious that the response of spores to dry heat depends upon the a_w before treatment (conditioning a_w) and the a_w during treatment (treatment a_w) (Angelotti *et al.*, 1968; Bruch and Smith, 1968; Hoffman *et al.*, 1968; Mullican and Hoffman, 1968; Drummond and Pflug, 1970). Reduction in either conditioning or treatment a_w from high-high values renders spores more sensitive to dry heat. The conditioning of objects at a low a_w environment prior to treatment increases the probability of achieving sterilization and a further increase can be obtained by lowering the treatment a_w (Drummond and Pflug, 1970). Moisture may also be a factor for the increasing dry heat resistance of spores occluded in crystals of glycine or sodium chloride (Mullican and Hoffman, 1968; see also Angelotti, 1968; Angelotti *et al.*, 1968) although a possible alternative, that of poor heat transfer, has also been considered (Doyle and Ernst, 1967).

VI. *Uses of Dry Heat*

A detailed discussion of the uses of dry heat is clearly outside the scope of this book, and the interested reader is referred to Carter (1972) for a comprehensive treatise. Only a few brief comments will thus be made here.

Products or equipment which may be sterilized by dry heat include sutures (which, as a result of their processing, may be heavily contaminated with *Cl. tetani* spores: Dawson, 1962); powders for topical use, such as talc, kaolin and sulphonamides which prior to sterilization may be heavily contaminated with bacterial spores; oils and oily injections (British Pharmacopoeia, 1980); glassware; glass syringes (Report, 1962); and various instruments and materials in space research (see

Sneath, 1968; Bond *et al.*, 1971; Puleo *et al.*, 1973, 1977, 1978: Trauth, 1973).

VII. *Testing of Sterilizers*

Bacteriological testing of gas-operated hot-air ovens has been carried out by using samples of earth and spores of *B. subtilis* and *B. stearothermophilus* (Patrick *et al.*, 1961). It was found that 180°C for 10 min was sufficient to kill the spores, but unfortunately no details as to the strains of test organisms or the method of recovery were provided. Moreover, earth samples may show considerable variation in composition, and hence in response to dry heat, and *B. stearothermophilus* does not appear to be particularly resistant to dry heat (Darmady *et al.*, 1958; Bruch *et al.*, 1963; Quesnel *et al.*, 1967).

Bacillus globigii has been recommended as a biological indicator (BI) in monitoring dry heat processes (Ernst, 1968). Quesnel *et al.* (1967) suggested that a mixture of *B. globigii* and *B. subtilis* MD2 (which seems to possess above-average resistance to dry heat: Gurney and Quesnel, 1980) would provide a suitable BI.

Another organism which has been proposed as a BI has been a non-toxigenic strain of *Cl. tetani* (Darmady *et al.*, 1958), with the suggestion (Darmady *et al.*, 1961) that the holding time at the selected sterilizing temperature should be 1½ times that required to kill all these spores at a temperature 10°C below that selected, e.g. the minimum lethal time (i.e. TDT) for this organism at 160°C was found to be 12 min (Table 3.1). Thus if a sterilizing temperature of 170°C were used, the holding time would be 1½ × 12 or 18 min.

Some bacterial spores are too resistant to dry heat to be employed as a BI. Into this category would undoubtedly come *Bacillus* species ATCC 27380 (Bond *et al.*, 1973), the *D*-values of which at 125° and 150°C are no less than 139 and 2·5 h respectively (Bond and Favero, 1975).

Myers (1978) describes the selection of sterilization criteria for both moist and dry heat. This is based on a z-value of 10°C when an autoclave is used and of 21°C when dry heat is employed. Then, if Δt is the time interval between F_0 measurements, T the temperature of the product at time t,

$$F_0 = \Delta t \ 10^{T-121/z} \text{ for moist heat} \tag{5}$$

and

$$F_0 = \Delta t \ 10^{T-160/z} \text{ for dry heat.} \tag{6}$$

References

Angelotti, R. (1968). *In* "Sterilization Techniques for Instruments and Materials as Applied to Space Research" (P. H. A. Sneath, ed.). Cosper Technique Manual Series No. 4, pp. 59–74. Paris.

Angelotti, R., Maryanski, J. H., Butler, T. F., Peeler, J. T. and Campbell, J. E. (1968). *Applied Microbiology* **16**, 735–745.

Augustin, J. A. L. and Pflug, I. J. (1967). *Applied Microbiology* **15**, 266–276.

Bond, W. W. and Favero, M. S. (1975). *Applied Microbiology* **29**, 859–860.

Bond, W. W., Favero, M. S., Petersen, N. J. and Marshall, J. H. (1970). *Applied Microbiology* **20**, 573–578.

Bond, W. W., Favero, M. S., Petersen, N. J. and Marshall, J. H. (1971). *Applied Microbiology* **21**, 832–836.

Bond, W. W., Favero, M. S. and Korber, M. R. (1973). *Applied Microbiology* **26**, 614–616.

Brannen, J. P. (1970). *Biophysik* **7**, 55–59.

Brannen, J. P. (1971). *Journal of Theoretical Biology* **32**, 331–334.

Brannen, J. P. and Garst, D. M. (1972). *Applied Microbiology* **23**, 1125–1130.

British Pharmacopoeia (1980). Pharmaceutical Press, London.

Bruch, C. W., Koesterer, M. G. and Bruch, M. K. (1963). *Developments in Industrial Microbiology* **4**, 334–342.

Bruch, M. K. and Smith, F. W. (1968). *Applied Microbiology* **16**, 1841–1846.

Carter, S. J. (1972) (Ed.) "Tutorial Pharmacy" 6th edn. Pitman Medical Publishing Co., Bath.

Chiasson, L. P. and Zamenhof, S. (1966). *Canadian Journal of Microbiology* **12**, 43–46.

Collier, C. P. and Townsend, C. T. (1956). *Food Technology* **10**, 477–481.

Darmady, E. M. and Brock, R. B. (1954). *Journal of Clinical Pathology* **7**, 290–299.

Darmady, E. M., Hughes, K. E. A. and Jones, J. D. (1958). *Lancet* **2**, 766–769.

Darmady, E. M., Hughes, K. E. A., Jones, J. D., Prince, D. and Tuke, W. (1961). *Journal of Clinical Pathology* **14**, 38–44.

Dawson, J. O. (1962). *Pharmaceutical Journal* **188**, 159–163.

Doyle, J. E. and Ernst, R. R. (1967). *Applied Microbiology* **15**, 726–730.

Drummond, D. W. and Pflug, I. J. (1970). *Applied Microbiology* **20**, 805–809.

Ernst, R. R. (1968). *In* "Disinfection, Sterilization and Preservation" (C. A. Lawrence and S. S. Block, eds), pp. 703–740. Lea and Febiger, Philadelphia.

Ernst, R. R. (1977). *In* "Disinfection, Sterilization and Preservation" (S. S. Block, ed.), 2nd edn, pp. 481–521. Lea and Febiger, Philadelphia.

Fox, K. and Eder, B. D. (1969). *Journal of Food Science* **34**, 518–521.

Fox, K. and Pflug, I. J. (1968). *Applied Microbiology* **16**, 343–348.

Francis, A. E. (1956). *Journal of Pathology and Bacteriology* **72**, 351–352.

Gould, G. W. (1977). *Journal of Applied Bacteriology* **42**, 297–309.

Gould, G. W. and Measures, J. C. (1977). *Proceedings of the Royal Society of London, Series B* **278**, 151–166.

Gurney, T. R. and Quesnel, L. B. (1980). *Journal of Applied Bacteriology* **48**, 231–247.

Heckley, R. J. and Dimatteo, J. (1975). *Applied Microbiology* **29**, 565–566.

Hoffman, R. K., Gambill, V. M. and Buchanan, L. M. (1968). *Applied Microbiology* **16**, 1240–1244.

Knox, R. (1961). *Journal of Clinical Pathology* **14**, 11–17.

Koesterer, M. G. (1965). *Developments in Industrial Microbiology* **6**, 268–276.

Molin, G. (1977a). *Journal of Applied Bacteriology* **42**, 111–116.

Molin, G. (1977b). *Journal of General Microbiology* **101**, 227–231.

Molin, G. (1977c). *In* "Spore Research 1976" (A. N. Barker, J. Wolf, D. J. Ellar, G. J. Dring and G. W. Gould, eds), pp. 487–500. Academic Press, London and New York.

Molin, G. (1982). *In* "Principles and Practice of Disinfection, Preservation and Sterilization" (A. D. Russell, W. B. Hugo and G. A. J. Ayliffe, eds) pp. 454–468. Blackwell Scientific Publications, Oxford.

Molin, G. and Östlund, K. (1975). *In* "Spores VI" (P. Gerhardt, R. N. Costilow and H. L. Sadoff, eds), pp. 556–559. American Society of Microbiology, Washington D.C.

Molin, G. and Östlund, K. (1976). *Canadian Journal of Microbiology* **22**, 359–363.

Molin, G. and Svensson, M. (1976). *Antonie van Leeuwenhoek Journal of Microbiology and Serology* **42**, 387–395.

Molin, G. and Snygg, B. G. (1967). *Applied Microbiology* **15**, 1422–1426.

Mullican, C. L. and Hoffman, R. K. (1968). *Applied Microbiology* **16**, 1110–1113.

Mullican, C. L., Buchanan, L. M. and Hoffman, R. K. (1971). *Applied Microbiology* **22**, 557–559.

Murray, T. J. (1931). *Journal of Infectious Diseases* **48**, 457–467.

Murray, T. J. and Headlee, M. R. (1931). *Journal of Infectious Diseases* **48**, 436–456.

Murrell, W. G. (1964). *Australian Journal of Pharmacy* S40–S46.

Murrell, W. G. and Scott, W. J. (1957). *Nature, London* **179**, 481–482.

Murrell, W. G. and Scott, W. J. (1966). *Journal of General Microbiology* **43**, 411–425.

Myers, R. B. (1978). *Journal of the Parenteral Drug Association* **32**, 216–225.

Niepokojczycka, E. and Zakrweski, K. (1972). *Acta Microbiologica Polonica, Series B*, **4**, 141–153.

Northrop, J. and Slepecky, R. A. (1967). *Science, New York* **155**, 838–839.

Oag, R. K. (1940). *Journal of Pathology and Bacteriology* **51**, 137–145.

Patrick, G. A. K., Wharton, R. H., Prentis, K. and Signy, A. G. (1961). *Journal of Clinical Pathology* **14**, 62–65.

Pflug, I. J. (1960). *Food Technology* **14**, 483–487.

Pflug, I. J. (1973). *In* "Industrial Sterilization" (G. B. Phillips and W. S. Miller, eds), pp. 239–282. Duke University Press, Durham, N.C.

Pflug, I. J. and Holcombe, R. G. (1977). *In* "Disinfection, Sterilization and Preservation" (S. S. Block, ed.), 2nd edn, pp. 933–994. Lea and Febiger, Philadelphia.

Pflug, I. J. and Schmidt, C. F. (1968). *In* "Disinfection, Sterilization and Preservation" (S. S. Block, ed.), pp. 63–105. Lea and Febiger, Philadelphia.

Pheil, C. G., Pflug, I. J., Nicholas, R. C. and Augustin, J. A. L. (1967). *Applied Microbiology* **15**, 120–124.

Prado Filho, L. G. (1975). *Lebensmittel-Wissenschaft ünd Technologie* **8**, 29–33.

Puleo, J. R., Oxborrow, G. S., Fields, N. D., Herring, C. M. and Smith, L. S. (1973). *Applied Microbiology* **26**, 838–845.

Puleo, J. R., Favero, M. S., Oxborrow, G. S. and Herring, C. M. (1975). *Applied Microbiology* **30**, 786–790.

Puleo, J. R., Fields, N. D., Bergstrom, S. L., Oxborrow, G. S., Stabekis, P. D. and Koukol, R. C. (1977). *Applied and Environmental Microbiology* **33**, 379–384.

Puleo, J. R., Bergstrom, S. L., Peeler, J. T. and Oxborrow, G. S. (1978). *Applied and Environmental Microbiology* **36**, 473–479.

Put, H. M. C. and Aalsberberg, W. I. J. (1967). *Journal of Applied Bacteriology* **30**, 411–419.

Quesnel, L. B., Hayward, J. M. and Barrett, J. W. (1967). *Journal of Applied Bacteriology* **30**, 518–528.

Report (1962). "The Sterilization, Use and Care of Syringes". Medical Research Council Memorandum No. 41, H.M.S.O., London.

Richards, J. W. (1968). "Introduction to Industrial Sterilization". Academic Press, London and New York.

Rowe, A. J. and Silverman, G. J. (1970). *Developments in Industrial Microbiology* 11, 311–326.

Russell, A. D. (1971). *In* "Inhibition and Destruction of the Microbial Cell" (W. B. Hugo, ed.), pp. 451–612. Academic Press, London and New York.

Savage, R. H. M. (1959). *In* "The Operation of Sterilizing Autoclaves", pp. 1–11. Pharmaceutical Press, London.

Simko, G. J., Devlin, J. D. and Wardle, M. D. (1971). *Applied Microbiology* 22, 491–495.

Sneath, P. H. A. (1968) (Ed.) "Sterilization Techniques for Instruments and Materials as Applied to Space Research", Cospar Technique Manual Series No. 4, Paris.

Soper, C. J. and Davies, D. J. G. (1973). *Journal of Applied Bacteriology* 36, 119–130.

Sundberg, A. D. and Carlin, A. F. (1976). *Journal of Food Science* 41, 451–452.

Sykes, G. (1965). "Disinfection and Sterilization", 2nd edn. Spon, London.

Sykes, G. (1966). *Process Biochemistry*, August, pp. 1–5.

Trauth, C. A. Jr. (1973). *Space Life Sciences* 4, 357–367.

Wardle, M. D., Brewer, W. A. and Peterson, M. L. (1971). *Applied Microbiology* 21, 827–831.

Willing, W. G. (1979). *Pharmaceutical Technology International* 2, 23–30.

Zamenhof, S. (1960). *Proceedings of the National Academy of Sciences, U.S.* 46, 101–105.

4

Effects of Ionizing Radiation on Bacterial Spores

I. *Introduction*

Studies in which microorganisms have been exposed to different types of radiation have, particularly over the past two decades, revealed a powerful process employing ionizing radiations which can be used for the sterilization of various medical and pharmaceutical products, especially those which are too thermolabile to be sterilized by conventional heat processes. These studies have also provided a considerable amount of information on (a) the factors which influence the radiation sensitivity of bacteria, (b) at least some of the reasons responsible for the above-average resistance of certain bacteria and (c) the mechanism(s) of inactivation of bacteria and bacterial spores. These aspects are considered in this chapter.

The types of radiation that are bactericidal can, to all practical intents, be divided into ionizing radiation and ultraviolet radiations: these are dealt with separately, since the types of damage inflicted on bacteria are somewhat different. The effects of ultraviolet radiation are thus considered in the subsequent chapter.

A. **Types of Radiation**

The types of ionizing radiations, which strip off electrons from the atoms of the material through which the radiations pass, are X-rays, γ-rays, high-speed electrons (β-rays), protons and α-rays (positively charged helium atoms). Essentially all the chemical effects are produced by these electrons. Ultraviolet light causes excitation of atoms, i.e. an alteration of electrons within their orbits, but does not possess enough energy to eject an electron to produce an ion, and is thus not an ionizing radiation. Infrared radiations have the ability to raise rapidly the temperature of objects which they strike and are thus used for their heating effect (Chapter 3).

X-rays and γ-rays consist of very short wavelengths, the latter being produced from radioactive sources such as Cobalt-60 (^{60}Co), and the former from machines. High-speed electrons were originally produced from radioactive isotopes, but had little penetration; various machines have since been developed which accelerate atomic particles to give them the energies for penetrating deeply (Stewart and Hawcroft, 1977).

The energy of all these ionizing radiations is expressed as electron-volts (eV). Usually, X-rays, γ-rays and high-speed electrons are used. X-radiation and γ-radiation are conventionally distinguished by being produced by non-nuclear and nuclear reactions, respectively, but they are similar forms of electromagnetic radiation. X-rays and γ-rays have considerable penetrating power. In contrast, α-particles are charged and heavy, consisting of helium nuclei ($^4_2$He) and have little penetrating power; they thus find no use as a sterilizing agent.

B. Units of Radiation

The units of radiation are the rep or, more usually, the rad or Gray. The original unit, the roentgen, defined the amount of radiation applied; its use was limited by X-radiation and γ-radiation up to 3 million electron volts (3 MeV).

The rad is a unit for the measurement of the energy absorbed from ionizing radiation by the matter through which the radiation passes.

The more modern (S.I.) unit is the Gray (Gy) which also measures the energy absorbed; a Gy is defined as the deposition of 1 J/kg energy in tissue, whereas 1 rad is the deposition of 10^{-2}J/kg (or 100 erg/g) energy.

Thus, 1 Gy = 100 rad,

or 1 Mrad = 10 000 Gy.

However, virtually all the published work on the activity and action of radiation on bacteria or bacterial spores lists the dose in rad, kilorad (krad) or megarad (Mrad). This convention will be continued in this chapter and in other relevant parts of this book.

II. *Dose-Survivor Curves*

Survival curves are expressed by plotting surviving fraction, on a logarithmic scale, along the ordinate, against the irradiation dose in kilorads (krad) or megarads (Mrad) on an arithmetic scale, along the abscissa. As with spores exposed to heat, survivor curves of various

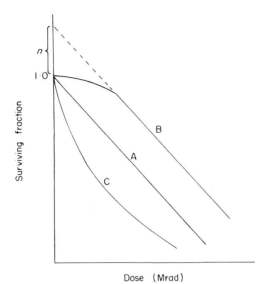

Fig. 4.1   Types of inactivation curves (n = extrapolation number).

types may be produced, and these are depicted in Fig. 4.1. Much time has been spent on attempting to assess the type of damage inflicted on various spores, as judged from the shape of the dose–survivor curve, and this point will be considered later.

A. Exponential Inactivation

In Fig. 4.1, curve A represents a straight line or exponential rate kill. Examples of such a response have been provided by Woese (1958, 1959) who showed that *B. subtilis*, *B. brevis* and *B. mesentericus* were inactivated exponentially when exposed to X-rays; by Silverman *et al.* (1967), who noted a straight-line order of death when *B. globigii* was exposed to γ-irradiation, with wet spores irradiated in air, vacuum-dried spores irradiated in air, and vacuum-dried spores irradiated in vacuum; by Thornley (1963), for *Cl. perfringens*; by Pepper *et al.* (1956) for *Cl. sporogenes* and *B. pumilus*, although these straight lines may be more apparent than real; by Christensen and Holm (1964, 1967), Christensen (1967) and Christensen *et al.* (1967) for spores of *B. subtilis*, *B. globigii* and *B. pumilus*; and by Roberts and Derrick (1975) for *Cl. putrefaciens*.

B. Non-exponential Inactivation

A more usual type of response, however, is that depicted by curve B in

Fig. 4.1, in which an initial shoulder on the curve is followed by an exponential rate of death (Bridges, 1964; Silverman and Sinskey, 1977; Alper, 1979; Harm, 1980). Curve B occurs with certain non-sporing bacteria such as *Micrococcus radiodurans* (Moseley and Laser, 1965a, b; Bridges, 1976) and, under certain conditions, with *Streptococcus faecium* (Christensen, 1964; Christensen and Kjems, 1965; Christensen *et al.*, 1982). Curve B also occurs with various spores, including *B. megaterium, B. cereus, B. mycoides, B. pumilus, B. stearothermophilus, B. subtilis, B. pantothenticus, B. licheniformis, Cl. sporogenes, Cl. botulinum* types A, B and E and other clostridia (Woese, 1958, 1959; Kempe, 1955; Levinson and Hyatt, 1960; Burt and Ley, 1963a; Ley and Tallentire, 1964; Grecz, 1965; Roberts and Ingram, 1965a, b; Briggs, 1966; Hitchins *et al.*, 1966; Grecz *et al.*, 1967, 1977; Silverman *et al.*, 1967). Irradiation-induced spore activation can occur with several *Clostridium* species (Roberts and Ingram, 1965a, b) and with some but not all *Bacillus* species (Gould and Ordal, 1968).

The extent of the shoulder can be measured by extrapolating the exponential part of the graphical responses so that it cuts the ordinate; in Fig. 4.1, curve B, n refers to the extrapolation number. The smaller the value of n, the smaller is the shoulder; in *B. pumilus* strain E601 irradiated in air, for instance, there is only a slight shoulder, and n is of the order of 2 (Burt and Ley, 1963a). With a large shoulder, followed by exponential death the following expression is employed:

$$S \text{ (or } N/N_0) = 1 - (1 - \exp[1 - kD])^n \tag{1}$$

in which N_o is the initial number of cells, N the final number, S the proportion of cells surviving an irradiation dose D, k is the slope of the exponential part of the curve, and n is the extrapolation number.

C. Resistant Tail

The response depicted by curve C in Fig. 4.1, in which an exponential rate of kill is followed by a decreasing rate of spore inactivation, is encountered less frequently. Spores of *Cl. botulinum* strains 62A and 213B in irradiated chopped ham exhibit a diphasic order of death, an initial rapid death rate decreasing in slope as the dose increases (Greenberg *et al.*, 1965). Radiation survival curves of *Cl. botulinum* 33A spores show an exponential reduction which accounts for most of the population followed by a tail comprising a very small residual number of spores (Anellis *et al.*, 1965a, b). Similar tailing-off phenomena have been noted by other authors for some sporing and non-sporing bacteria (Dunn *et al.*, 1948; Brown *et al.*, 1960; Erdman *et al.*, 1961a, b; Wheaton and

Pratt, 1962; Dyer *et al.*, 1966). Tallentire (1973) considers that technical problems are responsible for the tailing phenomenon, which thus might represent an artefact.

The reason for this tailing-off effect is not known; a slight increase in the resistance of *Cl. botulinum* type A spores by daily exposure to γ-radiation has been found (Erdman *et al.*, 1961a, b) and thus the production of radiation-resistant mutants (Wheaton and Pratt, 1962) remains as a possible reason for the tailing phenomenon. Repeated passage of resistant survivors of *vegetative* cell suspensions through successive sublethal irradiation doses has produced a 4·5 increase in resistance, this increase being accompanied by an increase in *spore* resistance and eventually by the loss of ability to produce spores (Parisi and Antoine, 1974).

D. Target Theory

The theoretical numbers of spore targets which must be inactivated by irradiation have been calculated. Where exponential death occurs, one event (or a very small number of events) is responsible for death (Lea, 1956). For the target theory to be applicable, destruction must not be influenced by concentration, temperature or dose rate, whereas as demonstrated in subsequent sections, these factors may affect the radiation sensitivity of spores.

With an exponential rate of death, then, a single "hit" on the sensitive site (presumably DNA) is responsible for cell death, whereas with survival curves of type B (Fig. 4.1), several hits (multi-hit theory) on DNA are necessary to bring about inactivation.

A method for determining the number of hits required for inactivation, estimated from non-linear multi-hit survivor curves by a least square fit of the experimental data was described by Grecz (1965), who used the following equation:

$$\text{Surviving fraction } (N/N_0) = 1 - (1 - e^{-Kx})^N \tag{2}$$

in which N is the number of surviving organisms, N_0 the initial viable count, $e = 2·7183$, x the dose in Mrad, N the number of hits to inactivate the organism, and K a constant ($Mrad^{-1}$) for describing radioresistance.

Based on this method, the estimated numbers of hits to inactivate one spore of *Cl. botulinum* strain 33A and strain 12885A were 90 and 13, respectively.

Woese (1958, 1959) noted two types of inactivation curves with irradiated spores: a single-hit, straight line response with *B. subtilis, B.*

brevis and *B. mesentericus*, and a multi-hit, initial shoulder response with *B. megaterium*, *B. cereus* and *B. mycoides*. He also reported that "multiple target" spores had a higher content of DPA.

However, to put the target theory in its proper perspective, a statement of Ginoza (1967) should be considered, viz. that:

> "the obvious lack of direct quantitative correlation between the initial hit events occurring in the bacterial cells and their reproductive death serves as a reminder that the parameters associated with any bacterial survival curve are too numerous for target theory to be of direct help".

Moseley (1968), also, considered that too much attention was being paid to explain variation in resistance in terms of cellular targets rather than to the repair of radiation injury (see Section IV and Chapter 5). Some bacteria possess the ability to repair the damage to DNA caused by ionizing radiations at lower doses, and this may account for the initial shoulder in the dose–survivor curve.

III. *Mathematical Aspects*

Some, but not all, of the terms employed in heat sterilization studies are also used in irradiation sterilization. These terms are considered below.

A. *D*-value

This is the dose, usually expressed in krad or Mrad, to reduce the initial spore population by 90% (i.e. to 10%). When the dose-survival curve is a straight line (Fig. 4.1, curve A), it is possible to read the *D*-value from the graph. When the dose–survival curve shows an initial shoulder (Fig. 4.1, curve B), the *D*-value can be obtained from the straight line portion (exponential part) of the graph. If this is done, however, the extent of the shoulder should also be stated, for instance by quoting the *n*-value (extrapolation number).

The *D*-value may also be obtained from the equation:

$$D\text{-value} = \text{Radiation dose}/\log N_0 - \log N \qquad (3)$$

in which N_0 and N are as described in equations 1 and 2 (Schmidt and Nank, 1960).

Other methods of determining *D*-values include partial spoilage data (Anellis *et al.*, 1965a, 1967: see also Chapter 2), the presence of toxin, as with *Cl. botulinum* (Anellis *et al.*, 1967), the use of incremental radiation doses (Whitby and Gelda, 1974), and the Spearman-Kärber assay (Anellis and Werkowski, 1968).

As described later, several factors influence the rate of death of bacterial spores exposed to radiation, and thus a knowledge of the composition of the medium in which the spores are held during irradiation is essential when comparing D-values. This aspect is considered in Table 4.1, which lists the D-values of irradiated spores under various conditions. The figures are those listed by the authors, or have been calculated by the present writer from their results.

From this table, the following conclusions concerning D-values may be made:

(a) The D-values in Mrad of spores in general are given as 0·25 to 0·375 or 0·4 by Clouston and Sangster (1964) and Christensen *et al.* (1966). However, it can be seen from the values quoted in Table 4.1 for actual experimental results that values considerably lower than 0·25 Mrad are frequently obtained. The upper limit of 0·4 Mrad is generally satisfactory, only isolated examples of higher D-values being obtained: see also Whitby and Gelda (1979), however.

(b) A considerable variation may exist between different strains of the same organism.

(c) The irradiation conditions markedly influence the resistance of bacterial spores. This is particularly so with *Cl. botulinum* types A and B, where the response depends on the medium and on the temperature. Anoxic and aerobic conditions influence the response of *B. pumilus* and this aspect is considered in more detail in Section IV.D and in Chapter 9.

(d) *Clostridium botulinum* type E spores are considerably less radiation resistant than types A and B.

(e) Among *Bacillus* species, *B. pumilus* spores are generally the most resistant, and at one time these spores were suggested as being suitable for use as biological indicators (BIs: see Section VII.A).

B. D_{37}-value

The D_{37}-value is the irradiation dose which reduces the spore population to 37% of its original value. The term is based on the half-way point (0·5) of the $\log_{10}$ scale on the ordinate, 0·5 being the logarithm (base 10) corresponding to 37% survival. The D_{37} is, however, rarely used nowadays: see, for example, Bott and Lundgren (1964), Tanooka and Sakakibara (1968) and Terano *et al.* (1969).

E

Table 4.1. *D*-values of irradiated bacterial spores

Organism	Strain	Irradiation conditions	*D*-value (Mrad)	Reference
Spores (in general)		—	0·25–0·4	Clouston and Sangster (1964)
			0·25–0·375	Christensen et al. (1966)
B. subtilis	E152	Aqueous	0·146	Borick and Fogarty (1967)
	E163	Aqueous	0·114	Borick and Fogarty (1967)
	Statens Serumin-stitut	Spores dried after suspension in various media	0·24, 0·34, 0·035, 0·25, 0·26	Christensen and Sehested (1964)
		Spores dried on to polythene foil	0·25–0·35	Christensen and Holm (1964)
	23	Aqueous	0·1	Zamenhof et al. (1965)
	ATCC 9466	Aqueous	0·18	
	NCTC 8236	Aqueous	0·22	Briggs (1966)
	NCIB 8054	Aqueous	0·23	Härnulv and Snygg (1973)
		Glycerol (a_w 0·96–0·00)	0·28–0·42	
B. pumilus	E601	Aqueous	0·175	Borick and Fogarty (1967)
	E601	Aqueous	0·171	Borick and Fogarty (1967)
	E601	Phosphate buffer, aerobic	0·175	Burt and Ley (1963a)
	—	—	0·170	Rubbo and Gardner (1965)
	—	Buffer, anoxic	0·30	Ley (1966)
	—	Buffer, aerobic	0·17	
	E601	Spores dried on to polythene foil	0·26	Christensen and Holm (1964)
	E601	Spores on dry filter paper strips	0·175	Prince (1976)
	E601	Aqueous	0·255	Prince (1978)
	E601	Catgut	0·225	
	E601	Wet preparation (sealed in glass vial)	0·19–0·34	Kereluk (1977)
	E601	Dried preparation (paper strip)	0·12–0·20	
B. megaterium	ATCC 8245	Phosphate buffer: irradiated in:		
		Nitrogen	0·27	Ewing et al. (1974)
		Nitrogen + PNAP[a]	0·21	
		Nitrous oxide + PNAP[a]	0·175	
		Nitrous oxide	0·15	
		Oxygen	0·125	

Table 4.1–*continued*

Organism	Strain	Irradiation conditions	D-value (Mrad)	Reference
	ATCC 8245	Aqueous buffer, pH 7: irradiated in:		
		Equilibrium with air	0·15	
		Anoxia	0·32	
		Anoxia + PNAP[a]	0·28	
		Acetone: irradiated in		
		Equilibrium with air	0·18	Tallentire *et al.*
		Anoxia	0·28	(1972)
		Anoxia + PNAP[a]	0·28	
		Ethanol: irradiated in		
		Equilibrium with air	0·2	
		Anoxia	0·4	
		Anoxia + PNAP[a]	0·4	
B. globigii	E154	Aqueous	0·165	Borick and Fogarty (1967)
	ATCC 9372	Spores dried on to polythene foil	*ca.* 0·3	Christensen and Holm (1964)
B. mesentericus	E40	Aqueous	0·118	Borick and Fogarty (1967)
B. cereus	E190	Aqueous	0·107	Borick and Fogarty (1967)
Cl. botulinum				
Type A, various		Aqueous	0·10–0·14	
Type B, various		Aqueous	0·10–0·11	
Type C		Aqueous	0·14	Roberts and Ingram
Type D		Aqueous	0·22	(1965b)
Type E, various		Aqueous	0·08–0·16	
Type F		Aqueous	0·25	
33A			0·221	
36A			0·214	
12885A		Sliced cured bacon	0·188	Anellis *et al.*
9B			0·205	(1965a)
41B			0·160	
53B			0·199	
33A			0·235	
36A			0·218	Anellis *et al.*
1288A		Cured ham	0·242	(1967)
9B			0·171	
41B			0·175	
53B			0·164	
Type A		Food	0·35	Ley (1964)
Type B		Broth	0·20	Ley (1964)
33A		Chopped ham	0·197–0·226	Greenberg *et al.* (1965)
33A		Phosphate buffer, 0°C	0·29	
		−196°C	0·396	Grecz *et al.* (1965)
33A		Ground beef, 0°C	0·453	
		−196°C	0·680	

Table 4.1–*continued*

Organism	Strain	Irradiation conditions	D-value (Mrad)	Reference
33A		Buffer	0·295 ⎫	Anellis *et al.*
		Pork pea broth	0·396 ⎭	(1965b)
53B		Beef slices, temperature range −196 to +200°C	0·4–0·268	El-Bisi *et al.* (1967)
53B		Phosphate buffer, 5°C	0·19	
		−40°C	0·196	
		−190°C	0·218	El-Bisi *et al.*
		Beef, 5°C	0·300	(1967)
		−40°C	0·310	
		−190°C	0·340	
Type E				
Alaska			0·137	
Beluga		Beef stew	0·136	Schmidt *et al.*
Iwandi			0·125	(1962)
VH			0·128	
8E			0·138	
33A		Aqueous suspension, atmosphere of nitrogen	0·253	Durban *et al.* (1970)
51B			0·101	
Cl. aerofoetidium			0·16	
Cl. bifermentans			0·14–0·20	
Cl. butyricum			0·15	
Cl. caloritolerans			0·15	
Cl. chauvoei			0·20	
Cl. fallax			0·25	
Cl. histolyticum			0·18–0·22	
Cl. oedematiens,	Type A		0·19	
	Type B		0·18	
	Type C		0·16	
Cl. septicum			0·16	
Cl. sordellii			0·15	
Cl. sphenoides		Aqueous	0·21	Roberts and Ingram
Cl. sporogenes			0·16–0·22	(1965b)
Cl. subterminale			0·16	
Cl. tetani			0·24	
Cl. tertium			0·16	
Cl. tetanomorphum			0·18–0·23	
Cl. welchii (*perfingens*)				
	Type A		0·12	
	Type B		0·17	
	Type C		0·18	
	Type E		0·12	
	Type F		0·20	
Cl. putrefaciens	NCTC 9836		0·16	Roberts and Derrick (1975)

---

[a] PNAP, *p*-nitroacetophenone.

Table 4.2. Inactivation Dose (D_I) for some irradiated bacteria[ab]

Non-sporing organism	D_I (Mrad)	Spores	D_I (Mrad)
Ps. aeruginosa		B. subtilis	1·5
Staph. aureus		B. globigii	<1
Strep. viridans		B. pumilus E601	2·5
Strep. faecalis	<1	B. stearothermophilus	1·5
E. coli		Cl. perfringens	2
M. tryophilus		Cl. tetani	<1

[a] 100 paper discs per organism were irradiated at each of 4 dose levels.
[b] Based on the data of Darmady *et al.* (1961).

C. Inactivation Dose (D_I)

Several items are taken, and contaminated with a spore suspension. Replicates are then irradiated at a series of dose levels, and afterwards incubated in appropriate recovery media. The lowest irradiation dose at which all the replicates are sterile is the Inactivation Dose (D_I) for that suspension.

D_I will, of course, depend markedly on the initial viable count (bioburden) per item. Some examples of D_I are given in Table 4.2. These are based on the results of Darmady *et al.* (1961b), who irradiated 100 paper discs per organism at each of four dose levels. Unfortunately, the number of spores per disc varied from species to species, the lowest being $1·6 \times 10^5$ and the highest $5·8 \times 10^7$. Other examples of D_I are provided in the papers of Pepper *et al.* (1956) and Bridges (1964).

D. Inactivation Factor (IF)

As with heat sterilization studies (Chapter 2), IF is defined as the initial number of viable spores divided by the final number. For medical and pharmaceutical products, an irradiation dose of 2·5 Mrad is normally employed (see later) and Table 4.3 provides examples of the IF of different spores at this dose level. The figures have either been quoted by the authors or have been calculated by the present writer from their results.

In general, at a dose of 2·5 Mrad (Table 4.3), the IF for bacterial spores varies between 10^6 and 10^7 up to 10^9 to 10^{10}. Under the same conditions, the IF for *Staph. aureus* is ca. 10^{15}, for corynebacteria about 10^{15} also, whereas with *M. radiodurans* very few are killed at this dose, and a 7 Mrad dose is needed for an IF of about 6×10^7 to be achieved.

Table 4.3. Inactivation Factors (IF) for some bacterial spores irradiated at a dose of 2·5 Mrad

Organism	Strain	IF	Reference
Spores, in general	—	Between 10^6 and 10^7 to 10^9	Christensen *et al.* (1967)
		10^7 to between 10^9 and 10^{10}	Clouston and Sangster (1964)
B. subtilis	Statens Seruminstitut, Copenhagen	Between 10^7 and 10^8 to 10^{10}	Christensen and Holm (1964)
B. globigii	ATCC 9372	Between 10^7 and 10^8	Christensen and Holm (1964)
		ca. $2·5 \times 10^7$	Christensen and Holm (1964)
B. pumilus		Between 10^9 and 10^{10}	Christensen and Holm (1964)
	E601	10^9	Christensen and Holm (1964)
	E601[a]	10^{15}	Burt and Ley (1963a)
	E601[b]	10^7	Burt and Ley (1963a)
	E601[c]	10^4	Ley and Tallentire (1965)

[a] Irradiation under aerobic conditions.
[b] Irradiation under anoxic conditions.
[c] Irradiation in the presence of H_2S.

The influence of the presence of aerobic or anoxic conditions and of hydrogen sulphide is also apparent. The sensitivity of *Cl. botulinum* type E in comparison to types A and B, and of the highly heat-resistant *B. stearothermophilus* are to be noted (Russell, 1971).

E. Sterilizing Dose

This term is used in the food industry, and is based on the proposal by Schmidt (1963) that a microbiologically safe process should conform with a 12-log spore reduction of *Cl. botulinum*, i.e. sterilizing dose = $D_{10} \times 12$, or IF = 10^{12} (see also Anellis and Werkowski, 1971).

The sterilizing dose may, alternatively, be estimated by the formula $S + (D_{10} \times n)$, where S is the experimentally established minimal sterilizing dose (2 Mrad) based on flat, non-toxic, sterile cans for the actual spore density used, and n is the number of log cycles needed to adjust the initial spore density by a hypothetical 10^{11} spores (Anellis *et al.*,

1965a, b, 1967, 1969, 1972, 1977). Thus, a 12-log cycle would mean a reduction to 10^{-1} spore.

Dose-survivor curves of *Cl. botulinum* show an initial shoulder or lag (*L*: see curve B, Fig. 4.1), and it has been proposed that this should be taken into consideration in determining the minimal radiation dose (M.R.D.) for sterilizing foodstuffs (El-Bisi *et al.*, 1967). This is still based on the safety concept of a 10^{-12} lethality, but *L* is included as shown in the following equation.

$$\text{M.R.D.} = (12 \times D\text{-value}) + L \qquad (4)$$

The sterilizing dose and the inactivation dose (D_I) described earlier must obviously be related. However, the latter is based on the radiation dose necessary to sterilize all the replicates in a given sample, whereas the former, as can be seen, is based on the concept of a 12-log spore reduction of *Cl. botulinum* in the food industry. It is, perhaps, rather unfortunate that there are two such terms; however, it must be remembered that D_I as such is, in fact, rarely employed.

IV. *Factors Influencing the Sensitivity of Irradiated Spores*

Bacterial spores are generally more resistant to ionizing radiations than yeasts, fungi or non-sporulating bacteria (Bridges *et al.*, 1956; Koh *et al.*, 1956; Pepper *et al.*, 1956; Roberts and Hitchins, 1969; Russell, 1971; Silverman and Sinskey, 1977). The range of resistance among bacteria is extremely large. *Bacillus subtilis* spores are about 10–12 times as resistant as the corresponding vegetative cells (Zamenhof *et al.*, 1965) and a factor of approximately 50 separates the *D*-values against pseudomonads and the spores of *Cl. botulinum* (Thornley, 1963). The most resistant organism currently known is still *M. radiodurans*, the inactivation curve of which shows a large shoulder, becoming exponential only at very high radiation doses (*ca.* 5–6 Mrad: Moseley, 1968). This organism possesses an extremely efficient repair process against both ionizing and ultraviolet radiation (Bridges, 1976; Moseley and Williams, 1977). Another non-sporing organism, *Strep. faecium*, is radiation-resistant only under special circumstances (see Section VII.A for a fuller discussion).

Several factors influence the radiation resistance of bacteria in general, and these have been considered by Bridges and Horne (1959), Goldblith (1967, 1971) and Silverman and Sinskey (1977). This section discusses those factors that affect the radiation sensitivity of bacterial spores.

A. Inoculum Size

As would be expected, the higher the initial population of bacterial spores, the greater is the dose required to kill them (Edwards *et al.*, 1954; Kempe *et al.*, 1954; Farkas, *et al.*, 1967; Borick and Fogarty, 1967). However, the initial cell density does not appear to affect the radiation resistance of spores (Farkas *et al.*, 1967) and the slopes of the dose-survivor curves of *B. coagulans* spores are the same for spore suspensions of varying population sizes (Morgan and Reed, 1954).

Nevertheless, the initial number of organisms or (to use the more recently adopted term) bioburden is of importance in selecting an appropriate radiation dose for sterilization purposes (Whitby and Gelda, 1979).

B. Type and Strain of Organism

Differences in radiation resistance occur within *Bacillus* and *Clostridium* species (Pepper *et al.*, 1956; Russell, 1971). Among the clostridia, *Cl. botulinum* types A and B spores are the most resistant (Anellis and Koch, 1962; Thornley, 1963), the particularly heat-resistant Putrefactive Anaerobe (PA) 3679 being slightly more sensitive (Thornley, 1963; see Table 4.1). *Clostridium botulinum* type E spores are, in general, much more sensitive to radiation than are types A and B (Schmidt *et al.*, 1962; Roberts and Ingram, 1965a, b). According to Plecas *et al.* (1969) *Cl. histolyticum* is highly resistant to radiation, with *Cl. perfringens* highly sensitive. The radiation resistance of *Cl. botulinum* type F strains, unknown before 1960, has only recently been studied: the non-proteolytic Eklund 83F strain is as resistant as strain 33A, whereas the proteolytic Walls 8G-F strain is much more sensitive (Anellis and Berkowitz, 1977). Among *Bacillus* spp., *B. pumilus* strain E601 (ATCC 27142) is probably the most resistant organism and has been widely used, especially in the United State, as a Biological Indicator (BI) (Kereluk, 1977).

C. Pre-irradiation Treatment of Spores

The radiation sensitivity of bacterial spores is known to depend on the prior treatment of spores. Such treatment includes the effects of freeze-drying from sugars, of drying from various media and of the composition of the sporulation medium.

1. *Freeze-drying from sugars*

Freeze-drying from a 5% aqueous solution of glucose produces a marked radioprotection of *B. subtilis* spores in contrast to freeze-drying from aqueous suspension (Cook and Roberts, 1964). Glucose can be replaced by lactose or fructose but not by maltose (Cook *et al.*, 1964). Protection may be linked to the presence of a glass, since the most marked glass and the greatest protection is associated with fructose, whereas no obvious glass and no protection occurs with maltose.

2. *Drying in various media*

Christensen and Sehested (1964) investigated the irradiation sterilization of spores of *B. globigii* and *B. subtilis* dried in various media (serum broth, water, methanol and phosphate-buffered saline). Before drying, the spores were washed or unwashed; unwashed spores showed the greatest resistance to ionizing radiation after suspension and drying in serum broth. Washed spores suspended and dried in methanol had less resistance to radiation than buffered saline, which in turn was less than in serum broth. The non-sporing organism, *Strep. faecium* was also most resistant when suspended and dried in serum broth. In the case of *B. pumilus* strain E601, when the spores were dried from buffer, nutrient broth and serum on to different supporting surfaces (glass, Perspex, polystyrene, aluminum or stainless steel) and then irradiated in the presence of air, the *D*-values were not significantly different, whereas if dried from polyvinyl alcohol solution or from a greasy base,

Table 4.4. *D*-Values of *B. pumilus* E601 dried from different suspending media on to different supporting media and irradiated in the presence of air[a]

Supporting surface	Suspending medium from which dried				
	Buffer	Broth	Serum	Polyvinyl alcohol	Greasy
Glass	0·169[b]	0·156	0·153	0·282	0·342
Perspex	0·159	0·151		0·321	
Polystyrene	0·178				
Aluminium	0·165	0·144	0·154	0·283	
Stainless steel	0·155				
Polyvinyl alcohol film	0·211	0·324	0·329	0·363	

[a] Data of Burt and Ley (1963a).

[b] Figures are *D*-values.

the *D*-values obtained from the subsequent irradiation treatment (see Table 4.4) were considerably higher (Burt and Ley, 1963a). However, since polyvinyl alcohol represented an artificial situation, it could be concluded that for practical purposes of radiation sterilization, the radiation resistance of air-dried spores of *B. pumilus* was independent of the media from which they were dried (Burt and Ley, 1963a).

D. **The Oxygen Effect**

This concerns the effect on bacterial spores of the gaseous environment during and after irradiation. It was shown several years ago that dried *B. subtilis* spores were more sensitive when irradiated under air than under reduced pressure (Tallentire, 1958). It was also found that the lethal efficiency of a radiation dose depended on the subsequent conditions under which the spores were stored; the highest level of inactivation occurred with post-irradiation storage in oxygen and the lowest with post-irradiation storage for 15 min in nitric oxide before exposure to oxygen (Tallentire and Dickinson, 1962). Oxygen present during or after the irradiation process can thus markedly influence the radiation resistance of bacterial spores of this species, and a similar oxygen effect takes place with *B. megaterium, B. globigii* and *B. stearothermophilus* (Silverman *et al.*, 1967). When dried spores of *B. megaterium* are irradiated in oxygen, their sensitivity is at the highest level; when irradiated in nitrogen the sensitivity is intermediate; and when irradiated in nitric oxide, their radiation sensitivity is least (Powers, 1962, 1965, 1966). However, Russell (1966) considered that the presence of 0·5% nitric oxide in nitrogen during the irradiation process caused slight sensitiziation of wet spores of *B. megaterium*. The scavenging role of nitric oxide during post-irradiation storage may be due to its removal of radiation-induced free radicals which on exposure to oxygen combine to produce damage lethal to the spore (Powers *et al.*, 1960 a, b; Tallentire and Davies, 1962).

In the following, pressure of water vapour is expressed as Torr, in accordance with the terminology adopted by various authors. One Torr (or mm Hg) $\times$ 0·1333 = kPa, the currently used S.I. unit.

When the amount of water in the dry spores is varied, marked changes occur in their radiation sensitivity (Tallentire and Dickinson, 1962; Tallentire *et al.*, 1963; Tallentire, 1970). Tallentire and Powers (1963) equilibrated *B. megaterium* spores to known pressures of water vapour over the range $2·5 \times 10^{-5}$ to 22 Torr, and subjected the spores to three different gaseous environments during and after X-irradiation.

Their results, based on the three categories of mechanisms leading to lethal damage in the standard air-dried spore (Powers *et al.*, 1960b) may be summarized as follows:

(i) **Class I:** this consists of oxygen-independent, temperature-dependent mechanisms, and occurs during irradiation in nitrogen. Post-irradiation treatment of dry spores (equilbrated to a water vapour pressure of $<10^{-5}$ torr) with nitric oxide or with water vapour resulted in each case in a value of the slope, k, of the dose-survivor curve of 0.013 krad^{-1}. Thus exposure to 22 Torr water vapour after irradiation has the same effect as nitric oxide (see above). The effects of changes in the equilibrium water vapour pressure at the time of irradiation on the inactivation constant, k, are given in Table 4.5 which shows that when irradiation is carried out at pressures of 5×10^{-2} Torr and below, k is 0.013 krad^{-1}, whereas at a pressure of 22 Torr, the value is 0.017 krad^{-1}. Thus, at the highest water contents, there is an enhancement of damage.

(ii) **Class II:** this consists of oxygen-dependent and temperature-dependent mechanisms that involve very short-lived chemical species. This part of the radiation effect is observed only if oxygen is present at the time of irradiation. As can be seen in Table 4.5, the

Table 4.5. Oxygen effect and the irradiation of *B. megaterium*[a]

Equilibrium water vapour pressure (Torr)[b] during irradiation	Irradiation conditions		Inactivation constant (k) in krad^{-1}	Type of damage[c]
	During	After		
5×10^{-2} or less	N_2	H_2O	0.013	
5×10^{-1}	N_2	H_2O	0.013	Class I
22	N_2	H_2O	0.017	
ca. 10^{11}	O_2	O_2	0.117	
2.5×10^{-5}	O_2	O_2	0.100	
4×10^{-4}	O_2	O_2	0.094	Class II
2.5×10^{-1}	O_2	O_2	0.053	
22	O_2	O_2	0.032	
5×10^{-4}	N_2	O_2	0.057	
10^{-1}	N_2	O_2	0.040	Class III
22	N_2	O_2	0.017	

[a] Based on the data of Tallentire and Powers (1963).
[b] One Torr (or mm Hg) $\times$ 0.1333 = kPa.
[c] See text for details.

inactivation constant, k (and hence the probability of lethal damage) decreases with an increase in water content.

(iii) **Class III:** this comprises oxygen-dependent mechanisms that involve long-lived free radicals. When spores irradiated in nitrogen are exposed to oxygen with no intervening treatment, the damage is a combination of that brought about by Class I mechanisms plus that by free radicals which interact with oxygen. The post-irradiation is strongly temperature-dependent. Table 4.5 shows that as the water content increases, there is a decrease in the mechanisms involving post-irradiation reaction.

Thus, the above findings indicate that most of the change in the radiation sensitivity of spores irradiated at different water contents is due to the effect of water on the oxygen-dependent parts of the damage. With the oxic spore, resistance is maximal at the highest spore water content (Tallentire, 1970), the spore being most radiation sensitive in its driest state (Powers, 1977). With the anoxic spore, however, a decrease in resistance occurs with increasing water content (Tallentire, 1970). Under anoxic conditions, spores of *B. subtilis* and *B. stearothermophilus* become more resistant as a_w falls; this can be achieved by means of increasing glycerol concentrations. This leads to a consideration of whether glycerol is, in fact, dehydrating the cell. However, glycerol — unlike sucrose — penetrates rapidly (Gould, 1978) and dehydration is thus unlikely to be the correct explanation. Another possibility is that glycerol is acting as a scavenger for toxic radiolysis products of water (Härnulv and Snygg, 1973).

Following exposure to ketonic agents, bacterial spores in anoxic buffer suspension become sensitized to ionizing radiation (Tallentire and Jacobs, 1972; Tallentire *et al.*, 1972; Ewing *et al.*, 1974; Fielden *et al.*, 1974; Ewing, 1973, 1975; Jacobs and Tallentire, 1974). Increased concentrations enhance sensitization, but the maximal increase is only about 40% of the oxygen effect. Scavengers of the hydroxyl radical ($^{\cdot}OH$), such as tertiary butanol or high ethanol concentrations reduce, but do not completely eliminate, the maximum amount of sensitization (Powers *et al.*, 1972a, b; Ewing, 1976, 1980). Various agents (nitrogen dioxide, potassium permanganate and silver salts) also sensitize bacterial spores in anoxic conditions (Powers and Cross, 1970; Tallentire and Jones, 1973; Richmond and Powers, 1974), whereas cobalt (III) complexes sensitize spores in oxic and anoxic conditions (Richmond *et al.*, 1975). Under anoxic conditions, hydrogen peroxide may be associated with the lethal effects of ionizing radiation (Cross *et al.*, 1972). The significance of these findings is discussed more fully in Chapter 9; see also Powers (1972).

The sensitivity of *B. megaterium* spores under anoxic conditions increases with increasing dose rate (Purdie *et al.*, 1974).

E. Temperature Effect

Only a brief discussion will be given here of the effect of temperature on the efficacy of radiation, since the subject is covered in greater detail in Chapter 9 (Section IV.A–C). Morgan and Reed (1954) and Kempe (1955) found that a preliminary heat-shocking treatment did not affect the subsequent lethal effect of radiation on *Cl. botulinum* spores, and Anderson *et al.* (1967) showed that heat-treated spores of *Cl. botulinum* type A became more resistant to radiation.

A divergence of opinion is again apparent on the effects of temperature during irradiation. Low temperatures have been found to have little effect on the sterilizing dose of radiation on *Cl. botulinum* spores in pork (Denny *et al.*, 1959; Ingram and Thornley, 1961). In contrast, the radiation sensitivity of spores of *Cl. botulinum* 33A in phosphate buffer or in ground beef increases with increasing temperature over the range of -196 to $0°C$, whereas in pork pea broth temperature has virtually no effect on radiation sensitivity over this range (Grecz *et al.*, 1965, 1967). El-Bisi *et al.* (1967) observed that lower irradiation doses were needed to inactivate spores of *Cl. botulinum* 53B in food as the temperature increases in the range of -196 to $20°C$.

A "paradoxical inversion" (or "thermorestoration" effect) is sometimes noted in that, as temperature increases, resistance increases up to a certain point, beyond which a rise in temperature is associated with a rapid increase in sensitivity. This, however, occurs only in model systems (and then not invariably so) but not necessarily when spores are irradiated in foods at different temperatures. This is considered more fully in Chapter 9, together with the effects of pre-irradiation on thermal resistance.

F. Effect of Environment

Both the composition and pH of the suspending medium may influence the radiation resistance of bacterial spores. The composition of the suspending medium may be extended to include the presence of additives, since these may increase or decrease the sensitivity to irradiation of bacterial spores. For convenience, however, additives are considered briefly in a separate subsection, and in more detail in Chapter 9.

1. *Composition of the suspending medium*

Generally, spores are more sensitive when irradiated in phosphate buffer than in various foodstuffs such as ground beef, beef and pork pea broth. Examples (Table 4.1) have been provided for *Cl. botulinum* 33A (Anellis *et al.*, 1965a, b; Grecz *et al.*, 1965) and 53B (El-Bisi *et al.*, 1967) and for *Cl. perfringens* type A (Midura *et al.*, 1965). However, whereas some food substrates protect *Cl. botulinum* spores, others (such as canned bacon) appear to sensitize them (Grecz, 1965).

2. *pH of the suspending medium*

From the rather limited evidence available, it seems that there is little effect of pH on the radiation resistance of spores (Edwards *et al.*, 1954), except possibly at pH values below 5 (Farkas *et al.*, 1967).

3. *Presence of additives*

The presence of additives may increase or decrease the radiation sensitivity of spores, the additives then acting as sensitizers or protectors, respectively. This aspect is considered more fully in Chapter 9; see also Deasy *et al.* (1970a, b, 1971).

4. *Dried spores*

The spores of certain species are more resistant to γ-radiation when exposed on wet discs than those on dry discs (Borick and Fogarty, 1967) and sterilization is more difficult with spores on agar dosimeters than in suture material (Borick and Fogerty, 1967). The radiation resistance of air-dried spores of *B. pumilus* E601 is only influenced by the supporting surface if this is soluble, as occurs with a polyvinyl alcohol film. Irrespective of the suspending medium from which the spores are dried, *D*-values are always higher when the supporting during the irradiation process is a polyvinyl alcohol film, which suggests (Burt and Ley, 1963a) that the spores are trapped in the film during drying, thereby leading to local anoxic conditions (Section IV.D).

G. Continuous or Interrupted Radiation

No significant difference between *D*-values of *B. pumilus* E601 spores occurs when irradiation doses are delivered continuously or given in fractions at various storage intervals (Burt and Ley, 1963b). It has also been pointed out, however, that with food, growth could occur in the intervals between the radiation treatment, unless the sterilization of materials was performed and maintained in the frozen state (Borick and

Fogarty, 1967). It must also be borne in mind that the radiation resistance of *B. pumilus* spores may be altered by repeated irradiation treatment of surviving spore populations (Parisi and Antoine, 1975, 1977). Vegetative cells of this strain also show radiation resistance after multiple radiation treatments (Parisi and Antoine, 1974).

H. Partial Cell Irradiation

Partial cell irradiation is a procedure involving bombardment of cells with electrons of low incident energy so that their trajectories terminate within the spore. By means of this technique, it has been shown that the germination-like changes that occur in irradiated spores (Levinson and Hyatt, 1960; Gould and Ordal, 1968) result from peripheral cell damage to the cells (Lefebvre and Preiss, 1970; Lefebvre, 1973; Stogaitis and Lefebvre, 1976, 1977). The loss of optical density that results in such treated spore suspensions is considered more fully in Section V.B; see also Davis (1954).

I. Stage of Sporulation

During the formation of spores of *B. megaterium*, the cysteine and cystine content in the protein increases (Vinter, 1959), the proteins of spores containing about five times as much of these as vegetative cells prior to spore formation. The period of formation of cysteine-rich structures precedes slightly the formation of the refractile structure of spores of *B. cereus* (Vinter, 1961a), and the radioresistance of sporulating cells appears simultaneously with the formation of cystine structures, being closely followed by the formation of the refractile structures (Vinter, 1961a). Resistance to UV or gamma-radiation takes place about 2 h before the onset of heat resistance (Durban *et al.*, 1970).

Vinter (1961b) proposed the separation of normal spore maturation into two stages: first, the development of a cystine-rich protein structure in the spore coat and the simultaneous attainment of radioresistance, and second, which was only successfully initiated after completion of the first stage, the synthesis of a Ca–DPA complex and concurrent increase in heat resistance (see Chapters 1 and 2). In *B. cereus*, the development of radioresistance is parallelled by the formation of proteins containing markedly increased concentrations of -SH and -SS groups (Vinter, 1962, 1967). Bott and Lundgren (1964), in studies of a wild-type, WT, strain of *B. cereus*, a mutant C-1 of WT and strain T, were unable to establish a direct relationship between SS content and radioresistance, but noted that an increased SS/SH ratio accompanied the development of radioresistance, and concluded that this SS/SH level could be "part of a more complex mechanism which influences radioresistance". Hitchins *et al.* (1966) treated spores of *B. cereus* strain PX with thioglycollic acid, which ruptured at least 10–30% of spore S–S bonds by reducing them to thiol groups; spores thus treated remained viable, but remained as resistant as control (untreated) spores to γ-radiation. These results imply that if these disulphide bonds had a radioprotective role, then the thioglycollate-treated spores should have become more sensitive to radiation. Although -SH containing compounds can act as scavangers of radiation-induced chemical species that effect radiobiological damage (Tallentire, 1970), the findings of Hitchins *et al.* (1966) demonstrate that the S–S rich protein structure is unlikely to afford resistance to the spore against radiation. Additional studies involving mercapoethanol- or alkali-treated spores likewise show that spores do not possess a "protective barrier" against ionizing radiation (Gould *et al.*, 1970).

J. Germinating Spores

Upon incubation in germination media at 37°C, spores of *B. cereus* lose their resistance to X-rays at a rapid rate, becoming even more sensitive than vegetative cells (Stuy, 1956). This is to be contrasted with the situation (Chapter 5) where germinating spores become, for a short period, more resistant to ultraviolet light. This UV resistance, which as stated occurs over a short period, is not apparent from the findings of Durban *et al.* (1970) in which, with viable counts at extended intervals, there is an apparently simultaneous loss of resistance to heat, γ-radiation and UV radiation.

K. Post-irradiation Recovery and Revival of Bacterial Spores

This aspect is a very important consideration in determining the sensitivity of spores to ionizing radiation, but regrettably is a factor that is too often ignored, although it was shown several years ago that dormancy may be more pronounced after irradiation than after heat treatment (Riemann, 1960).

Those factors (such as composition and pH of the recovery medium, incubation temperature, period of incubation, etc.) that could influence the recovery and revival of treated spores will be discussed fully in Chapter 10. Recent studies have shown, for example, that the post-irradiation incubation temperature (Chowdhury *et al.*, 1976) and the sodium chloride content of recovery media (Kiss *et al.*, 1978) deserve attention.

V. *Possible Mechanisms of Inactivation of Bacterial Spores*

There are several possibilities for the comparatively high radiation resistance of bacterial spores. These include the presence of radioprotective substances in the spore coat (discounted in Section IV.I), the water content of the spore, the possible differences in DNA present in spores and vegetative cells and the possible ability of the cell to repair damage (Tallentire, 1970). A possible relationship between DPA content and γ-radiation has also been suggested (Berg and Grecz, 1970). Although these may be implicated in resistance, it is worth mentioning them in the context of inactivation since in many ways the two areas are inextricably linked. This will become apparent from the following discussion, in which the effect of irradiation on DNA will be considered in some detail (Section V.C). Research has also been devoted to a possible relationship between spore death and DPA loss and this is discussed below (Section V.A).

A. Loss of DPA

No significant release of DPA occurs from X-irradiated spores of *B. megaterium* at a dose of 60 krad although spore viability is considerably reduced (Rode and Foster, 1960). At higher doses (*ca.* 1·2 Mrad or above), *B. megaterium* spores lose turbidity fairly rapidly (Levinson and Hyatt, 1960). Spores of PA 3679 also lose viability although higher radiation doses (2·5 Mrad) are required to achieve this effect. These doses also induce the loss of DPA in the two organisms (Table 4.6) but the *D*-values are approximately 0·2 and 0·5 Mrad, respectively, which suggests that DPA loss occurs only after a considerable killing effect has taken place. Substances leaking from irradiated spores resemble those characterizing the exudate of physiological germination, with an absorption peak of 270 nm (the UV_{max} for DPA), but the leakage from irradiated spores occurs only at high radiation doses (Farkas and Kiss, 1964).

These findings all point to the conclusion that DPA loss occurs only after a considerable killing effect on the spores has taken place, and is, therefore, a consequence rather than a cause of death.

B. Loss of Optical Density

A loss of optical density (O.D.) of spore suspensions after exposure to ionizing radiation was referred to briefly above. Loss of O.D. occurs after partial cell irradiation of *B. megaterium* spores in the absence of

Table 4.6. Retention of Dipicolinic acid (DPA) in irradiated spores[a]

Radiation dose (Mrad)	Approximate retention (%) of DPA in irradiated spores of		
	B. megaterium	PA 3679	*B. cereus*
0	100	100	100
0·25	—	—	103·4
0·4	100	—	—
0·5	—	100	97
0·95	95	—	—
1·0	—	—	88
1·2	65	—	—
1·5	40	100	—
2·0	—	—	34
2·5	—	82	—
5·0	—	71	—

[a] Data of Levinson and Hyatt (1960) for *B. megaterium* and PA 3679, and of Farkas and Kiss (1964) for *B. cereus*.

added germination stimulants of lytic enzymes (Lefebvre, 1977). *Bacillus cereus* spores become progressively more "activated" after exposure to γ-radiation, in the context that they germinate more rapidly in the presence of germinants, which suggests that ionizing radiation causes tertiary-structure changes in macromolecules (Gould and Ordal, 1968; see also Chapter 1).

C. Effects on DNA and Repair Processes

Ultraviolet light, X-rays and nitrogen mustard (HN2) all produce structural defects in DNA, which, unless repaired, are likely to inhibit DNA synthesis or cause some error in protein synthesis, which leads to cell death (Haynes, 1964). Haynes (1964) stated that bacterial survival is determined by the net probability that these defects either persist and prove lethal, or are repaired (after irradiation) during the first few hours of incubation on the plating medium. According to Haynes (1966), there is no indication that DNA is the only target relevant to inactivation, although it seems that it is the principal target. Szybalski and Lorkiewicz (1962) found that the increase in X-ray sensitivity produced by 5-bromouracil was closely parallelled by a corresponding increase in the sensitivity of the transforming DNA extracted from the same cultures. Further, the X-ray sensitivity of various organisms may be correlated with their total DNA content (see Haynes, 1964, 1966; Ginoza, 1967) and DNA base composition, for Kaplan and Zavarine (1962) observed an interesting correlation between the guanine–cytosine content and X-ray sensitivity in a series of bacterial species. In irradiated vegetative bacteria, breakdown of DNA has been observed (Stuy, 1960; McGrath *et al.*, 1966; Grady and Pollard, 1967), and Haynes (1966) stated that "reproductive death in bacteria treated with X-rays, ultraviolet or HN2 arises primarily from formation of structural defects in DNA which serve to block DNA replication".

Some interesting studies on *Micrococcus radiodurans* are important in considering the mechanism of irradiation inactivation. Moseley and Laser (1965a) suggested that recovery of this organism from radiation damage was due to repair of damaged DNA by an active cellular, probably enzymic (Moseley and Laser, 1965b), process which occurs in the lag period (i.e. when cells are transferred to a growth medium) after irradiation. This repair of damage has since been the subject of several notable reviews (Bridges, 1976; Moseley and Williams, 1977). Hitchins *et al.* (1966) wondered whether, as spores did not appear to contain a radioprotective substance (Section IV.I), they possessed a repair mechanism, the term "repair" here and above implying the actual enzymatic steps involved in restoring damaged DNA molecules to a biologically functional form (Haynes, 1964; see later, also).

In viruses and in the more complex bacterial cell, the evidence points to the primary target as being DNA, the reasons that some bacteria are more resistant than others being that they possess a more efficient DNA-repair mechanism (Ginoza, 1967). Thus, unless they are repaired, the structural defects in DNA prove lethal to the bacterial cell. Alper (1977, 1979) considers also that the cellular membrane to which DNA is attached is another target site.

When *B. subtilis* spores are irradiated under dry, anoxic conditions (see Section IV.D) the transforming ability of extracted DNA is more radioresistant than DNA from irradiated vegetative cells (Tanooka and Hutchinson, 1965). The radioresistance of transforming DNA is the same in spores or in spheroplasts formed from them (spore-spheroplasts) but is less in lysed spheroplasts (Tanooka and Sakakibara, 1968). Spore-spheroplasts retain some of the dormant properties of spores themselves (Sakakibara and Ikeda, 1969) and it is interesting to note here that spore-specific UV photoproducts (see Chapter 5) are formed in spores and spore-spheroplasts but not in lysed spheroplasts (Tanooka, 1968; Tanooka and Terano, 1970a). When DNA is extracted from spores and is then exposed to radiation, its transforming ability is equivalent to that of extracted, then irradiated DNA from the corresponding vegetative cell (Tanooka and Sakakibara, 1968). The DNA in spores, however, is much more resistant than the DNA in vegetative cells to single-strand and double-strand breaks (Tanooka and Terano, 1970b). Tanooka and Sakakibara (1968) considered that spore-specific chemical protection was partly responsible for radioresistance and that repair was not involved. Equally, however, it could be claimed that the DNA itself exists in a different state in spores and in vegetative cells. Spore DNA does not appear to be protected from X-irradiation damage, and Zamenhof *et al.* (1965) have claimed that there is no evidence that the radiation resistance of cells or spores can be ascribed to differences in the radiation resistance of their DNA.

Repair of damage caused by ionizing or UV radiation can, as stated above, be responsible for the resistance shown by some bacteria (Moseley, 1968; Bridges, 1976; Moseley and Williams, 1977). However, the types of damage inflicted by ionizing and UV radiations are different; the former induces single-strand or double-strand scission of DNA, whereas UV induces the formation of thymine dimers in the DNA of vegetative cells or of spore photoproducts in spore DNA (Chapter 5). Single-strand breaks can be repaired in spores during post-irradiation germination (Terano *et al.*, 1969) but this rejoining is not affected by chloramphenicol (Terano *et al.*, 1971). More recently, spores of the same species with widely differing radiation resistances (*Cl. botulinum*, highly resistant 33A and highly sensitive 51B) have been studied (Durban *et al.*, 1974). The results appear to show that in strain 33A there is direct repair (rejoining) or single strand DNA breaks during or after irradiation in spores existing under non-physiological conditions at 0°C and in the absence of germination. EDTA inhibits much of this repair. In the sensitive strain, 31B, no significant repair occurs under conditions of spore dormancy. No post-irradiation repair of DNA from spores of both organisms occurs during germination. The obvious objection to this theory is, of course, the normally negligible level of metabolic activity in resting spores.

During germination, the radiation resistance of spores is lost. If, however, the just-germinated cells are quickly suspended in strong sucrose solution and are then irradiated the resistance is restored. This finding suggests that the water content of the spore core is a major factor in the resistance of spores to radiation (Gould, 1978), i.e. resistance is associated with a dry core. This hypothesis cannot, as yet, be reconciled with the findings of Tallentire and Powers (1963), Iwasaki *et al.* (1974) and Tallentire *et al.* (1974) who have demonstrated that under oxic conditions the resistance of spores is maximal at the highest spore water content, whereas under anoxic conditions resistance decreases as the a_w rises (Tallentire, 1970; Härnulv and Snygg, 1973).

The various theories of cellular inactivation by ionizing radiation are well discussed by Alper (1979).

VI. *Uses of Ionizing Radiation*

A comprehensive discussion of the applications and uses of ionizing radiation is outside the scope of this book. What follows, therefore, should be regarded as being only a summary. Additional information can be obtained by consulting Ley (1971), Gaughran and Goudie (1974), Diding (1975), Silverman and Sinskey (1977), International Atomic Energy Agency (IAEA), Vienna (1975), Alper (1979) and Harm (1980).

A. Sterilization of Medical Products

Several uses of ionizing radiations in the sterilization of medical and pharmaceutical items or equipment have been described. One of the earliest, and certainly one of the most useful, was published by the Association of British Pharmaceutical Industry (Report, 1960) in which the effects of radiations on various drugs were reported. Several papers have appeared subsequently describing the uses of this method of sterilization. Ionizing radiation has been employed for the sterilization of the following:

(i) Disposable syringes (Hunter, 1961; Tattersall, 1966; Cook and Berry, 1967; Richards, 1968).

(ii) Sutures (Pandula *et al.*, 1967; Dawson, 1975), although it must be noted that catgut, irradiated dry, is degraded by the direct action of radiation, whereas when irradiated in the wet state, or if covalent links are introduced (e.g. by pre-irradiation treatment with chromium salts or formaldehyde) radiation resistance of catgut is increased (Gupta, 1975).

(iii) Sterilization of pharmaceutical powders (Igali, 1967; Barker *et al.*, 1980; British Pharmocopoeia, 1980).

(iv) Sterilization of adhesive and other dressings (Dow, 1961; Aronson *et al.*, 1975; Morganstern, 1977).

(v) Sterilization of eye ointments with retention of potency and freedom from toxicity (Kulkarni and Gopal, 1975).

(vi) Intravenous infusion sets (Kulkarni and Gopal, 1975; Singson and Ibe, 1975).

Ogg (1967) has described the applications of γ-ray sterilization in ophthalmology.

Generally, pharmaceutical products are more stable in the solid rather than liquid state to ionizing radiation (Report, 1960; Gupta, 1975; Blackburn *et al.*, 1975; Gopal *et al.*, 1975; Kulkarni and Gopal, 1975). Radiation may be a useful method of sterilizing medical and pharmaceutical products, but safety and efficacy must be determined for each product (Kulkarni and Gopal, 1975; Hangay, 1977).

In general terms, ionizing radiation should be of considerable use as a sterilizing procedure because when used normally, there is no increase in temperature and the process would thus be expected to find application in the sterilization of thermolabile products. Items sterilized by other methods and used should not be resterilized by ionizing radiation.

Another avenue which has been explored is the combination of heat (moist or dry) with ionizing radiation. This is discussed in Chapter 9.

B. Food Sterilization

Several investigations have been made of the possible sterilization by radiation of various foodstuffs, and the choice of sterilizing dose is considered in Section VII.B. In the United Kingdom, a Committee was set up by the (then) Ministry of Health to report on this matter (Report, 1964). This Committee considered *Cl. botulinum* to be the most important organism in the context of sterilization, not only because of the nature of the spores themselves but also because of the toxin produced. Additionally, the possible physical and chemical changes in irradiated foods were discussed, since there could be changes in taste and in colour such that the food becomes unacceptable for human consumption.

Frohnsdorff (1974) emphasized that a general acceptance or irradiated food had yet to be achieved, but pointed out two areas where radiation had become established, viz. (i) the diet of experimental animals bred and reared in sterile environments, (ii) the sterilization of food required for human patients undergoing treatment in isolated sterile rooms.

VII. *Choice of Sterilizing Dose*

A. Medical and Pharmaceutical Products

The most important considerations in selecting a particular sterilizing dose are (i) destruction of microorganisms, (ii) no alterations in the product being sterilized. Thus, a knowledge of the type and number of organisms per unit prior to sterilization is of considerable value (Osterberg, 1973) and various studies have been devoted to this problem. Kelsey (1961), in considering the choice of organisms for various sterilization processes, proposed that the number of test organisms should represent the maximum contamination likely to be encountered in practice, together with a safety margin, and suggested it was convenient to aim at the total sterilization of a test object containing 10^5 or 10^6 organisms. However, Tattersall (1966) has shown that disposable syringes are contaminated, prior to sterilization, with relatively small numbers of organisms and Cook and Berry (1967) found that of the unsterilized syringes (from various manufacturers) which they examined, 16–48% were initially sterile, and of the others there were 20–70 organisms per contaminated syringe. The most common organisms were coagulase-negative Gram-positive cocci. Spore-forming rods are often present on sutures prior to radiation sterilization (Osterberg, 1973).

It is also essential to know the resistance of these organisms during and after irradiation in a given environment (Christensen and Holm, 1967; Christensen *et al.*, 1967; Christensen, 1977).

A dose of 2·5 Mrad has been recommended as one which provides complete safety (Artandi and van Winkle, 1959; Report of the Association of British Pharmaceutical Industry, 1960). Artandi and van Winkle (1959) established the minimal killing dose for more than 150 different species of microorganisms, and found the maximum dose that could safely be tolerated by surgical catgut; they chose 2·5 Mrad as the sterilizing dose, which was 40% above the minimum dose (1·8 Mrad) to kill the most resistant microorganism. Catgut could tolerate 5 Mrad before showing properties inferior to heat-sterilized gut. Darmady *et al.* (1961) found that, of the organisms they tested, spores of *B. pumilus* strain E601 were the most resistant, and could, therefore, be used as a test organism for irradiation; a dose of 2·5 Mrad was still, however, satisfactory. For these spores, the IF is 10^{15} or 10^7, depending on whether the spores are irradiated under aerobic or anoxic conditions, respectively (Burt and Ley, 1963a). A dose of 2·5 Mrad has also been recommended by Powell (1961). Ley and Tallentire (1965) have discussed the reasons for the choice of the 2·5 Mrad sterilizing dose in the United Kingdom, and have stated that the most convincing evidence of a given sterilizing dose will arise from a study of the naturally contaminated production items themselves, rather than an experimental situation designed in the laboratory. A dose of 2·5 Mrad has been found to be satisfactory in practice (van Winkle *et al.*, 1967). In the United States, sterilizing doses of less than 2·5 Mrad have been used with no hazardous consequences (Whitby and Gelda, 1979).

In Denmark, studies with *Streptococcus faecium* have resulted in the recommendation that a dose of 4·5 Mrad is the minimum necessary for the radiation sterilization of dry, disposable plastic equipment. Under certain conditions (strains dried on polythene foil in the presence of serum broth) strains of this organism are more resistant than bacterial spores (Christensen *et al.*, 1966, 1967; Christensen and Holm, 1967; Holm and Christensen, 1967; Christensen, 1967; International Atomic Energy Agency, 1967). When *Strep. faecium* is irradiated in air in heart infusion broth, however, an IF of more than 10^{20} is obtained at 2·5 Mrad (Matsuyama *et al.*, 1964). Thus, the method of drying, in serum broth, influences its radiation resistance. The resistance of spores, also, can be altered by changing the conditions under which they are irradiated; when irradiated at 2·5 Mrad in the presence of hydrogen sulphide (a situation unlikely to be encountered in practice), in air or under anoxic conditions, *B. pumilus* spores have IF values of, respectively, 10^4, 10^{15} and 10^7 (Ley, 1966). *Streptococcus faecium* has been encountered only infrequently as a contaminant and then only at low levels (van Winkle *et al.*, 1967).

Ley and Tallentire (1965) considered that the usual procedures, viz. the use of sterility testing and of biological indicators, in monitoring radiation sterilization were of minor importance. Instead, they suggested that the sterilizing process, used at 2·5 Mrad, should be routinely challenged with medical products that had been deliberately exposed to all "natural" conditions known to yield high contamination levels.

Several theoretical studies have been made of the influence of the initial numbers of contaminants (and their radiation resistance) on the quality assurance of sterilized products (Ley, 1971; Tallentire *et al.*, 1971, 1977; Ley *et al.*, 1972; Tallentire, 1973; Tallentire and Khan, 1975, 1977; Khan *et al.*, 1977). The principle of this is the development of a mathematical model, using subprocess data, which examines the dependence on radiation dose of the proportion of items contaminated in a population undergoing irradiation. This model is based upon the concept that sterility testing (Kirshbaum, 1971; Outschoorn, 1977) of samples after substerilizing radiation doses would give a number of positive samples from which it would be possible to deduce the likelihood of positives at much higher radiation doses (see also Whitby and Gelda, 1979).

B. Food Preservation

Any process of food sterilization must ensure not only the destruction of microorganisms but also the continued nutritive value and palatability of the food. The extent of the damage to, or changes in, the irradiated food depends on (i) the radiation dose applied, the more severe the treatment, the greater the damage (Kempe *et al.*, 1957; Ley, 1967); (ii) the nature of the particular food (Ley, 1967) and (iii) the conditions prevailing during and after irradiation (Ley, 1967). Irradiation is known to bring about changes in proteins, carbohydrates and fats, but as a general rule, a dose of 6 Mrad causes an amount of destruction of vitamins equivalent to that caused by cooking (Report, 1964). However, the nutritive value of food irradiated with a dose of 5 Mrad or less is very small (Report, 1964). Hannen (1955) had earlier discussed the possible uses of radiation for sterilizing foodstuffs or eliminating pathogens in foods, or for increasing the shelf life of foods by reducing the level of spoilage organisms.

The two pathogens of greatest significance in food sterilization are undoubtedly *Cl. botulinum* and *Cl. perfringens (welchii)* (Report, 1964); the reason for this is their relative resistance to radiation, this applying particularly to the former organism, on which most studies appear to have been carried out. Based upon the work of Morgan and Reed (1954), Bridges and Horne (1959) showed that for food containing only 1–10 *Cl. botulinum* spores/g, the sterilizing dose would be 3 Mrad; if 10^3 spores/g were present, a dose of 4 Mrad would be required.

Many of the approaches involved in the thermal sterilization of foodstuffs have been applied to sterilization by ionizing radiations, although many irradiated organisms are not inactivated logarithmically. Bellamy (1959) pointed out that if the criterion used in heat sterilization studies of an IF of 10^{12} were adopted, then a sterilizing dose of 4·5 Mrad would have to be used in food sterilization. The most direct concept proposed for the application of ionizing radiations in food sterilization is, in fact, regarded as the $12 \times D$-value concept (Niven, 1958; Schmidt, 1963; Clifford and Anellis, 1975; Silverman and Sinskey, 1977). A dose of 4·5 Mrad has also been suggested by Clouston and Sanger (1964) for foods where *Cl. botulinum* was a problem. However, Ley (1967) has pointed out that, in the case of irradiated fresh meats, a dose high enough to deal with *Cl. botulinum* causes objectionable odour and flavour changes, and does not effectively control enzyme activity, which must be stopped to ensure preservation of texture during storage at room temperature. El-Bisi *et al.* (1967) considered that *Cl. botulinum* types A and B had the greatest radioresistance among common food-borne sporogenic bacteria in both laboratory reference menstrua and model food systems, and also stated that the potential hazard of botulism in such a product was a challenge of the highest order from a public health viewpoint. Their calculated irradiation dose consisted of the critical minimal radiation dose (MRD) × lag (*L*) where MRD was 12 × *D*-value (see Section III.E). Depending on the temperature of irradiation, the dose used varied between 5·276 and 3·532 Mrad. However, it should also be borne in mind that different radiation doses may need to be used for different food products, for Grecz (1965) has found varying *D*-values for *Cl. botulinum* irradiated in, e.g., canned chicken and canned bacon.

Greenberg *et al.* (1965) found that the *D*-value of *Cl. botulinum* strains 33A and 41B in chopped ham was 0·197–0·226 Mrad, so that the calculated 12 × *D*-value would be between 2·36 and 2·712 Mrad. *Anellis et al.* (1965a, b, 1967) carried out experiments on sliced, cured bacon, packed in cans and seeded with 6 × 10^5 or 3 × 10^6 spores/can (depending on the strain) of various strains of *Cl. botulinum*. *D*-values were calculated from (i) partial spoilage data, and (ii) recovery of *Cl. botulinum* from non-spoiled cans, after the cans had been γ-irradiated to various dose levels. The theoretical 12 log reduction dose (i.e. 12 × *D*-value) was 2·67 or 2·87 Mrad, depending on the method of calculation, the experimental minimal sterilizing dose was 2·0 Mrad, and 4·5 Mrad was adequate as the sterilizing dose.

The use of a "pasteurizing" dose of irradiation has been considered by Bellamy (1959) and Report (1964). Such a dose, used at 1 Mrad (Bellamy, 1959) has been employed to cover either the control of the spoilage organisms or the pathogens which are most likely to be troublesome or dangerous in the food that is to be irradiated. However, a pasteurization process might result in surviving organisms which were mutants, or which could proliferate more readily in irradiated than in unirradiated foods; moreover, sufficient pathogens might survive to "allow their rapid and unusual proliferation in the virtual absence of other microbes, the latter having been destroyed by the radiation" (Report, 1964).

In addition to the destruction of *Cl. bolulinum*, the inactivation of botulinum toxin needs to be considered. Skulberg and Coleby (1960) and Skulberg (1965) showed that the *D*-values of types A and B toxins were 1·25–2·9 Mrad and 0·65–4·12 Mrad, depending on the condition employed, and 2·1 Mrad for type E toxin. Grecz and Lin (1967) found that a dose of 4·5 Mrad reduced 100 000 minimum lethal doses (M.L.D.) of vegetative toxin to 2300 M.L.D. Thus, radiation doses capable of producing commercial sterilization in foods cannot be relied upon to destroy significant amounts of preformed toxin, whether this toxin is present in the spores of *Cl. botulinum* or in the medium (Skulberg, 1965; Grecz and Lin, 1967).

Goresline *et al.* (1964) suggested the following definitions for the main types of irradiation treatment intended to kill microorganisms in food:

(i) **Radappertization**, which is the application to foods of doses of ionizing radiations sufficient to reduce the number and/or activity of viable organisms to such an extent that very few, if any, are detectable in the treated food, while no spoilage or toxicity of microbial origin is detectable. This is thus equivalent to "commercial sterility": see Rowley *et al.* (1974) for a discussion of radappertization of meats.

(ii) **Radicidation**, which is the application to foods of doses of ionizing radiations sufficient to reduce the number of viable specific non-spore-forming pathogenic microorganisms, other than viruses, so that none is detected in the treated food.

(iii) **Radurization**, which is the application to foods of doses of less than 1 Mrad of ionizing radiations sufficient to enhance the keeping quality (i.e. extend the storage life) by causing a substantial reduction in the numbers of viable specific organisms.

Of these, radicidation at doses of less than $0 \cdot 75 \times 10^6$ is considered to be most useful in removing salmonellae in eggs, in animal feeds and in frozen chicken; radurization for extending the storage life of cod, haddock, shrimp and strawberries; whereas radappertization is the least useful because of the problem of wholesomeness and because thermally processed and frozen foods are so widely used in civilized countries (Goldblith, 1970).

References

Adams, G. E. and Stratford, I. J. (1977). *In* "Sterilization of Medical Products by Ionizing Radiation" (E. R. L. Gaughran and A. J. Goudie, eds), pp. 81–96. Multiscience Publications, Montreal.

Alper, T. (1977). *In* "Sterilization of Medical Products by Ionizing Radiation" (E. R. L. Gaughran and A. J. Goudie, eds), pp. 9–29. Multiscience Publications, Montreal.

Alper, T. (1979). "Cellular Radiobiology". Cambridge University Press, Cambridge.

Anderson, A. W., Corlett, D. A. and Krabbenkroft, K. L. (1967). *In* "Botulism 1966" (M. Ingram and T. A. Roberts, eds), pp. 76–88. Chapman and Hall, London.

Anellis, A. and Berkowitz, D. (1977). *Applied and Environmental Microbiology* **34**, 600–601.

Anellis, A. and Koch, R. B. (1962). *Applied Microbiology* **10**, 326–330.

Anellis, A. and Werkowski, S. (1968). *Applied Microbiology* **16**, 1300–1308.

Anellis, A. and Werkowski, S. (1971). *Canadian Journal of Microbiology* **17**, 1185–1187.

Anellis, A., Grecz, N., Huber, D. A., Berkowitz, D., Schneider, M. D. and Simon, M. (1965a). *Applied Microbiology* **13**, 37–42.

Anellis, A., Grecz, N. and Berkowitz, D. (1965b). *Applied Microbiology* **13**, 397–401.

Anellis, A., Berkowitz, D., Jarboe, C. and El-Bisi, H. M. (1967). *Applied Microbiology* **15**, 166–177.

Anellis, A., Berkowitz, D., Jarboe, C. and El-Bisi, H. M. (1969). *Applied Microbiology* **18**, 604–611.

Anellis, A., Berkowitz, D., Kemper, D. and Rowley, D. B. (1972). *Applied Microbiology* **23**, 734–739.

Anellis, A., Shattuck, E., Morin, M., Srisara, B., Qvale, S., Rowley, D. B. and Rose, E. W., Jr. (1977). *Applied and Environmental Microbiology* **34**, 823–831.

Aoki, H. and Slepecky, R. (1974). *In* "Spore Research 1973" (A. N. Barker, G. W. Gould and J. Wolf, eds), pp. 93–102. Academic Press, London and New York.

Aronson, M., Eisenberg, E. and Lepidot, M. (1975). *In* "Radiosterilization of Medical Products 1974", pp. 447–458. Proceedings of a Symposium, International Atomic Energy Agency, Vienna.

Artandi, C. and van Winkle, W. (1959). *Nucleonics* **17**, 86–90.

Barker, D. J. W., Tallentire, A. and Ley, F. J. (1980). *In* "Microbial Growth and Survival in Extremes of Environment" (G. W. Gould and J. E. L. Corry, eds), pp. 195–204. Society for Applied Bacteriology Technical Series No. 15. Academic Press, London and New York.

Bellamy, W. D. (1959). *Advances in Applied Microbiology* **1**, 49–73.

Berg, P. E. and Grecz, N. (1970). *Journal of Bacteriology* **103**, 517–519.

Blackburn, R., Iddon, B., Moore, J. S., Phillips, G. O., Power, D. M. and Woodward, T. W. (1975). *In* "Radiosterilization of Medical Products 1974", pp. 351–363. Proceedings of a Symposium, International Atomic Energy Agency, Vienna.

Borick, P. M. and Fogarty, M. G. (1967). *Applied Microbiology* **15**, 785–789.

Bott, K. F. and Lundgren, D. G. (1964). *Radiation Research* **21**, 195–211.

Bridges, A. E., Olivo, J. P. and Chandler, V. L. (1956). *Applied Microbiology* **4**, 147–149.

Bridges, B. A. (1964). *Progress in Industrial Microbiology* **5**, 283–326.

Bridges, B. A. (1976). *In* "The Survival of Vegetative Microbes" (T. R. Gray and J. R. Postgate, eds), pp. 183–208. 26th Symposium of the Society for General Microbiology. Cambridge University Press, Cambridge.

Bridges, B. A. and Horne, T. (1959). *Journal of Applied Bacteriology* **22**, 96–115.

Briggs, A. (1966). *Journal of Applied Bacteriology* **29**, 490–504.

British Pharmacopoeia (1980). Pharmaceutical Press, London.

Brown, W. L., Vinton, C. and Gross, C. E. (1960). *Food Technology* **14**, 622–625.

Burt, M. M. and Ley, F. J. (1963a). *Journal of Applied Bacteriology* **26**, 484–489.

Burt, M. M. and Ley, F. J. (1963b). *Journal of Applied Bacteriology* **26**, 490–495.

Christensen, E. A. (1964). *Acta Pathologica Microbiologica Scandinavica* **61**, 483–486.

Christensen, E. A. (1967). *In* "Radiosterilization of Medical Products", pp. 1–3. Proceedings of a Symposium, International Atomic Energy Agency, Vienna.

Christensen, E. A. (1977). *In* "Sterilization of Medical Products by Ionizing Radiation" (E. R. L. Gaughran and A. J. Grudie, eds), pp. 50–64. Multiscience Publication, Montreal.

Christensen, E. A. and Holm, N. W. (1964). *Acta Pathologica Microbiologica Scandinavica* **60**, 253–264.

Christensen, E. A. and Holm, N. W. (1967). *Archiv for Pharmaci og Chemi* **74**, 847–857.

Christensen, E. A. and Kjems, E. (1965). *Acta Pathologica Microbiologica Scandinavica* **63**, 281–290.

Christensen, E. A. and Sehested, K. (1964). *Acta Pathologica Microbiologica Scandinavica* **62**, 448–458.

Christensen, E. A., Kristensen, H. and Sehested, K. (1982). *In* "Principles and Practice of Disinfection, Preservation and Sterilization" (A. D. Russell, W. B. Hugo and G. A. J. Aycliffe, eds), pp. 513–533. Blackwell Scientific Publications, Oxford.

Christensen, E. A., Holm, N. W. and Juul, F. (1966). *Riso Report*, No. **140**.

Christensen, E. A., Holm, N. W. and Juul, F. (1967). *In* "Radiosterilization of Medical Products", pp. 265–281. Proceedings of a Symposium, International Atomic Energy Authority, Vienna.

Chowdury, M. S. U., Rowley, D. B., Anellis, A. and Levinson, H. S. (1976). *Applied and Environmental Microbiology* **32**, 172–178.

Clifford, W. J. and Anellis, A. (1975). *Applied Microbiology* **29**, 861–863.

Clouston, J. G. and Sangster, D. F. (1964). *Australian Journal of Pharmacy* **45**, 548–551.

Cook, A. M. and Berry, R. J. (1967). *In* "Radiosterilization of Medical Products", pp. 295–308. Proceedings of a Symposium, International Atomic Energy Agency, Vienna.

Cook, A. M. and Roberts, T. A. (1964). *Journal of Pharmacy and Pharmacology* **16**, 529–532.

Cook, A. M., Roberts, T. A. and Widdowson, J. P. (1964). *Journal of General Microbiology* **34**, 185–193.

Cross, M. H., Simic, M. and Powers, E. L. (1972). *Nature New Biology* **238**, 260–261.

Darmady, E. M., Hughes, K. E. A., Burt, M. M., Freeman, B. M. and Powell, D. B. (1961). *Journal of Clinical Pathology* **14**, 55–58.

Davis, M. (1954). *Archives of Biochemistry and Biophysics* **48**, 469–481.

Dawson, J. O. (1975). *In* "Radiosterilization of Medical Products 1974", pp. 265–268. Proceedings of a Symposium, International Atomic Energy Agency, Vienna.

Deasy, P. B., Kusser, E. and Timoney, R. F. (1970a). *Applied Microbiology* **20**, 455–460.

Deasy, P. B., Kusser, E. and Timoney, R. F. (1970b). *Applied Microbiology* **20**, 461–464.

Deasy, P. B., Kusser, E. and Timoney, R. F. (1971). *Applied Microbiology* **22**, 567–570.

Denny, C. B., Bohrer, C. W., Perkins, W. E. and Townsend, C. E. (1959). *Food Research* **24**, 44–50.

Diding, N. (1975). *Acta Pharmaceutica Suecica* **12**, Supplement, 35–43.

Donnellan, J. E. and Setlow, R. B. (1965). *Science, New York*, **149**, 308–310.

Dow, J. (1961). *In* "Recent Developments in the Sterilization of Surgical Materials", pp. 29–31. Report of a Symposium. Pharmaceutical Press, London.

Dunn, C. G., Campbell, W. L., Fran, H. and Hutchins, A. (1948). *Journal of Applied Physics* **19**, 605–615.

Durban, E., Goodnow, R. and Grecz, N. (1970). *Journal of Bacteriology* **102**, 590–592.

Durban, E., Grecz, N. and Farkas, J. (1974). *Journal of Bacteriology* **118**, 129–138.

Dyer, J. K., Anderson, A. W. and Dutiyabodhi, P. (1966). *Applied Microbiology* **14**, 92–97.

Edwards, R. B., Peterson, L. J. and Cummings, D. G. (1954). *Journal of Food Technology* **8**, 284–290.

El-Bisi, H. M., Snyder, D. P. and Levin, R. E. (1967). *In* "Botulism 1966" (M. Ingram and T. A. Roberts, eds), pp. 89–107. Chapman and Hall, London.

Erdman, E., Thatcher, F. S. and MacQueen, K. F. (1961a). *Canadian Journal of Microbiology* 7, 199–206.

Erdman, E., Thatcher, F. S. and MacQueen, K. F. (1961b). *Canadian Journal of Microbiology* 7, 207–215.

Ewing, D. (1973). *International Journal of Radiation Biology* 24, 505–515.

Ewing, D. (1975). *International Journal of Radiation Biology* 28, 165–176.

Ewing, D. (1976). *Radiation Research* 68, 459–468.

Ewing, D. (1980). *Radiation Research* 21, 288–296.

Ewing, D., Fielden, E. M. and Roberts, P. B. (1974). *Radiation Research* 58, 481–488.

Farkas, J. and Kiss, I. (1964). *Communications of the Central Food Research Institute, Budapest* No. 3, pp. 1–11.

Farkas, J., Kiss, I. and Andrassy, E. (1967). *In* "Radiosterilization of Medical Products", pp. 343–354. Proceedings of a Symposium, International Atomic Energy Agency, Vienna.

Fielden, E. M., Ewing, D. and Roberts, P. B. (1974). *Radiation Research* 58, 489–497.

Frohnsdorff, R. S. M. (1974). *In* "Sterilization by Ionizing Radiation" (E. R. L. Gaughran and A. J. Goudie, eds), pp. 425–453. Multiscience Publishers, Montreal.

Gaughran, E. R. L. and Goudie, A. J. (1974) (Eds). "Sterilizing by Ionizing Radiation", Multiscience Publishers, Montreal.

Ginoza, W. (1967). *Annual Review of Microbiology* 21, 315–368.

Goldblith, S. A. (1967). *In* "Radiosterilization of Medical Products", pp. 3–22. Proceedings of a Symposium, International Atomic Energy, Agency Vienna.

Goldblith, S. A. (1970). *Journal of Food Technology* 5, 103–110.

Goldblith, S. A. (1971). *In* "Inhibition and Destruction of the Microbial Cell" (W. B. Hugo, ed.), pp. 285–305. Academic Press, London and New York.

Gopal, N. G. S., Rajagopalan, S. and Sharma, G. (1975). *In* "Radiosterilization of Medical Products 1974", pp. 387–402. Proceedings of a Symposium, International Atomic Energy Agency, Vienna.

Goresline, H. E., Ingram, M., Mocquot, G., Mossel, D. A. A., Niven, C. F. Jr. and Thatcher, F. S. (1964). *Nature, London* 204, 237–238.

Gould, G. W. (1978). *In* "Spores VII" (G. Chambliss and J. C. Vary, eds), pp. 21–26. American Society for Microbiology, Washington D.C.

Gould, G. W. and Ordal, Z. J. (1968). *Journal of General Microbiology* 50, 77–84.

Gould, G. W., Stubbs, J. M. and King, W. L. (1970). *Journal of General Microbiology* 60, 347–355.

Grady, L. J. and Pollard, E. C. (1967). *Biochimica et Biophysica Acta* 145, 837–839.

Grecz, N. (1965). *Journal of Applied Bacteriology* 28, 27–35.

Grecz, N. and Lin, C. A. (1967). *In* "Botulism 1966" (M. Ingram and T. A. Roberts, eds), pp. 302–322. Chapman and Hall, London.

Grecz, N., Snyder, O. P., Walker, A. A. and Anellis, A. (1965). *Applied Microbiology* 13, 527–536.

Grecz, N., Upadhyay, J. and Tang, T. C. (1967). *Canadian Journal of Microbiology* 13, 287–293.

Grecz, N., Lo, H., Kang, T. W. and Farkas, J. (1977). *In* "Spore Research 1976" (A. N. Barker, J. Wolf, D. J. Ellar, G. J. Dring and G. W. Gould, eds), pp. 602–630. Academic Press, London and New York.

Greenberg, R. A., Bladel, B. and Zingleman, W. J. (1965). *Applied Microbiology* 13, 743–748.

Gupta, B. L. (1975). *In* "Radiosterilization of Medical Products 1974", pp. 179–190. Proceedings of a Symposium, International Atomic Energy Agency, Vienna.

Hangay, G. (1977). *In* "Sterilization of Medical Products by Ionizing Radiation" (E. R. L. Gaughran and A. J. Goudie, eds), pp. 247–263. Multiscience Publications, Montreal.

Hannen, R. S. (1955). Scientific and Technological Problems involved in using Ionizing Radiations for the Preservation of Food. Special Report No. 61. H.M.S.O., London.

Harm, W. (1980). "Biological Effects of Ultraviolet Radiation". Cambridge University Press, Cambridge.

Harnülv, B. G. and Snygg, B. G. (1973). *Journal of Applied Bacteriology* **36**, 677–682.

Haynes, R. H. (1964). *Photochemistry and Photobiology* **3**, 429–450.

Haynes, R. H. (1966). *Radiation Research Supplement* **6**, 1–29.

Hitchins, A. D., King, W. L. and Gould, G. W. (1966). *Journal of Applied Bacteriology* **29**, 505–511.

Holm, N. W. and Christensen, E. A. (1967). *Archiv for Pharmaci og Chemi* **74**, 858–866.

Holm, N. W. and Christensen, E. A. (1975). *Acta Pharmaceutica Suecica* **12**, Supplement, 26–34.

Hunter, C. L. F. (1961). *In* "Recent Developments in the Sterilization of Surgical Materials", pp. 32–33. Report of a Symposium. Pharmaceutical Press, London.

Igali, S. (1967). *In* "Radiosterilization of Medical Products", pp. 339–341. Proceedings of a Symposium, International Atomic Energy Agency, Vienna.

Ingram, M. and Thornley, M. J. (1961). *Journal of Applied Bacteriology* **24**, 94–103.

International Atomic Energy Agency (1967). *In* "Radiosterilization of Medical Products". Report of a Panel: Recommended Code of Practice for Radiosterilization of Medical Products, Vienna.

International Atomic Energy Agency (1975). Symposium, "Radiosterilization of Medical Products 1974", Vienna.

Iwasaki, T., Tallentire, A., Kimber, B. F. and Powers, E. L. (1974). *Radiation Research* **57**, 306–310.

Jacobs, G. P. and Tallentire, A. (1974). *In* "Spore Research 1973" (A. N. Barker, G. W. Gould and J. Wolf, eds), p. 249. Academic Press, London and New York.

Kaplan, H. S. and Zavarine, R. (1962). *Biochemical and Biophysical Research Communications* **8**, 432–436.

Kelsey, J. C. (1961). *Journal of Clinical Pathology* **14**, 313–319.

Kempe, L. L. (1955). *Applied Microbiology* **3**, 346–352.

Kempe, L. L., Graikoski, J. T. and Gillis, R. A. (1954). *Applied Microbiology* **2**, 330–332.

Kempe, L. L., Graikoski, J. T. and Bonventre, P. F. (1957). *Applied Microbiology* **5**, 292–295.

Kereluk, K. (1977). *Developments in Industrial Microbiology* **18**, 373–385.

Khan, A. A., Tallentire, A. and Dwyer, J. (1977). *Journal of Applied Bacteriology* **43**, 205–213.

Kirshbaum, A. (1971). *Bulletin of the Parenteral Drug Association* **25**, 226–232.

Kiss, I., Rhee, C. O., Grecz, N., Roberts, T. A. and Farkas, J. (1978). *Applied and Environmental Microbiology* **35**, 533–539.

Knauss, H. P. (1956). *Science, New York* **124**, 182.

Koh, W. Y., Morehouse, C. T. and Chandler, V. L. (1956). *Applied Microbiology* **4**, 143–146.

Kulkarni, R. D. and Gopal, N. G. S. (1975). *In* "Radiosterilization of Medical Products 1974", pp. 403–408. Proceedings of a Symposium, International Atomic Energy Agency, Vienna.

Lea, D. E. (1956). "Actions of Radiations on Living Cells". Cambridge University Press, Cambridge.

Lefebvre, G. M. (1973). *Radiation Research* **54**, 234–238.

Lefebvre, G. M. and Preiss, J. W. (1970). *Radiation Research* **42**, 488–497.

Levinson, H. S. and Hyatt, M. T. (1960). *Journal of Bacteriology* **80**, 441–451.

Ley, F. J. (1966). *In* "Ionizing Radiations and the Sterilization of Medical Products", pp. 51–62. Riso, 1964. Taylor and Francis, London.

Ley, F. J. (1967). *Chemistry in Britain* **3**, 298–300.

Ley, F. J. (1971). *Journal of the Society of Cosmetic Chemists* **22**, 711–723.

Ley, F. J. and Tallentire, A. (1964). *Pharmaceutical Journal* **193**, 59–61.

Ley, F. J. and Tallentire, A. (1965). *Pharmaceutical Journal* **195**, 216–218.

Ley, F. J., Winsley, B., Harbord, P., Keall, A. and Summers, T. (1972). *Journal of Applied Bacteriology* **35**, 53–61.

Matsuyama, A., Thornley, M. J. and Ingram, M. (1964). *Journal of Applied Bacteriology* **27**, 125–133.

McGrath, R. A., Williams, R. W. and Swartzenruber, D.C. (1966). *Biophysical Journal* **6**, 113–122.

Midura, T. F., Kempe, L. L., Graikoski, J. T. and Milone, N. A. (1965). *Applied Microbiology* **13**, 244–247.

Morgan, B. H. and Reed, J. M. (1965). *Food Research* **19**, 357–366.

Morganstern, K. H. (1977). *In* "Sterilization of Medical Products by Ionizing Radiation" (E. R. L. Gaughran and A. J. Goudie, eds), pp. 371–391. Multiscience Publications, Montreal.

Moseley, B. E. B. (1968). *Advances in Microbial Physiology* **2**, 173–194.

Moseley, B. E. B. and Laser, H. (1965a). *Nature, London* **206**, 373–375.

Moseley, B. E. B. and Laser, H. (1965b). *Proceedings of the Royal Society, Series B* **162**, 210–222.

Moseley, B. E. B. and Williams, E. (1977). *Advances in Microbial Physiology* **16**, 100–156.

Niven, C. F. Jr. (1958). *Annual Review of Microbiology* **12**, 507–524.

Ogg, A. J. (1967). *In* "Radiosterilization of Medical Products", pp. 49–54. Proceedings of a Symposium, International Atomic Energy Agency, Vienna.

Osterberg, B. O. (1973). *Applied Microbiology* **26**, 354–358.

Outschoorn, A. S. (1977). *Developments in Industrial Microbiology* **18**, 387–397.

Pandula, E. L., Farkas, E. and Racz, I. (1967). *In* "Radiosterilization of Medical Products", pp. 83–89. Proceedings of a Symposium, International Atomic Energy Agency, Vienna.

Parisi, A. and Antoine, A. D. (1974). *Applied Microbiology* **28**, 41–46.

Parisi, A. and Antoine, A. D. (1975). *Applied Microbiology* **29**, 34–39.

Parisi, A. and Antoine, A. D. (1977). *Radiation Research* **69**, 267–275.

Pepper, R. E., Buffer, N. T. and Chandler, V. L. (1956). *Applied Microbiology* **4**, 149–152.

Plecas, M., Bittner, J. and Voinescu, V. (1969). *Acta Biologica et Medica Germanica* **23**, 921–923.

Powell, D. B. (1961). *In* "Recent Developments in the Sterilization of Surgical Materials", pp. 9–16. Report of a Symposium. Pharmaceutical Press, London.

Powers, E. L. (1962). *Physics in Medicine and Biology* **7**, 3–28.

Powers, E. L. (1965). *In* "Proceedings of the XIth International Congress of Radiology", pp. 1451–1457. Rome, 1965.

Powers, E. L. (1966). *In* "Electron Spin Resonance and the Effects of Radiation on Biological Systems", pp. 137–159. Nuclear Science Series, Report 43. National Academy of Sciences, National Research Council, Washington D.C.

Powers, E. L. (1972). *Israel Journal of Chemistry* **10**, 1199–1211.

Powers, E. L. (1977). *In* "Sterilization of Medical Products by Ionizing Radiation" (E. R. L. Gaughran and A. J. Grudie, eds), pp. 97–118. Multiscience Publications, Montreal.

Powers, E. L. and Cross, M. (1970). *International Journal of Radiation Biology* **17**, 501–514.

Powers, E. L., Webb, R. B. and Ehret, C. F. (1960a). *Radiation Research Supplement* **2**, 94–121.

Powers, E. L., Webb, R. B. and Kaletta, B. F. (1960b). *Science, New York* **132**, 959–960.

Powers, E. L., Cross, M. and Simic, M. (1972a). *International Journal of Radiation Biology* **22**, 237–243.

Powers, E. L., Richmond, R. C. and Simic, M. (1972b). *Nature New Biology* **238**, 260–261.

Prince, H. N. (1976). *Applied and Environmental Microbiology* **31**, 999–1000.

Prince, H. N. (1978). *Applied and Environmental Microbiology* **36**, 392–393.

Purdie, J. W., Ebert, M. and Tallentire, A. (1974). *International Journal of Radiation Biology* **26**, 435–443.

Report (1960). Report of the Association of British Pharmaceutical Industry. "The Use of Gamma Radiation Sources for the Sterilization of Pharmaceutical Products".

Report (1964). Report of the Working Party on Irradiation of Food: Ministry of Health, H.M.S.O., London.

Richards, J. W. (1968). "Introduction to Industrial Sterilization". Academic Press, London and New York.

Richmond, R. C. and Powers, E. L. (1974). *Radiation Research* **58**, 470–480.

Richmond, R. C., Simic, M. and Powers, E. L. (1975). *Radiation Research* **63**, 140–148.

Riemann, H. (1960). *Nordic Veterinary Medicine* **12**, 86–104.

Roberts, T. A. and Hitchins, A. D. (1969). *In* "The Bacterial Spore" (G. W. Gould and A. Hurst, eds), pp. 611–670. Academic Press, London and New York.

Roberts, T. A. and Derrick, C. M. (1975). *Journal of Applied Bacteriology* **38**, 33–37.

Roberts, T. A. and Ingram, M. (1965a). *Journal of Applied Bacteriology* **28**, 125–139.

Roberts, T. A. and Ingram, M. (1965b). *Journal of Food Science* **30**, 879–885.

Rode, L. J. and Foster, J. W. (1960). *Journal of Bacteriology* **79**, 650–656.

Rowley, D. B., Anellis, A., Wierbicki, E. and Baker, A. W. (1974). *Journal of Milk and Food Technology* **37**, 86–93.

Rubbo, S. D. and Gardner, J. F. (1965). "A Review of Sterilization and Disinfection". Lloyd-Luke, London.

Russell, A. D. (1971). *In* "Inhibition and Destruction of the Microbial Cell" (W. B. Hugo, ed.), pp. 451–612. Academic Press, London and New York.

Russell, C. (1966). *Experientia* **22**, 80.

Sakakibara, Y. and Ikeda, Y. (1969). *Biochimica et Biophysica Acta* **179**, 429–438.

Schmidt, C. F. (1963). *Journal of Applied Radiation Isotopes* **14**, 19–26.

Schmidt, C. F. and Nank, W. K. (1960). *Food Research* **25**, 321–327.

F

Schmidt, C. F., Nank, W. K. and Lechowich, R. V. (1962). *Journal of Food Science* **27**, 77–84.

Silverman, G. J. and Sinskey, T. I. (1977). *In* "Disinfection, Sterilization and Preservation" (S. S. Block, ed.), 2nd edn, pp. 542–561. Lea and Febiger, Philadelphia.

Silverman, G. J., Davis, N. S. and Beecher, N. (1967). *Applied Microbiology* **15**, 510–515.

Singson, C. C. and Ibe, L. D. (1975). *In* "Radiosterilization of Medical Products 1974", pp. 459–465. Proceedings of a Symposium, International Atomic Energy Agency, Vienna.

Skulberg, A. (1965). *Journal of Applied Bacteriology* **28**, 139–141.

Skulberg, A. and Coleby, B. (1960). *Riso Report* No. **16**, pp. 59–60.

Stewart, J. C. and Hawcroft, D. M. (1977). "A Manual of Radiobiology." Sedgwick and Jackson, London.

Stogaitis, G. and Lefebvre, G. M. (1976). *Applied and Environmental Microbiology* **32**, 217–221.

Stogaitis, G. and Lefebvre, G. M. (1977). *Radiation Research* **69**, 76–82.

Stuy, J. H. (1956). *Biochimica et Biophysica Acta* **22**, 241–246.

Stuy, J. H. (1960). *Journal of Bacteriology* **79**, 707–715.

Szybalski, W. and Lorkiewicz, Z. (1962). *Abhandlungen der Deutschen Akademie der Wissrenchafren zu Berlin, Klasse für Medizin* **1**, 63–71.

Tallentire, A. (1958). *Nature, London* **182**, 1024–1025.

Tallentire, A. (1970). *Journal of Applied Bacteriology* **33**, 141–146.

Tallentire, A. (1973). *International Journal of Radiation Sterilization* **1**, 85–103.

Tallentire, A. and Davies, D. J. G. (1961). *Experimental Cell Research* **24**, 148–150.

Tallentire, A. and Dickinson, N. A. (1962). *Journal of Pharmacy and Pharmacology* **14**, 127T–128T.

Tallentire, A., Dickinson, N. A. and Collett, J. H. (1963). *Journal of Pharmacy and Pharmacology* **15**, 180T–181T.

Tallentire, A. and Jacobs, G. P. (1972). *International Journal of Radiation Biology* **21**, 205–213.

Tallentire, A. and Jones, A. B. (1973). *International Journal of Radiation Biology* **24**, 345–354.

Tallentire, A. and Khan, A. A. (1975). *In* "Radiosterilization of Medical Products", pp. 3–14. Proceedings of a Symposium, International Atomic Energy Agency, Vienna.

Tallentire, A. and Khan, A. A. (1977). *In* "Sterilization of Medical Products by Ionizing Radiations" (E. R. L. Gaughran and A. J. Goudie, eds), pp. 65–80. Multiscience Publications, Montreal.

Tallentire, A. and Powers, E. L. (1963). *Radiation Research* **20**, 270–287.

Tallentire, A., Dwyer, J. and Ley, F. J. (1971). *Journal of Applied Bacteriology* **34**, 521–534.

Tallentire, A., Jones, A. B. and Jacobs, G. P. (1972). *Israel Journal of Chemistry* **10**, 1185–1197.

Tallentire, A., Hayes, J. R. and Kimber, B. F. and Powers, E. L. (1974). *Radiation Research* **57**, 300–305.

Tallentire, A., Maughan, R. L., Michael, B. D. and Stratford, I. J. (1977). *In* "Spore Research 1976" (A. N. Barker, J. Wolf, D. J. Ellar, G. J. Dring and G. W. Gould, eds), pp. 549–654. Academic Press, London and New York.

Tanooka, H. (1968). *Biochimica et Biophysica Acta* **166**, 581–583.

Tanooka, H. and Hutchinson, F. (1965). *Radiation Research* **24**, 43–56.

Tanooka, H. and Sakakibara, Y. (1968). *Biochimica et Biophysica Acta* **155**, 130–142.

Tanooka, H. and Terano, H. (1970a). *Journal of Biochemistry* **67**, 735–736.

Tanooka, H. and Terano, H. (1970b). *Radiation Research* **43**, 613–626.

Tattersall, K. (1966). *In* "Ionizing Radiations and the Sterilization of Medical Products", pp. 15–21. *Riso.* Taylor and Francis, London.

Terano, H., Tanooka, H. and Kadota, H. (1969). *Biochemical and Biophysical Research Communications* **37**, 66–71.

Terano, H., Tanooka, H. and Kadota, H. (1971). *Journal of Bacteriology* **106**, 925–930.

Thornley, M. J. (1963). *Journal of Applied Bacteriology* **26**, 334–345.

van Winkle, W., Borick, P. M. and Fogarty, M. (1967). *In* "Radiosterilization of Medical Products", pp. 169–180. Proceedings of a Symposium, International Atomic Energy Agency, Vienna.

Vinter, V. (1959). *Nature, London* **193**, 998–999.

Vinter, V. (1961a). *Nature, London* **189**, 589–590.

Vinter, V. (1961b). *In* "Spores III" (H. O. Halvorson, ed.), pp. 127—141. Burgess Publishing Company, Minneapolis.

Vinter, V. (1962). *Folia Microbiologica* **7**, 275–287.

Vinter, V. (1967). *Folia Microbiologica* **12**, 89–100.

Wheaton, E. and Pratt, G. B. (1962). *Journal of Food Science* **27**, 327–334.

Whitby, J. L. and Gelda, A. K. (1979). *Journal of the Parenteral Drug Association* **33**, 144–155.

Woese, C. (1958). *Journal of Bacteriology* **75**, 5–8.

Woese, C. (1959). *Journal of Bacteriology* **77**, 38–42.

Zamenhof, S., Bursztyn, H., Ramechandry, T. K. R. and Zamenhof, P. J. (1965). *Journal of Bacteriology* **90**, 108–115.

5

Effect of Ultraviolet Radiation on Bacterial Spores

I. *Introduction*

Ultraviolet (UV) radiation has a wavelength range of between about 328 and 210 nm (3280 and 2100 Å), with maximal bactericidal activity at 240–280 nm (Sykes, 1963), 254–280 nm (McCulloch, 1945), 250–280 nm (Setlow and Boling, 1965) and 265 nm (Thimann, 1963; Schechmeister, 1968; Morris, 1972). Modern mercury vapour lamps emit more than 90% of their radiations at 253·7 nm (Morris, 1972). Since the quantum of energy liberated is low, UV radiation has less penetrating ability than other radiations and therefore is less effective as a microbiocidal agent.

Several reviews deal with the action and uses of UV radiation, and with microbial repair processes, notably those by Hollaender (1955),

Roberts and Hitchins (1969), Smith and Hanawalt (1969), Witkin (1969, 1976), Russell (1971, 1982), Morris (1972), Howard-Flanders (1973), Bridges (1976), Moseley and Williams (1977), Hanawalt *et al.* (1979), Alper (1979) and Harm (1980). Sporulation of *B. licheniformis* is inhibited by broad-spectrum light (Propst-Ricciuti and Lubin, 1976).

II. *Dose–Survival Curves*

As with bacteria exposed to heat or ionizing radiations, the dose–survival curves obtained when bacteria are exposed to UV radiation and the results plotted semi-logarithmically ($\log_{10}$ viable numbers, or surviving fraction, vs. UV dose) are of various types:

(a) a straight-line response has been observed with non-sporulating bacteria such as *Sal. typhimurium*, *E. coli* B_{s-1} and *E. coli* K12 strain AB2480 (Moseley and Laser, 1965a,b; Haynes, 1966, Tyrrell *et al.*, 1972) and vegetative cells of *B. subtilis* (Munakata and Ikeda, 1968);

(b) an initial shoulder, followed by exponential death.

Vegetative cells of *B. subtilis*, when exposed to UV light, show a very slight shoulder, followed by an exponential death rate, whereas dormant spores of this organisms show a much greater initial shoulder (Fig. 5.1: Stafford and Donnellan, 1968). The extent of the shoulder may, in fact, vary with the sporulation stage (Germaine *et al.*, 1973). A large initial shoulder has also been noted with some strains of *Staph. aureus*,

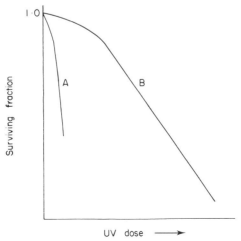

Fig. 5.1   Inactivation curves of (A) vegetative cells, (B) spores, of a *Bacillus* species exposed to UV light.

E. coli and *Micrococcus lysodeikticus* (Haynes, 1964, 1966; Tyrrell *et al.*, 1972) but most noticeably with *M. radiodurans*, which is highly resistant to both UV and ionizing radiations. Survival curves for this organism exposed to either type of radiation have large initial shoulders with high extrapolation numbers (Moseley and Laser, 1965a,b; Moseley, 1968). Organisms that are resistant to UV radiation may possess highly efficient repair processes and may thus survive high radiation doses.

Curves of type (b) would suggest that several "hits" are needed to inactivate one organism, in contrast to those of type (a), where only one "hit" is needed to induce death of an organism. This, however, ignores the possibility of repair processes which are mentioned above and which are discussed in more detail in Section III.C. For theoretical concepts of UV-induced inactivation curves in bacteria, the paper by Miller (1970) should be consulted.

III. *Factors Influencing Bacterial Sensitivity*

A. Type of Organism

Bacterial spores are generally more resistant to UV irradiation than are vegetative cells (Duggar and Hollaender, 1934; Wells, 1955; Sykes, 1965; Ashwood-Smith and Bridges, 1967), although as described earlier the stage of sporulation influences the sensitivity shown. Similarly, as will be considered below, for a short period during germination, there is a marked increase in resistance. McCulloch (1945) considered that Gram-negative rods were the organisms most easily killed by UV light, staphylococci and streptococci requiring about 5–10 times, bacterial spores about 10 times, and mould spores 50 times, as much irradiation, to destroy them. Zamenhof and Reddy (1967) showed that at low UV doses, the dose ratio at the same survival for spores and vegetative cells of *B. subtilis* was about 20–40. Duggar and Hollaender (1934) found that *B. megaterium* spores were more resistant than those of *B. subtilis*, and according to Johansen and Myhrstad (1978) spores of the latter organisms are considerably more sensitive to UV radiation than many non-sporulating organisms. The UV sensitivity of bacilli varies with the stage of sporulation or germination (Section IV).

Bacillus subtilis spores are more resistant to UV radiation when tested in the form of a "dust suspension" than when exposed as an aerosol (Sykes, 1965). Likewise, a small but significant increase in UV radiation is required for disinfection of dried, as opposed to wet, droplets of *B. globigii* spores (Morris, 1972). *Bacillus pumilus* spores are considered to possess above-average resistance to UV (Abshire *et al.*, 1980). Spores produced on different media may have different susceptibilities to UV radiation (Bayliss *et al.*, 1981).

UV inactivation of the microbial insecticide, *B. thuringiensis*, has been described (Krieg, 1975; Griego and Spence, 1978).

B. Low Temperatures

The majority of microorganisms tested by Ashwood-Smith and Bridges (1967) were supersensitive to UV irradiation at low temperatures. This increase in sensitivity occurred only when the bacteria were frozen and was independent of the effects of freezing and thawing. Enhancement factors for the lethal effects of UV irradiation at $-79°C$ compared with irradiation at $+22°C$ were: *E. coli* strain B/r, 7; *Staph. aureus*, 5·2; *B. subtilis*, vegetative cells, 5·0; and *B. subtilis*, spores, 2·5. *Micrococcus radiodurans* was not supersensitive at low temperatures. Of interest was the finding that photoreactivating light (Section III.C) was ineffective following irradiation at $-79°C$. This is a most interesting finding and one that will be returned to again later (Section IV.B,C). In contrast to low temperatures, the sensitivity of bacteria to UV is only slightly influenced by temperature within the range 5–37°C (Hollaender, 1942).

C. Repair Processes

Under appropriate conditions, many bacterial species can repair the damage induced by UV radiation. Such repair processes involve photoreactivation (light repair) and dark repair (excision and recombination). The isolation of mutants which are defective in one or more of these repair systems has accelerated a better understanding at the molecular level of the nature of UV damage and of repair processes. The composition of the recovery medium may be important with vegetative *B. subtilis* cells (Hadden, 1976).

1. Photoreactivation

The exposure of UV-irradiated *E. coli* to suitable visible light (below 51100 Å, 510 nm) results in the recovery of a large portion of the cells from what would otherwise have been death (Kelner, 1949a,b). This effect of reactivating light was termed "photoreactivation" (PR). Kelner also differentiated between "dark survivors" and "light survivors", and this will be considered below.

PR has since been defined (Jagger, 1958) as being the reversal with near-ultraviolet or visible light of UV radiation damage to a biological system, or as being the restoration of UV radiation lesions in a biological system with light of wavelength longer than that of the damaging radiation.

If N_0 is the total number of viable cells before irradiation, N_D (which refers to dark survival) the number of survivors after treatment, and N_L (which refers to light survival) the number of survivors after PR, then (after Jagger, 1958):

Fractional light survival is N_L/N_0, from which % light survival

$$(\text{or } \% \text{ survival}) = 100 \times \frac{N_L}{N_0} \tag{1}$$

$$\text{Degree of PR} = \frac{N_L - N_D}{N_0 - N_D}$$

$$\text{From which } \% \text{ PR} = 100 \times \frac{N_L - N_D}{N_0 - N_D} \tag{2}$$

There is, however, a wide divergence among bacteria in their capacity to be photoreactivated. Organisms which can be photoreactivated include *Streptomyces griseus* and *E. coli* (Kelner, 1951), vegetative cells of *B. mycoides*, *B. pumilus*, *B. megaterium* and three out of four strains of *B. cereus*, but not *B. subtilis*, *B. polymyxa* and *B. circulans*. It was subsequently reported (Stuy, 1956a,b) that of 15 *Bacillus* strains investigated, only two showed good PR, four showed moderate photoreactivation and the others were not photoreactivable. With three cultures of bacilli (Stuy, 1955), PR could be achieved with light of wavelength 366, 405 or 436 nm after UV inactivation. These radiations also have an inactivating effect, however, so that the photoreactivation would be small, and not observable when the dose-rate of the incident light is too great. Thus, the diversity in response among *Bacillus* spp. to photoreactivating light is obviously linked with their degree of sensitivity to such light. Spores of photoreactivable strains of vegetative bacilli are not reactivated by light after UV inactivation (Stuy, 1955, 1956b), and resting spores of *B. cereus* after UV treatment cannot be photoreactivated until they are transferred to a nutrient medium on which they can germinate (Stuy, 1956c). This is an important finding, and is discussed in more detail in Section IV. Sporulating cultures of *B. cereus* completely lose their photoreactivability at the same time as UV resistance increases (Romig and Wyss, 1957).

2. Dark Repair

Dark repair of damaged DNA occurs in non-sporulating bacteria, such as *M. radiodurans*, which possess the means of repair in the absence of photoreactivating light. This type of process involves removal by excision repair (which involves excision of the damaged portion and employment of DNA on the opposite strand as a template) or by post-replication recombination ("crossing-over") repair. Dark repair may also occur in UV-exposed bacterial spores during germination (Section V).

IV. *Mechanisms of Bacterial Death and Repair*

The effects of UV radiation on bacteria, and the repair processes that may be possessed by the organisms, provide one of the most fascinating aspects of molecular biology. This section will compare the UV-induced damage in bacterial spores with that in germinating spores and non-sporulating organisms and will also consider the role of low temperature in supersensitivity to UV.

A. UV-induced Mutations in Bacteria

Intensive UV radiation of spores serves as a potent mutagenic agent, but at similar survival levels, ionizing radiation is more mutagenic than UV for total auxotrophs but about equally mutagenic for revertants (Zamenhof and Reddy, 1967). For the same survival, the frequency of mutants induced in vegetative cells is lower than that induced in spores (Zamenhof and Reddy, 1967). During sporulation in *B. cereus*, a period of increased sensitivity to UV occurs prior to acquisition of resistance of the spores, and during this period of sensitivity the organisms are more susceptible to the mutagenic effects of both UV and ionizing radiations (McDonald and Wyss, 1959; Vogt *et al.*, 1967).

The isolation of a mutant of *B. subtilis* producing UV-sensitive spores, derived from a mutant producing UV-sensitive vegetative cells, has been described by Munakata and Ikeda (1968) and Munakata (1969, 1974). Consideration of these spores will be deferred until later.

B. Effect of UV Irradiation of Non-sporulating Bacteria

Exposure of non-sporulating bacteria to UV radiation results in the formation of thymine dimers (TT) between adjacent thymine molecules

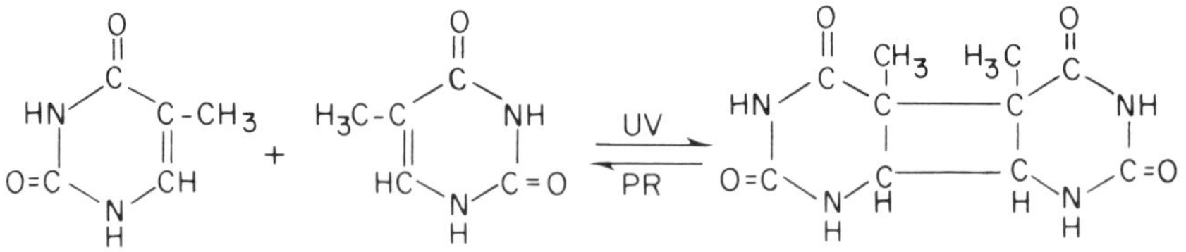

Fig. 5.2   UV-induced production of thymine dimers and photoreactivation in non-sporing bacteria. T, thymine; TT, thymine dimer; PR, photoreactivation.

in the same strand of DNA (Witkin, 1969, 1976; Eisenstark, 1971; Bridges, 1976; Moseley and Williams, 1977; Fig. 5.2). Other dimers may also be formed, such as a uracil-thymine heterodimer. Repair of this damage to DNA may occur by PR, a process in which bacteria are exposed to light of a higher wavelength. This involves the removal, by a photoreactivating enzyme, of the thymine dimers from DNA by monomerization of the dimers *in situ* (Fig. 5.2). Other repair mechanisms include (a) an excision mechanism (dark repair) which is a multienzyme process, and (b) post-replication recombination repair.

The most resistant organism to both ionizing radiation and UV radiation is *M. radiodurans*. This appears to possess a remarkable ability to repair DNA damage (Bridges, 1976), especially by excision repair, although why this is more efficient than with other organisms is as yet unknown.

In the frozen state, bacteria are usually more sensitive to UV light. One reason for this is the fact that PR light is ineffective (Bridges, 1976). In contrast, *M. radiodurans* shows no difference in sensitivity at temperatures down to −60°C and actually becomes more resistant to UV radiation between −60°C and −120°C, presumably because it can repair damage resulting from the formation of another thymine photoproduct (Ashwood-Smith and Bridges, 1967).

Some of these aspects will be reconsidered later (Section IV.C).

C. Effect of UV Irradiation on Bacterial Spores

1. *Spore photoproducts*

Bacterial spores are more resistant than vegetative bacteria to UV radiation, but at certain times during germination the cells become much more resistant. Following exposure of spores to UV light, thymine-containing photoproducts accumulate in spore DNA which are different from the thymine-containing cyclobutane dimers (Fig. 5.2) produced in vegetative cells (Donnellan and Setlow, 1965). These spore photoproducts do not disappear after a PR process but appear to be eliminated from DNA by a dark-repair mechanism which is different from that found for thymine dimers in non-sporulating bacteria (Donnellan and Stafford, 1968).

The spore photoproduct (5-thyminyl-5, 6-dihydrothymine, TDHT: Fig. 5.3) has been shown to be identical to a photoproduct that accumulates in hydrolysates of DNA exposed to dry or as a frozen solution to UV radiation (Rahn and Hosszu, 1968, 1969; Varghese, 1970a,b, 1971). With the exception of *M. radiodurans*, vegetative cells in the frozen state are supersensitive to UV radiation and a photoproduct (presumably TDHT) other than thymine dimers accumulates which is less susceptible to repair. UV-sensitive mutants of UV-resistant *B. subtilis* spores form the same photoproduct (TDHT) and to the same extent for a given radiation dose as the resistant spores, and thus the ability to remove TDHT is linked to UV resistance (Munakata and Rupert, 1972). Two genetically-controlled mechanisms have been

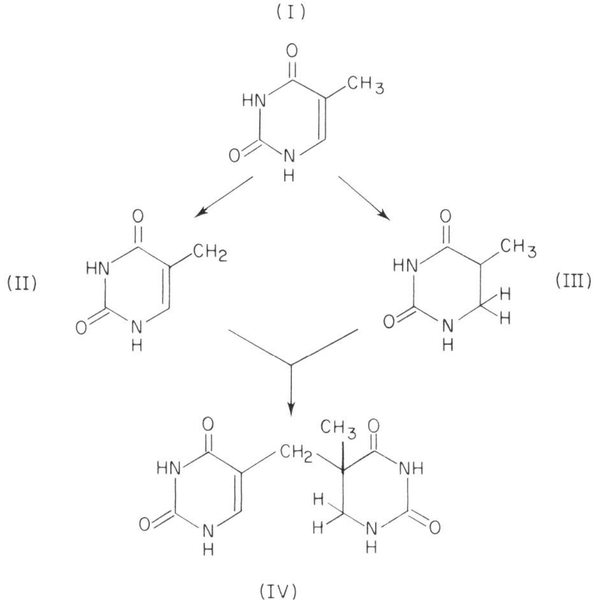

Fig. 5.3 Postulated formation of "spore photoproduct" (5-thyminyl-5, 6-dihydrothymine; TDHT) (after Varghese, 1971). I, thymine; II, thyminyl radical; III, thymyl radical; IV, TDHT.

described for this removal, the first ("spore repair") involving the early elimination of TDHT during germination, although vegetative growth is not required; and the second, demonstrated in a mutant lacking the first mechanism, requires further development towards the vegetative cell for operation, and is an excision resynthesis mechanism. TDHT is not removed from spores of high UV sensitivity in which both mechanisms are blocked (Munakata and Rupert, 1972). The "spore repair" process changes the photoproduct (TDHT) to a harmless form *in situ*, and an energy source is necessary for any excision, and for the "spore repair" process to proceed beyond a limited removal of TDHT (Munakata and Rupert, 1974).

2. *Spore spheroplasts and transforming DNA*

Mutants of vegetative cells of *B. subtilis* have been classified as *uvs* (Hcr⁻), *uvs* (Hcr⁺) and *uvss* (Hcr⁻) on the basis of UV-sensitivity (*uvs*) or supersensitivity (*uvss*) and host cell reactivation ability (Munaka and Ikeda, 1969; Munakata, 1970). Restoration of the transforming activity was apparent in the wild-type, resistant *uvr* (Hcr⁺) strain but not in *uvs* (Hcr⁻) strains.

Spore spheroplasts of *B. subtilis* can be prepared by successive treatments with thioglycollic acid, urea and lysozyme. The transforming activity of DNA in these spore spheroplasts is resistant to UV radiation, but this resistance is greatly reduced when the spheroplasts are lysed (Tanooka, 1968). Thus, the spheroplast form retains most of the spore-specific characteristics of DNA (Tanooka and Terano, 1970).

3. *Sporulation and UV resistance*

During sporulation, marked changes in the cellular response to UV radiation occur. These changes are associated with stages III, mid-IV and post-IV (Germaine *et al.*, 1973), and PR declines to a very marked extent during the development of stage IV forespores (Baillie *et al.*, 1974). The ability to form spore photoproduct (TDHT) appears to be a property of both transition and spore DNA.

A correlation has been noted between the amount of spore photoproduct formed and the content of DPA in spores (Germaine and Murrell, 1973, 1974). Leif and Herbert (1960) had earlier noted that DPA could protect spores from UV radiation, and Berg and Grecz (1970) found that *B. cereus* T spores lacking in DPA (i.e. DPA⁻) are more sensitive to UV radiation than spores (DPA⁺) with a high DPA content. During sporulation of the DPA⁺ cultures, however, UV resistance precedes heat resistance and coincides with the formation of forespores and the synthesis of cystine-rich structures (Durban *et al.*, 1970). According to Grecz *et al.* (1973), resistance to UV is related to the spore content of dipicolinate, with DPA$^+$ spores being more resistant than DPA$^-$ ones. These findings are, however, in direct contrast to those of Germaine and Murrell (1973, 1974) who found that DPA$^-$ spores of *B. cereus* are more resistant than DPA$^+$ spores and that spore photoproducts are produced to a greater rate and extent in DPA$^+$ spores. DPA has also been shown to sensitize forespores to UV radiation (Germaine *et al.*, 1973).

During sporulation of *B. cereus*, a period of increased sensitivity to UV occurs just before the acquisition of spore resistance (Romig and Wyss, 1957). The period of maximum sensitivity to UV does not coincide with the maximum accumulation of poly-β-hydroxybutyrate (Vogt *et al.*, 1967).

4. *Germination and UV resistance*

At certain times in their germination, spores of *B. cereus* (Stuy, 1956), *B. subtilis* (Irie *et al.*, 1965; Stafford and Donnellan, 1968; Donnellan and Stafford, 1968) and *B. megaterium* (Stafford and Donnellan, 1968; Donnellan and Stafford, 1968) become much more resistant to UV light (curve at the 3 min point in Fig. 5.4). This phase is then followed by one in which an increase in sensitivity of the germinating spores to UV radiation takes place, these forms eventually becoming more sensitive than the dormant spores, with the population approaching the sensitivity of vegetative cells. The experiments of Stafford and Donnellan (1968) correlate this resistance during the early phase of germination to a decrease in the production of thymine-containing photoproducts. Their results may be summarized as follows:

(i)   At 3 min which is the time of peak resistance with *B. megaterium* (Fig 5.4a), the amount of thymine-containing photoproducts is only a fraction of that found in vegetative cells or dormant spores.

(ii) During germination, the amount of spore photoproduct for a given UV exposure falls rapidly. There is little or no vegetative cell photoproduct production for a period of 3 min (Fig. 5.4b) during which time UV survival increases rapidly.

(iii) After 3 min, spore photoproduct falls slightly, and UT and TT dimers (see below) rapidly begin to appear. At the same time, there is a decrease in UV resistance.

These findings led Stafford and Donnellan (1968) to state that "the qualitative changes in sensitivity during germination are explicable in terms of changes in spore-type and cyclobutane-type photoproducts",

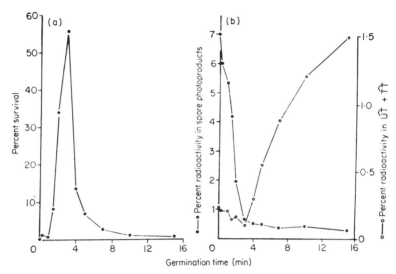

Fig. 5.4   UV-induced thymine photoproducts in *B. megaterium*.

(a) Survival of spores and germinating spores as a function of time.
(b) Percentage of thymine in photoproducts in germinating spores as a function of germination time.

Reprinted with permission from Stafford and Donellan (1968).

and that "the absence of both types of photoproducts at 3 minutes can explain the extreme resistance of bacterial spores at this time". These findings suggest that the DNA in spores, in germinating spores and in vegetative cells exists in different environments and could provide one reason as to why different types and amounts of photoproducts are produced in these UV-irradiated cells and why there are differences in survival after irradiation. Donnellan and Setlow (1965) had earlier shown that when bacterial spores were irradiated, thymine-containing photoproducts were produced which were different from the thymine-containing cyclobutane dimers produced in vegetative cells. In UV-irradiated vegetative cells of *B. megaterium*, thymine dimers, consisting of a uracil–thymine, UT heterodimer (formed by deamination during hydrolysis of a cytosine–thymine dimer) and of a thymine–thymine, TT homodimer, were produced, in amounts equivalent to those produced in vegetative cells of other organisms (Section IV.B). Three unidentified photoproducts were also produced. Subsequently, Smith and Yoshikawa (1966) showed that, whereas in UV-irradiated vegetative cells of *B. subtilis* the chief thymine photoproduct consisted of the cyclobutane-type dimer, in the spores of this organism, a new product, containing 28·4% of thymine occurred in greater amounts than the dimer (2·6% of thymine). It was also pointed out that this difference was also seen between the photoproducts of isolated DNA irradiated in solution and in the dry state, which suggested that the state of hydration was a critical factor. Dimers of UT and TT are considerably more effective in killing vegetative cells than spore photoproducts are in killing spores (Donnellan and Stafford, 1968).

In spores, these non-cyclobutane type photoproducts do not disappear after a photoreactivation process, i.e. upon exposure of UV-irradiated spores to long-wavelength light, but are eliminated from the DNA by a dark-repair mechanism different from that found for dimers in vegetative cells (Donnellan and Stafford, 1968). The lack of effect of photoreactivating light on UV-irradiated bacterial spores was pointed out above, and may be connected with the low enzymatic activity of spores. Schuster (1967) studied the fate of UV-induced thymine-containing dimers in the DNA of *B. subtilis*; in the wild-type (UV^R) strain, dimers were excised from the DNA but remained in the DNA of an UV light-sensitive (UV^S) mutant, when these were incubated in the dark.

The transition in UV resistance from dormant spores to vegetative cell over an extended time scale has been reinvestigated by Nokes and Powers (1977) who found that the major peak of UV resistance occurred after about 60 min incubation at 25°C, with a secondary peak of resistance at about 20 min. It was suggested that the reason for this was linked to DNA conformation, with at one extreme the "dry" DNA of spores and at the other the "wet" DNA of vegetative cells.

It now seems likely that germinating spores of *Bacillus* species can remove spore photoproduct via a combination of "excision repair" and "spore repair" processes (Munakata and Rupert, 1972, 1974, 1975). In highly UV-sensitive spores, blocked in both repair processes, the photoproduct remains in the TCA-insoluble fraction of UV-irradiated spores during germination; in a strain where only the "spore repair" functions, the TDHT disappears from the TCA-insoluble fraction but does not appear in the TCA-soluble fraction; in a strain in which "spore repair" is blocked, the photoproduct disappears slowly from the TCA-insoluble fraction and is all recovered in the TCA-soluble fractions. On the other hand, with the UVR strain (which shows wild type radiation sensitivity) both mechanisms play a part in removing photoproduct, and consequently only some of the TCA-insoluble fraction appears in the TCA-soluble material. These findings of Munakata and Rupert (1974) are summarized in Table 5.1. During germination, then, spores possessing the "spore repair" process can change the TDHT into a

Table 5.1. Removal of spore photoproduct from DNA in *B. subtilis* strains during germination[a]

Spore	Resistance to UV radiation	Repair process(es) operative[b]	Appearance of photo-product in fractions[c]
UVSSP-42-1	Low	None (both blocked)	Remains in TCA-insoluble
UVS-42	Moderate	Spore repair only	Disappears from TCA-insoluble, does not become TCA-soluble
SSP-1	Moderate	Excision repair only	Disappears slowly from TCA-insoluble, all trans-ferred to TCA-soluble
UVR	High	Spore repair + excision repair	Disappears from TCA-insoluble, part trans-ferred to TCA-soluble

[a] Based on the findings of Munakata and Rupert (1974).
[b] Two processes: "Spore repair" and "excision repair".
[c] Fractions: trichloroacetic (TCA)- insoluble and -soluble fractions.

product that is harmless *in situ* to the organism. This appears to be a direct, enzymatic dark repair in which the TDHT is converted to thymine, so that at the end of the "spore repair" process the DNA backbone is left intact (Van Wang and Rupert, 1977). UV-sensitive spores may produce comparatively UV-resistant germinated forms, this transitional phase then being followed by the normal vegetative level of sensitivity (Munakata, 1974).

D. Conclusions

The repair of UV damage in sporing and non-sporing bacteria provides a fascinating insight into molecular biology. There are obvious differences in the manner in which the two types of cells achieve repair of DNA injury. In non-sporing organisms, repair is achieved by photo-reactivation (PR) or by dark-repair mechanisms (excision, recombinational); in contrast, PR does not occur with spores, and the dark-repair mechanisms of excision repair (whereby TDHT-containing regions in DNA are transferred from the TCA-insoluble to the TCA-soluble fraction) and spore repair (in which TDHT is converted to thymine) take place only during germination.

A comparison of the repair processes in (a) non-sporing bacteria, and (b) bacterial spores during germination is presented in Fig. 5.5.

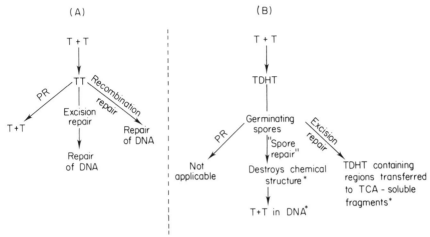

Fig. 5.5 A comparison of repair processes in (A) UV-exposed non-sporing bacteria, (B) UV-exposed bacterial spores. T, thymine; TT, tymine dimer; TDHT, spore photoproduct; PR, photoreactivation.
* For details, see text and Table 5.1.

Bacterial spores are almost invariably more resistant than non-sporing bacteria to UV radiation, although wide variations exist at different stages in the spore cycle. In the same way that thymine dimers are likely to be responsible for death in UV-exposed non-sporulating bacteria, so the occurrence of spore photoproducts (TDHT) will, unless removed, contribute to spore death. Low molecules weight, spore core proteins cross-linked to DNA, have also been implicated in UV resistance (Setlow and Setlow, 1979).

References

Abshire, R. L., Bain, B. and Williams, T. (1980). *Applied and Environmental Microbiology* **39**, 695–701.

Alper, T. (1979). "Cellular Radiobiology". Cambridge University Press, Cambridge.

Ashwood-Smith, M. J. and Bridges, B. A. (1967). *Proceedings of the Royal Society, Series B* **168**, 194–202.

Baillie, E., Germaine, G. R., Murrell, W. G. and Ohye, D. F. (1974). *Journal of Bacteriology* **120**, 516–523.

Bayliss, C. E., Waites, W. M. and King, N. R. (1981). *Journal of Applied Bacteriology* **50**, 379–390.

Berg, P. E. and Grecz, N. (1970). *Journal of Bacteriology* **103**, 517–519.

Bridges, B. A. (1976). *In* "The Survival of Vegetative Microbes" (T. G. R. Gray and J. R. Postgate, eds), 26th Symposium of the Society for General Microbiology, pp. 183–208. Cambridge University Press, Cambridge.

Donnellan J. E. and Setlow, R. B. (1965). *Science, New York* **149**, 308–310.
Donnellan, J. E. and Stafford, R. S. (1968). *Biophysical Journal* **8**, 17–28.
Duggar, B. M. and Hollaender, A. (1934). *Journal of Bacteriology* **27**, 241–256.
Durban, E., Goodnow, R. and Grecz, N. (1970). *Journal of Bacteriology* **102**, 590–592.
Eisenstark, A. (1971). *Advances in Genetics* **16**, 167–198.
Germaine, G. R. and Murrell, W. G. (1973). *Photochemistry and Photobiology* **17**, 145–154.
Germaine, G. R. and Murrell, W. G. (1974). *Journal of Bacteriology* **118**, 202–208.
Germaine, G. R., Coggiola, E. and Murrell, W. G. (1973). *Journal of Bacteriology* **116**, 823–831.
Grecz, N., Tang, T. and Frank, H. A. (1973). *Journal of Bacteriology* **113**, 1058–1060.
Griego, V. M. and Spence, K. D. (1978). *Applied and Environmental Microbiology* **35**, 906–910.
Hadden, C. T. (1976). *Journal of Bacteriology* **128**, 317–324.
Hanawalt, P. C., Cooper, P. K., Ganesan, A. K. and Smith, C. A. (1979). *Annual Review of Biochemistry* **48**, 783–836.
Harm, W. (1980). "Biological Effects of Ultraviolet Radiation". Cambridge University Press, Cambridge.
Haynes, R. H. (1964). *Photochemistry and Photobiology* **3**, 429–450.
Haynes, R. H. (1966). *Radiation Research Supplement* **6**, 1–29.
Hollaender, A. (1942). *In* "Aerobiology" (F. R. Moulton ed.), pp. 156–165. American Association for the Advancement of Science, Washington, U.S.A.
Hollaender, A. (1955). "Radiation Biology" Vol. 2. McGraw-Hill, New York.
Howard-Flanders, P. (1973). *British Medical Bulletin* **29**, 226–235.
Irie, R. N., Yano, N., Morichi, T. and Kembo, H. (1965). *Biochemical and Biophysical Research Communications* **20**, 389–392.
Jagger, J. (1958). *Bacteriological Reviews* **22**, 99–142.
Johansen, E. S. and Myhrstad, J. A. (1978). *NIPH Annals* **1**, 3–10 (National Institute of Public Health, Oslo, Norway).
Kelner, A. (1949a). *Proceedings of the National Academy of Sciences, U.S.* **35**, 73–79.
Kelner, A. (1949b). *Journal of Bacteriology* **58**, 511–522.
Kelner, A. (1951). *Journal of General Physiology* **34**, 835–852.
Krieg, A. (1975). *Journal of Invertebrate Pathology* **25**, 267–268.
Leif, W. R. and Herbert, J. E. (1960). *American Journal of Hygiene* **71**, 285–291.
McCulloch, E. C. (1945). "Disinfection and Sterilization". Kimpton, London.
McDonald, W. C. and Wyss, O. (1959). *Radiation Research* **11**, 409–417.
Miller, D. R. (1970). *Journal of Theoretical Biology* **26**, 383–398.
Morris, E. J. (1972). *Medical Laboratory Technology* **29**, 41–47.
Moseley, B. E. B. (1968). *Advances in Microbial Physiology* **2**, 172–194.
Moseley, B. E. B. and Laser, H. (1965a). *Nature, London* **206**, 373–375.
Moseley, B. E. B. and Laser, H. (1965b). *Proceedings of the Royal Society, Series B* **162**, 210–222.
Moseley, B. E. B. and Williams, E. (1977). *Advances in Microbial Physiology* **16**, 99–156.
Munakata, N. (1969). *Molecular and General Genetics* **104**, 258–263.
Munakata, N. (1970). *Japanese Journal of Genetics* **45**, 1–9.
Munakata, N. (1974). *Journal of Bacteriology* **120**, 59–65.
Munakata, N. and Ikeda, Y. (1968). *Biochemical and Biophysical Research Communications* **33**, 469–475.
Munakata, N. and Ikeda, Y. (1969). *Mutation Research* **7**, 133–139.

Munakata, N. and Rupert, C. S. (1972). *Journal of Bacteriology* **111**, 192–198.
Munakata, N. and Rupert, C. S. (1974). *Molecular and General Genetics* **130**, 239–250.
Munakata, N. and Rupert, C. S. (1975). *Mutation Research* **27**, 157–169.
Nokes, M. A. and Powers, E. L. (1977). *Photochemistry and Photobiology* **25**, 307–309.
Propst-Ricciuti, C. and Lubin, L. B. (1976). *Journal of Bacteriology* **128**, 506–509
Rahn, R. O. and Hosszu, J. L. (1968). *Photochemistry and Photobiology* **8**, 53–63.
Rahn, R. O. and Hosszu, J. L. (1969). *Biochimica et Biophysica Acta* **190**, 126–131.
Roberts, T. A. and Hitchins, A. D. (1969). *In* "The Bacterial Spore" (G. W. Gould and A. Hurst, eds), pp. 611–670. Academic Press, London and New York.
Romig, W. R. and Wyss, O. (1957). *Journal of Bacteriology* **74**, 386–391.
Russell, A. D. (1971). *In* "Inhibition and Destruction of the Microbial Cell" (W. B. Hugo, ed.), pp. 451–612. Academic Press, London and New York.
Russell, A. D. (1982). *In* "Principles and Practice of Disinfection, Preservation and Sterilization" (A. D. Russell, W. B. Hugo and G. A. J. Ayliffe, eds), pp. 534–547. Blackwell Scientific Publications, Oxford.
Schechmeister, I. L. (1968). *In* "Disinfection, Sterilization and Preservation" (C. A. Lawrence and S. S. Block, eds), pp. 761–768. Lea and Febiger, Philadelphia.
Schuster, R. C. (1967). *Journal of Bacteriology* **93**, 811–815.
Setlow, B. and Setlow, P. (1979). *Journal of Bacteriology* **139**, 486–494.
Setlow, R. B. and Boling, M. E. (1965). *Biochimica et Biophysica Acta* **108**, 259–265.
Smith, K. C. and Hanawalt, P. C. (1969). "Molecular Photobiology, Inactivation and Recovery" Academic Press, London and New York.
Smith, K. C. and Yoshikawa, H. (1966). *Photochemistry and Photobiology* **5**, 777–786.
Stafford, R. S. and Donnellan, J. E. (1968). *Proceedings of the National Academy of Science, U.S.* **59**, 822–828.
Stuy, J. H. (1955). *Biochimica et Biophysica Acta* **17**, 206–211.
Stuy, J. H. (1956a). *Biochimica et Biophysica Acta* **22**, 241–246.
Stuy, J. H. (1956b). *Biochimica et Biophysica Acta* **22**, 238–240.
Stuy, J. H. (1956c). *Antonie van Leeuwenhock* **22**, 337–349.
Sykes, G. (1963). *Chemistry and Industry* 885–893.
Sykes, G. (1965). "Disinfection and Sterilization", 2nd ed. Spon, London.
Tanooka, H. (1968). *Biochimica et Biophysica Acta* **166**, 581–583.
Tanooka, H. and Terano, H. (1970). *Journal of Biochemistry* **67**, 735–736.
Thimann, K. V. (1963). "The Life of Bacteria", 2nd edn. Macmillan Co., New York.
Tyrrell, R. M., Moss, S. H. and Davies, D. J. G. (1972). *Mutation Research* **16**, 1–12.
van Wang, T. C. and Rupert, C. S. (1977). *Photochemistry and Photobiology* **25**, 123–127.
Varghese, A. J. (1970a). *Biochemical and Biophysical Research Communications* **38**, 484–490.
Varghese, A. J. (1970b). *Biochemistry* **9**, 4781–4787.
Varghese, A. J. (1971). *Photochemistry and Photobiology* **13**, 357–364.
Vogt, J. C., McDonald, W. C. and Nakata, H. M. (1967). *Radiation Research* **30**, 140–147.
Witkin, E. (1969). *Annual Review of Genetics* **3**, 525–552.
Witkin, E. (1976). *Bacteriological Reviews* **40**, 869–907.
Wells, W. F. (1955). "Airborne Contagion and Air Hygiene", p. 75. Harvard University Press, Mass., U.S.A.
Zamenhof, S. and Reddy, T. K. R. (1967). *Radiation Research* **31**, 112–120.

6

Effect of Liquid-phase Antibacterial Agents on Bacterial Spores

I. *Introduction*

In general, bacterial spores are killed only slowly or not at all by many liquid phase antibacterial substances. It is, in fact, often stated that such substances are without action on spores, when what is meant is that they do not kill these forms. This is obviously an over-simplification of the matter, for the fact that these substances are often sporostatic indicates that they must have some effect on bacterial spores. Moreover, when the bactericidal activity of a new disinfectant is being considered, various tests should be carried out, including the effect of the substance under varying conditions of time, temperature and concentration, on a minimum of a Gram-negative faecal organism, a pyogenic staphylococcus, a pseudomononad, and an aerobic and anaerobic spore, and in the presence and absence of organic matter, including blood and serum (Berry, 1951; Cook, 1959; see also Kelsey and Maurer, 1974). There is general agreement, however, that spore-forming organisms should not be used in the standardization of disinfectants, as most disinfectants in common use are not very effective killing agents against such organisms (Sykes, 1962, 1970; Russell, 1971). The uses of disinfectants in routine practice, in industry and in the prevention of infection in hospital have been adequately described by Gillespie (1961) and Sykes (1963, 1965), and more recently by Spaulding *et al.* (1977), Ayliffe and Collins (1982) and Underwood (1982).

Most, if not all, antibacterial agents have been tested for their activity against bacterial spores, and the information so obtained is rather widely scattered throughout the literature. In recent years, an attempt has been made to bring together the various reports on sporicidal agents and to assess the correct usage of particular antibacterial substances or formulations (Report, 1965; Spaulding *et al.*, 1977; Ayliffe and Collins, 1982).

II. *Testing of Antibacterial Agents*

Methods of testing antibacterial agents against non-sporing bacteria have been described in detail by Sykes (1963). Methods of testing such agents against bacterial spores can be divided broadly into two groups (sporostatic and sporicidal tests) although effects on sporulation, germination and outgrowth will also be described.

A. **Sporostatic Tests**

Sporostatic tests are normally carried out in a manner similar to that

Table 6.1. Sporostatic and bacteriostatic concentrations of some commonly used antibacterial agents

Substance	Organism	Bacteriostatic or sporostatic concentration[a]	Reference
Cresol	E. coli	0·08 ⎫	
	Staph. aureus	0·06–0·1 ⎬	Russell (1967)
	B. subtilis	0·1 ⎭	
Chlorocresol	E. coli	0·02	Sykes (1958)
	Staph. aureus	0·025	Sykes (1958)
	B. subtilis	0·02	Russell (1967)
Phenol	E. coli	0·2 ⎱	Russell (1967)
	Staph. aureus	0·2 ⎰	
	B. subtilis	0·2	Loosemore (1964)
		0·2 (pH 5) ⎱	Sykes and
		0·25 (pH 7·5) ⎰	Hooper (1954)
Phenylmercuric nitrate	E. coli	0·0003	Sykes (1965)
		0·0001–0·0002	Russell (1967)
	Staph aureus	0·00001	Sykes (1965)
		0·00002	Russell (1967)
	B. subtilis	0·00008	Birkhaug (1933)
		0·00002	Russell (1967)
Benzalkonium chloride	E. coli	0·0016 ⎫	
	Salm. typhi	0·0004 ⎪	
	Cl. perfringens, Cl. tetani, Cl. histolyticum, Cl. oedematiens	0·0005 ⎬	Klarmann (1960)
Subtilin	B. polymyxa	2 ⎫	
	B. aterrimus, B. licheniformis, B. subtilis	5 ⎪	Gould (1964)
	B. fusiformis, B. brevis, B. globigii, B. cereus	10 ⎭	
Nisin	B. aterrimus	2 ⎫	
	B. coagulans, B. subtilis	5 ⎪	
	B. licheniformis	10 ⎬	Gould (1964)
	B. polymyxa, B. cereus, B. fusiformis, B. brevis	100 ⎭	

[a] Concentration expressed as μg/ml (Subtilin), Reading Units/ml (Nisin) and % w/v (all other substances).

used for bacteriostatic evaluations, viz. a spore suspension is added to a series of broth tubes (or is streaked on the surface of agar) containing gradually increasing concentrations of the substance under test. The tubes are incubated, and the presence or absence of growth is noted. The lowest concentration which prevents growth is the minimum inhibitory or sporostatic concentration. An alternative, microscopical, method in which the minimum concentration of a substance necessary to prevent germination may be used (Lund, 1962).

Examples of the sporostatic concentrations of various commonly used substances are given in Table 6.1. For the sake of comparison, the bacteriostatic concentrations (where known) of these substances against two non-spore forming bacteria, *E. coli* and *Staph. aureus*, are also given.

The term "sporostatic" unfortunately gives no information as to how, or at what stage, a substance inhibits the development of a spore to a vegetative cell, or whether it is the actual prevention of vegetative cell growth which is the observed effect. Examples of the stage(s) at which antibacterial agents act are provided, when appropriate, in this chapter. The simplest method of determining the effect of a substance on germination is to follow spectrophotometrically changes in optical density of spores + inhibitor either in a nutrient broth or in a more defined environment (p. 176).

B. Sporicidal Tests

1. *Viable counting technique*

The principle of this method is that spores are inoculated into a solution of the antibacterial substance, aliquots being removed at intervals, and the number of viable survivors determined (Reybrouch, 1982). This type of method has been employed in assessing the sporicidal activity of, e.g. phenol against spores of *B. subtilis* (Loosemore, 1964; Russell and Loosemore, 1964) and other bacilli (Briggs, 1966; Briggs and Yazdany, 1974), by Cousins and Allan (1967), Kelsey *et al.* (1974), Coates and Death (1978) and Death and Coates (1979) in determining the sporicidal properties of some halogens, and by Rubbo *et al.* (1967) and Thomas and Russell (1974a,b), who investigated the sporicidal activity of glutaraldehyde. A similar technique, except that spores were inoculated into a product (Experimental Muscle Relaxant Solution, pH 4·5) with and without a preservative, was used by Kenney *et al.* (1964). However, some of their results, such as those dealing with the sporicidal activity of benzalkonium chloride, must be accepted with reserve, since no mention was made of using any suitable neutralizing or inactivating agent (Russell *et al.*, 1979).

A rapid evaluation method of disinfectants, in which a mixed suspension of various vegetative bacteria, a spore (*B. cereus*) and yeast (*Saccharomyces cerevisiae*) were treated with the disinfectant for 5 min at 20°C, was described by Mossel (1963). A 1 ml sample was then transferred to a sterile "universal" neutralizing solution, and the number of survivors determined in infusion and in selective agar. A disinfectant was considered satisfactory if it effected at least 5 D.R.s* in non-sporing bacteria and the yeast. If less than 5 D.R.s took place with *B. cereus*, the chemical could still be considered effective, but if the manufacturer claimed it to be sporicidal, a minimum of 5 D.R.s in the viable spore count was also required.

A different technique, but one still involving viable counts, was made by Hare *et al.* (1963), who tested various antibacterial substances against various organisms, including one spore-former, *B. subtilis*. In their procedure, bacterial films were made by drying small volumes of a culture on the base of a sterile tube. The base of each tube was then held in a shallow layer of the antibacterial agent in a Petri dish or beaker, for the desired period. Excess of the inhibitory agent was then shaken off, and the lower end of the tube held for 25 s in a sterile 1 litre beaker through which tap water was flowing at the rate of 3 litres/min. As much water as possible was removed, and the bottom of the tube apposed to the surface of a culture plate and, after a slight rotation, removed. The plates were incubated for 48 h and the colonies counted. In some cases, it would seem that periods of longer than 15 min might have given more accurate and valuable results.

There are, however, certain criticisms of this technique; first, there could be detachment of bacterial films from the glass tube; second, there could be a carry-over of the antibacterial substance on to the subculture medium; third, there was no investigation into the use of neutralizing agents. The statement by Hare *et al.* (1963) that no such agents exist for some antibacterial substances is correct; however, suitable inactivating agents have been described for various disinfectants (Russell *et al.*, 1979; Russell, 1980).

The first two criticisms described above were, in fact, discussed by the authors of this paper, but were considered to have been overcome in practice.

In all testing procedures, it is important to standardize the conditions, including the spore culture, and the interested reader is referred

---

* One D.R. (decimal reduction) means that 90% of a bacterial population is killed, i.e. 10% remain viable. Thus, 5 D.R.s represent a kill of 99·999%.

to the excellent paper by Waites and Bayliss (1980) for further information and details. In the United States, the Association of Official Analytical Chemists (AOAC) has published a sporicidal test method which involves drying of spores on suitable carriers (see page 174). Stark *et al.* (1975) recommend that sporicidal efficacy be based on the results of these carrier tests and on "rate of spore-kill" tests. Both they and Forsyth (1975) suggest that spores should be prepared in chemically defined rather than in complex media (see also Hodges *et al.*, 1980), since the composition of the sporulation medium may influence the response of spores (Bayliss *et al.*, 1981).

2. *Filtration technique*

The principle of this method is that spores are added to the antibacterial substance, and when desired, the mixture is filtered through a suitable sterile bacteria-proof filter. The filter pad is washed *in situ*, and is then transferred either to a liquid recovery medium or to the surface of an agar plate. The technique can also, of course, be applied to disinfection studies using vegetative cells.

The earliest description of this technique appears to have been made by Davies and Fishburn (1946), and it was subsequently adopted by Davies and Davison (1947), who investigated the efficiency of chlorocresol against *B. subtilis* spores and who claimed this method to be far more sensitive than the usual colony counting method or one involving transference of an aliquot of the reaction medium to nutrient broth. The filter used was an adapted Seitz filter fitted with a Grade S.B. Sterimat. Subsequently, this technique, but with a membrane filter in place of a Seitz filter, has been used in the sterility testing of antibiotics (Holdowsky, 1957; Sykes and Hooper, 1959; Lightbown, 1961; European Pharmacopoeia, 1978). Of primary importance is the amount of antibiotic, or other antibacterial agent, retained by the membrane. In an attempt to determine this amount, spores of *B. subtilis* were added to antibiotic solutions immediately before filtration; at the end of the process, the filter was transferred to the surface of nutrient agar, and the numbers of colonies which developed were counted. Using this technique, Sykes and Hooper (1959) found that there was a high recovery of organisms from streptomycin, but not from neomycin, and Lightbown (1961) showed that there was a good recovery from bacitracin, dihydrostreptomycin, erythromycin, novobiocin, polymyxin, tetracycline and viomycin, a reasonable recovery from kanamycin and ristocetin, but no recovery from vancomycin.

In general, then, the filtration technique appears to be of value particularly in those cases where there is no known neutralizing agent for a particular antibacterial substance (see also Russell, 1980). This technique, employing membrane filters, has also been used for the enumeration of *B. stearothermophilus* in milk, which contains substances inhibitory to this organism (Busta and Speck, 1965).

3. *Extinction methods*

In extinction methods, spores are treated with the antibacterial agent, and at predetermined intervals are transferred to a suitable recovery medium, containing an appropriate neutralizing agent. The procedures of Ortenzio (1966), Friedl (1955, 1957, 1960), Ortenzio *et al.* (1953) and of Pepper and Chandler (1963) have used spores dried on suture loop carriers or cylinders, on which the spores must be dried for a reasonable period of time, e.g. *Cl. sporogenes* spores, from a 72 h culture, dried for 5 min did not resist constant boiling hydrochloric acid for 1 min, whereas dried for 30 min, they resisted a 10 min exposure to HCl, and dried for 22–26 h they resited 60, but not 120, min exposure. *Bacillus subtilis* spores were more sensitive. The reason for using HCl was that spores would be of a prescribed resistance, i.e. they had to resist HCl for at least 5 min (Ortenzio *et al.*, 1953). Basically, the procedure consisted of placing a dried contaminated suture loop carrier into each of four tubes of 10 ml constant boiling HCl at 20°C. After 5, 10, 20 and 30 min, the sutures were removed and transferred to thioglycollate subculture medium (Friedl, 1955). The criticism that acid was carried over to the subculture tubes was noted, and it was stated that this could be overcome by using a resubtransfer procedure, i.e. by transferring the loop carrier from thioglycollate subculture medium to fresh thioglycollate subculture meidum, and incubating all tubes at 37°C for 7 days. The addition of serum to the subculture medium has been found to give more positive results (Klarmann, 1956), but whether this acts by enriching the recovery medium, in the sense of rendering it recuperative for damages spores, or by neutralizing any inhibitory traces of germicide transferred into the medium is not clear. The AOAC procedure (AOAC, 1975) should also be consulted.

Various types of spore carrier have been studied. A silk suture loop carrier protected spores from death by HCl or peracetic acid, as compared to spores on the surface of a porcelain ring carrier (Friedl, 1957), presumably because more spores were adsorbed from a culture by the former surface. HCl, standardized on a basis of normality can replace the constant boiling HCl control without loss of precision, and can be more conveniently prepared and maintained in the testing laboratory; the optimum concentration of HCl is 2·5 N (Friedl, 1960). The spores used should then resist 2·5 N HCl for 2 min, and the post-treatment incubation was extended to 21 days (Ortenzio, 1966). In some cases, some subculture tubes which were negative after incubation could be induced to show growth if heated at 80°C for 20 min and reincubated at 37°C; however, this applied to *Cl. sporogenes* but not to *B. subtilis* (Ortenzio, 1966). Stuart (1967) has stated that, for routine evaluation, spores of *B. subtilis* ATCC 19659 and *Cl. sporogenes* ATCC 9081 should be used, although the method was also applicable for use with strains of *B. anthracis, Cl. tetani* and other spore-forming species.

Other types of extinction methods have been described by Weed and Ecker (1931, 1932) and by Birkhaug (1933), the basis of these methods being that loops of the reaction mixture (a mercury antibacterial agent plus spores) were transferred, when required, into recovery medium containing no neutralizing agent. According to these authors, the concentration of mercury compound in the subculture medium was not inhibitory. The use of a loop subculturing technique is inevitably open to several criticisms, and these have been fully and adequately considered by Sykes (1965). Such a procedure can, of course, provide useful preliminary information, but it is recommended that, wherever possible, an appropriate neutralizing agent be included in the recovery medium. This avoids any possibility that an inhibitory concentration of the antibacterial substance is transferred with the bacteria into the medium.

4. *Conclusions*

As with an assessment of the bactericidal activity of a substance against vegetative organisms, extinction methods obviously have some role to play in determining sporicidal activity. Their particular use in studying the inactivation of spores dried on carriers has been considered above. Nevertheless, despite the fact that they are laborious and rather tedious to perform, viable counting procedures provide more information on the inactivation process. It must be stressed, however, that in all procedures, due attention must be paid to adequate recovery and revival conditions for treated spores. Where no neutralizing agent is known for a particular antibacterial agent, prevention of the carry-over into the subculture medium of a high concentration of the chemical may be achieved either by "diluting out" the substance, for instance a phenol (Russell *et al.*, 1979), or by employing the filtration technique. Where a neutralizing agent is known, it must be included in the recovery medium; however, a dual role for such a substance, in that it must not only neutralize any antibacterial agent carried over into the medium but must also help in the revival of a sublethally injured spore (or vegetative cell), has been proposed by Berry (1951) who cited thioglycollate as an example of such a substance. Thioglycollate is, however, toxic to some spores (page 195).

C. Effects of Inhibitors on Sporulation

The sporulation process, whereby a cell forms a spore, is a complex process that is divided into seven stages (Fig. 1.5, Chapter 1). Addition of an antibacterial agent at the beginning of sporulation (after growth has ceased) may inhibit the process, and further information can be obtained by adding the substance at different stages to ascertain at which stage it acts. Information on this can be obtained microscopically (phase-contrast and electron microscopes), by measuring the rate of accumulation of spore constituents, or by studying the binding characteristics of a drug, e.g. penicillin, at different stages in sporulation.

Some substances may cause lysis of growing cells and of developing spores, but care must be taken to ensure that this is not a secondary effect induced by high drug concentrations.

D. Effects of Inhibitors on Germination and Outgrowth

Germination can be detected by several methods, including the release of DPA, oxygen uptake and the loss of refractility. Probably the easiest technique, however, is to measure the rate of decrease in optical density that occurs when spores are incubated in an appropriate germinative medium and thence to determine whether the antibacterial agent in question blocks this process.

Outgrowth can most easily be monitored by the further changes in optical density that follow germination. Antibacterial agents can thus be added at the onset of this phase to ascertain whether they inhibit this stage. Inhibitors of cell wall, protein, RNA and DNA syntheses can also be studied at this stage by measuring their effects on the incorporation of a labelled compound into the appropriate cell fraction.

Further information may be obtained by consulting the paper by Gould (1971).

III. *Effects of Antibiotics on Bacterial Spores*

Although early studies frequently indicated that bacterial spores were highly resistant to antibiotics, these compounds have, nevertheless, proved to be useful in studying various stages in the spore cycle. During the last decade, in particular, many investigations have been published of the effects of antibiotics such as penicillins, chloramphenicol, fusidic acid, rifampicin, cycloserine, tetracyclines and actinomycin D on the sporulation, germination and outgrowth processes. A considerable amount of useful information has accrued not only about the drugs themselves but also about peptidoglycan (murein, mucopeptide), protein, DNA and mRNA syntheses. It must also be remembered that sporing organisms when placed into a suitable growth medium, such as nutrient agar, are frequently employed in the biological assays of antibiotics (Board and Lovelock, 1975; Kavanagh, 1975; British Pharmacopoeia, 1980).

Other, non-chemotherapeutic antibiotics such as nisin and tylosin, may be employed as agents preventing food spoilage. This section will thus deal with both types of antibiotics.

A. Food Preservatives

1. *Nisin*

The antibiotic nisin is produced by *Streptococcus lactis*. Lewis *et al.* (1954) and O'Brien *et al.* (1956) investigated a wide range of antibiotics, but found that only nisin could reduce the heat resistance of spores of Putrefactive Anaerobe (PA) 3679. Nisin has been shown to be one of the few substances to reduce significantly the D-values of these spores at high temperatures (Michener *et al.*, 1959a). Nisin inhibits the gas production of sporing anaerobes in cheese (Hirsch *et al.*, 1951; McClintock *et al.*, 1952; Hirsch and Grinsted, 1954), probably more readily than it inhibits growth (Hirsch and Grinsted, 1954). Interestingly, it was suggested by Hirsch and Grinsted (1954) that spores were more sensitive to nisin than vegetative cells. Possible reasons for this will be considered later.

The experimental technique used in studying the activity of nisin on bacterial spores should be chosen with care, as much confusion has arisen as to whether the antibiotic is sporicidal or merely exerts a sporostatic action. Michener *et al.* (1959a,b) employed no inactivating agent in the recovery medium in their experiments, considering that the amount of nisin carried over into the medium was too small to prevent spores surviving the heat + nisin treatment from developing into vegetative cells and then producing colonies. According to Thorpe (1960) the carry-over of nisin into the recovery medium is not impor-

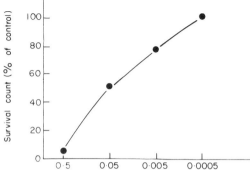

Fig. 6.1   Effect on survival count of *B. stearothermophilus* of the carryover of nisin into the recovery medium (Tramer, 1964).

tant, although subsequent work (Tramer, 1964) with *B. stearothermophilus* strains suggests that the carry-over of the antibiotic into the recovery medium does, in fact, govern the survival count and that the nisin must be diluted to *ca.* 0·0005 units/ml of agar for the maximum survival count to be obtained (see Fig. 6.1). Spores which have been autoclaved in the presence of 20 and 100 units nisin/ml remain viable, since they can still grow provided that nisin is inactivated by trypsin (Tramer, 1964).

Thorpe (1960) heated spores of *B. stearothermophilus* for various times in the presence and absence of nisin and, in the former case, with and without subsequent destruction of the antibiotic by trypsin. His results led him to conclude that the apparent lower heat resistance was caused by adsorption of the antibiotic on to the spores. However, nisin can be diluted out on plating, and thus does not become firmly adsorbed; in addition, it is equally effective if spores and nisin are heated together or if heated separately under comparable conditions (Tramer, 1964). These findings must, therefore, cast doubt on the conclusion of others that nisin reduces the heat resistance of bacterial spores; they also show that nisin is not firmly adsorbed by the spores, that it is the carry-over of nisin into the recovery medium which governs the survival count, and that whilst nisin is inhibitory to spores, it is not sporicidal. It does, in fact, seem likely that nisin is inhibitory to the outgrowth (see below) only of heat-damaged spores, especially in acid-type products (Segmiller *et al.*, 1965).

The point at which nisin is effective has been studied by various workers. Nisin does not prevent germination (Campbell and Sniff, 1959; Eastoe and Long, 1959; Segmiller *et al.*, 1965) whereas germinated spores are sensitive to the antibiotic (Ramseier, 1960). Gould (1964) found that nisin allowed germination to proceed normally, but that it prevented lysis or rupture of the spore wall; spores which normally outgrew by rupture of the spore wall were more sensitive than spores which outgrew by lysis of the wall. Hitchins *et al.* (1963) showed that germination swelling in the spores of *B. cereus* and *B. subtilis* was due mainly to an increase in the breadth of the spore, that it occurred in the absence of oxygen and that it was not inhibited by nisin; however, pre-emergence (post-germination) swelling was oxygen-dependent and was inhibited by nisin. The inhibitory effect of nisin may be increased in the presence of L-alanine (Mikolajcik *et al.*, 1965). The effect of nisin thus involves outgrowth and not germination in bacilli and in *Cl. botulinum* spores (Scott and Taylor, 1981a,b; Somers and Taylor, 1981).

The antibacterial activity of nisin appears to be restricted to its action on spores, since the growth and multiplication of the vegetative cells of many species of *Bacillus* are unaffected by concentrations of nisin much higher than those preventing colony formation of spore inocula on agar. Some examples of the minimum inhibitory concentrations of nisin on spores are given in Table 6.1.

Various methods, using *B. stearothermophilus* and other organisms, of assaying nisin in foods are described and discussed by Fowler *et al.* (1975).

Further information on nisin can be obtained in the book by Lueck (1980).

2. *Subtilin*

Anderson and Michener (1950) and Michener (1955) observed that subtilin was highly effective in reducing the heat resistance of spores of PA 3679, and subsequently, it was found (Michener *et al.*, 1959a,b) to be the most effective in this respect of a wide range of substances. However, Denny and Bohrer (1959) in a study of the effect of subtilin on the thermal death rate of food spoilage organisms at 100–115°C found that a subtilin-heat combination accelerated the death rate of *B. stearothermophilus* but had no significant effect on PA 3679. The effect of subtilin, in general, would appear to be sporostatic. Subtilin inhibits the same stage in outgrowth as does nisin (Gould, 1964).

3. *Tylosin*

The influence of this antibiotic in reducing the heat treatment or ionizing radiation treatment necessary to ensure microbiological sterility has been extensively studied (Denny *et al.*, 1961a,b; Farkas *et al.*, 1967b). Tylosin may reduce the thermal resistance of spores, but its effect is considered to be inhibitory and not sporicidal, and is more effective in reducing the radiation sensitivity of spores than is nisin. Tylosin does not prevent germination, but inhibits the outgrowth process in PA 3679 (Greenberg and Silliker, 1962). However, it inhibits a much later stage than do nisin and subtilin, for Gould (1964) has shown that inhibition is of vegetative cell growth rather than of growth from the spore. Vegetative cells of *B. cereus* outgrowing from spores in 1 μg/ml of tylosin become swollen and slowly elongate, but do not divide.

Tylosin is more effective than nisin in controlling spoilage of some foods but not others (Segmiller *et al.*, 1965).

B. Chemotherapeutic Antibiotics

1. *Introduction*

Early studies (Gardner, 1945; Curran and Evans, 1945) suggested that penicillin exerted a sporicidal action on *Bacillus* spores. Subsequently, it was shown that high concentrations of penicillin did not affect spore germination of *Clostridium* species (Wynne and Harrell, 1951), and a similar lack of effect of penicillin on the viability of bacterial spores has also been noted (Bittner and Voinescu, 1965). Streptomycin, also, has been shown to have no effect on germination and no sporicidal action (Wynne *et al.*, 1952). Brock (1962) studied the effects of antibiotics on endotrophic sporulation of *B. mycoides* and found that this process was inhibited by 10 μg/ml of chloramphenicol and tetracycline, by 25 μg/ml erythromycin and by 1000 μg/ml benzylpenicillin, whereas concentrations in excess of 1000 μg/ml of other antibiotics (neomycin, novobiocin, polymyxin B and streptomycin) did not inhibit the process. Polymyxin B resistance in *B. subtilis* is overcome in the presence of lysozyme or of a cell wall lytic substance released during spore germination (Galizzi *et al.*, 1975).

These and other antibiotics are now being used extensively to study changes occurring during sporogenesis and post-germination processes. Some have also been employed in attempts to obtain a better understanding of the high heat resistance of bacterial spores.

2. *Penicillins*

The effects of penicillins on bacterial spores may conveniently be considered in two parts:

(a) **Effects on sporulation.** Much of our early knowledge of the effects of penicillin on sporulation is derived from the studies of Vinter (1964), who found that the inhibitory action of the antibiotic depended on the stage of development of the *B. cereus* culture at which it was added. Penicillin can inhibit sporogenesis throughout almost the whole of the phase of accumulation of calcium in the spores and of DPA synthesis, in consequence of which these processes are arrested (see also Fitz-James, 1963). Calcium is released from the sporangia of the spores, the amount released depending on the stage when penicillin is added; DPA is also released, but at a slower rate. In the later stages of penicillin inhibition, Dap-containing structures are also destroyed. When calcium accumulation is complete, the development of spores is no longer affected by penicillin.

Vinter (1964) also studied the morphological changes which took place, and showed that whereas there is an increase in the refractility of spores in the sporangia in control cultures, in the penicillin-treated cultures, after the mildly refractile prespores have been formed, the development of refractility stops or even diminishes, the spore structures possibly even turning transparent. Fitz-James (1963) has also found that the addition of penicillin just prior to or early in cortex formation produces a spore of reduced refractility.

Penicillin and other antibiotics inhibit the sporulation septation stage (stage II) in bacterial spores (see Fig. 6.2; Hitchins and Slepecky, 1969). In fact, sporulating cultures of *B. megaterium* and *B. subtilis* show two intervals of enhanced binding, in contrast to non-sporulating bacteria (Lawrence *et al.*, 1971). The first increase in binding corresponds to the period of spore septum formation (stage II, Fig. 6.2) and the second to spore cortex formation (stage IV, Fig. 6.2; Lawrence *et al.*, 1971; Rogolsky *et al.*, 1973). Interestingly, it has been shown that there are two periods of peptidoglycan synthesis during the sporulation process (Pearce and Fitz-James, 1971a), with differences occurring in the structure of the cortical and germ cell wall peptidoglycan (Warth and Strominger, 1969). The cortical peptidoglycan contains a muramic lactam, a unique spore constituent (Fig. 1.4, Chapter 1). The two peaks of penicillin binding to sporulating cultures could either be due to the appearance of new penicillin binding proteins (PBPs) that are specific to the spore itself or to changes in the amounts of PBPs that are present in vegetative cells of the organism. The information currently available suggests that the latter is the correct conclusion (Anwar *et al.*, 1974). The inhibition of forespore septum development by penicillin is a reversible process, since it can be overcome by adding β-lactamase (Lawrence, 1974).

G

Table 6.2. Composition and heat resistance of spores of *B. cereus* T formed in the presence of methicillin[a]

Methi-cillin (μg/ml)	Hexosa-mine %	DPA %	Ca %	Mg %	Ca/DPA	Mg/Ca	D-value (min at 90°C)
0	5·55	11·1	2·06	0·19	0·77	0·152	36·1
18	5·35	8·59	1·96	0·18	0·95	0·158	23·2
36	5·44	9·15	1·96	0·18	0·89	0·158	13·0
54	5·19	8·51	1·98	0·20	0·97	0·166	11·1
108	4·42	6·84	0·94	0·16	0·57	0·282	5·8

[a] Data of Murrell and Warth (1965).

Spores formed in the presence of benzylpenicillin (Vinter, 1964) or of methicillin (Murrell and Warth, 1965) are less heat-resistant than control spores. Many spores of *B. cereus* are very labile at the higher methicillin concentrations (Table 6.2) and the range of heat resistance is about six-fold, with maximum heat resistance associated with a high hexosamine, calcium and DPA content, and with low Mg–Ca ratios (Murrell and Warth, 1965; Table 6.2).

(b) **Effects on germination and outgrowth.** Penicillin, even at high concentrations, has no effect on the germination of *Bacillus* or *Clostridium* spores (Wynne and Harrell, 1951; Scheibel and Lennert-Petersen, 1958; Treadwell *et al.*, 1958; Vinter, 1964). *Bacillus cereus* spores are capable of synthesizing cell wall material immediately after germination, although the cortex is degraded during germination and outgrowth. In this organism, the cells are relatively stable to penicillin in the early phases of post-germinative development, but during the later phase of elongation and first division they become highly sensitive to the penicillin-induced blockage of cell wall synthesis (Treadwell *et al.*, 1958; Vinter, 1965a,b,c, 1970). *Clostridium tetani* spores are greatly injured by penicillin during the early steps of outgrowth (Scheibel and Lennert-Petersen, 1958).

3. D-Cycloserine

The addition of D-cycloserine to sporangial suspensions of *B. cereus* spores reduces the amount of cortex formed in spores, and many spores at higher cycloserine concentrations lack any cortex development (Murrell and Warth, 1965; Murrell, 1967). Cycloserine has been shown to inhibit septation (Hitchins and Slepecky, 1969). The addition of cycloserine during the germination or post-germinative processes does not prevent swelling or the onset of elongation. With penicillins, the cells subsequently undergo disintegration during the elongation phase, whereas with D-cycloserine the elongation of the cells is merely arrested and is followed by atypical division (Vinter, 1965c). Thus, the early steps of outgrowth are relatively resistant to inhibition by cycloserine (Vinter, 1970).

4. *Chloramphenicol*

Penicillin-induced inhibition of sporogenesis in *B. cereus* is reversed by the simultaneous addition of chloramphenicol (Vinter, 1964). After the presporulation phase, sporogenesis is comparatively resistant to chloramphenicol but the whole process is slowed down to a marked extent. Chloramphenicol also affects the morphology of spores during their formation, since the spores are rounder and smaller, and inhibits the incorporation of labelled amino acids into the protein fraction of sporangia. Chloramphenicol has been shown to inhibit septation in *B. megaterium* (Hitchins and Slepecky, 1969; see also Young, 1976) and to inhibit the uptake of labelled cystine in the $A^{(-)}$ strain of *B. cereus* var. *alesti*, which is indicative of an inhibition of coat synthesis (Fitz-James, 1963). Chloramphenicol kills sporulating cells of *B. subtilis* only very slowly (Coote *et al.*, 1973), although it prevents the development of refractility and the formation of alkaline phosphatase in sporulating cultures (Sterlini and Mendelstam, 1969). In *Cl. perfringens*, net protein synthesis, sensitive to inhibition by chloramphenicol, continues during sporulation (Labbe and Duncan, 1976).

Bacterial spores will readily germinate in the presence of inhibitors of macromolecular synthesis such as chloramphenicol, which indicates that protein synthesis is not an essential feature of germination (Keynan and Halvorson, 1965). Thus, the germination process is resistant to chloramphenicol (Steinberg *et al.*, 1965; Steinberg and Halvorson, 1968a), whereas during the outgrowth phase the incorporation of leucine into proteins is inhibited (Steinberg *et al.*, 1965). Of interest is the finding that chloramphenicol does not retard the activity of the glucose oxidizing system, the first appearance of respiration coinciding with the fall in optical density that signifies germination (Steinberg *et al.*, 1965). An apparent disagreement with the conclusion that this antibiotic does not inhibit germination comes from the work of Waites and Wyatt (1974a) who found that chloramphenicol inhibited the germination of *Cl. bifermentans* spores in the presence of L-alanine, that the inhibition could be overcome by the addition of extra L-alanine, that chloramphenicol did not prevent the germination-like changes in optical density brought about by hydrogen peroxide (Section IV) or lysozyme, and that erythromycin (another inhibitor of protein synthesis: Franklin and Snow, 1981) did not inhibit germination. Thus, an inhibition of protein synthesis (a process that does not occur during germination: see also Chapter 1) can be ruled out as a possible explanation, and an alternative explanation must be sought, possibly a removal of reducing power (Waites and Wyatt, 1974a).

5. *Tetracyclines*

Studies on tetracycline antibiotics have been made on sporulating cells of bacilli characterized by an enormous accumulation of calcium (Vinter, 1970). Increased amounts of calcium were bound on the cells during the prespore phase. At the same time, the ability of cells of *B. cereus* and *B. megaterium* to bind chlortetracycline also markedly increased. At a concentration of 5 μg/ml, chlortetracycline or other tetracyclines inhibited to a great extent the incorporation of calcium into the cells and DPA synthesis in the sporangium by, it was postulated, blocking the cell surface.

Clostridium tetani spores germinating in the presence of a tetracycline stop development before visible outgrowth occurs (Scheibel and Lennert-Petersen, 1958).

6. *Fucidin*

Fucidin is an important chemotherapeutic antibiotic which is generally active against β-lactamase producing strains of *S. aureus*. It is effective against growing strains of bacteria, and acts by inhibiting the translocation step in protein synthesis by forming a complex with the extension factor associated with GDP on the ribosome.

During the transition period of growth to sporulation, there is an alteration in the structure and function of 70S ribosomes (see Kornberg *et al.*, 1968) and ribosomal proteins obtained from exponentially growing cells are different from those from sporulating cells of *B. subtilis* (Fortnagel and Bergmann, 1973). Exponential growth of *B. subtilis* cells is inhibited by fusidic acid (Fortnagel, 1973) whereas sporulation becomes resistant 3 h after the end of exponential growth which is 3 h before the formation of heat resistance (Fortnagel, 1973; Fortnagel and Bergmann, 1973). This resistance coincides with the formation of asymmetric prespore septa, and with the loss of ability of ribosomes to bind the antibiotic (Fortnagel and Freese, 1977).

7. *Rifampicin*

Rifampicin is a member of the rifamycin group of antibiotics, which have an important role to play in the treatment of tuberculosis. Rifampicin exerts its lethal effect on bacteria by binding to RNA polymerase and thus inhibiting DNA transcription (Franklin and Snow, 1981).

Doi *et al.* (1970) have studied a *B. subtilis* mutant selected for rifampicin resistance and have shown that in this mutant the RNA polymerase is resistant to inhibition by rifampicin, in contrast to the wild type enzyme. Further, the mutant produced spores with an altered morphology. Rifampicin rapidly inhibits sporulation and the formation of alkaline phosphatase (Leighton and Doi, 1971). Rifampicin at a concentration of 1 μg/ml is rapidly bactericidal to growing or sporulating cells after 120 min (Coote *et al.*, 1973). There are, however, significant changes in the morphology of vegetative cells and of cells initiated to sporulation when treated with rifampicin, with eventual lysis (Coote *et al.*, 1973). Leighton and Doi's (1971) assertion that the mRNA formed during sporulation is unstable is not necessarily correct, however, since no account was taken of the cytological damage produced by high rifampicin concentrations. In fact, rifampicin has been claimed to be too toxic for assessing the lifetime of mRNA (Coote *et al.*, 1973). Even a concentration of 1 μg/ml of antibiotic may be sufficiently high to induce secondary lethal effects. Sublethal concentrations as low as 0·005 μg/ml can still selectively inhibit some stages in the sporulation of *Cl. botulinum*; when added at the time of inoculation, rifampicin blocks spore development at stage III, whereas later addition of the antibiotic allows some cells to reach stages IV and V (Hawirko *et al.*, 1976).

Rifampicin added to stages IV or V does not prevent the incorporation of labelled amino acids nor does it inhibit the specific synthesis of a structural protein (enterotoxin) of the spore coat of *Cl. perfringens* (Labbe and Duncan, 1977).

8. *Actinomycin D*

Actinomycin D has found some use chemotherapeutically as an antibiotic in the treatment of some types of cancers.

It is antibacterial by virtue of its effect on the DNA-dependent RNA polymerase and inhibits RNA synthesis (Franklin and Snow, 1981).

Pearce and Fitz-James (1971b) studied spore refractility in *B. cereus* variants treated with actinomycin D. Addition of antibiotic at various times during stages IV and V was used to prevent the synthesis of lytic enzyme, thereby blocking the terminal lysis. Fitz-James (1963) had earlier shown that the early addition of actinomycin D blocks spore development, that addition at stage III but before cortex development results in the production of heat-resistant forms, and addition after cortex formation but before spore coat development gives rise to forms with varying degrees of refractility. An inhibition of spore development in *B. subtilis* has also been observed (Balassa, 1963; Szulmajster *et al.*, 1963; Nakayama *et al.*, 1980) although spore development appears to continue for some time after the addition of antibiotic (Aronson and del Valle, 1964). In this context it is interesting to note the studies of Sterlini and Mandelstam (1969) on the commitment to sporulation in *B. subtilis*, in which various points of commitment were noted, each after *ca*. 30 min no longer sensitive to actinomycin D. Concentrations greater than 1 μg/ml (and especially >10 μg/ml) induced lysis in this organism, but concentrations below 0·5 μg/ml did not completely inhibit sporulation. Cells that are rapidly lysing fail to sporulate. *Bacillus subtilis* cells committed to sporulation are killed more rapidly by rifampicin (1 μg/ml) than by the same concentration of actinomycin D (Coote *et al.*, 1973). Rifampicin-resistant *B. subtilis* mutants have also been described (Korch and Doi, 1971).

Spores will germinate readily in the presence of inhibitors of macromolecular synthesis such as chloramphenicol and actinomycin D, indicating that the synthesis of macromolecules is not an essential feature of germination (Keyman and Halvorson, 1965). Actinomycin D inhibits amino acid incorporation into proteins in outgrowing spores (Steinberg *et al.*, 1965) and further development is blocked within a short time after antibiotic addition (Vinter, 1970). Throughout the outgrowth process, the addition of actinomycin D blocks further RNA synthesis immediately, and added at zero time the antibiotic inhibits induction of α-glucosidase (Steinberg and Halvorson, 1968a).

9. Conclusions

This section has shown how useful studies with inhibitors of cell wall synthesis (penicillins), protein synthesis (chloramphenicol, fucidin, tetracyclines), RNA synthesis (actinomycin D, rifampicin) can be in studying changes that occur during sporulation, germination and outgrowth. Inhibitors of DNA synthesis, such as mitomycin C and nalidixic acid inhibit this process during outgrowth (Steinberg and Halvorson, 1968b; Keynan *et al.*, 1976). Recent studies on nalidixic acid (Takahashi, 1981) and gramicidin (Danders and Masahiel, 1981) should also be consulted. Figures 6.2 (effects on spore development)

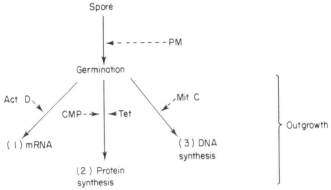

	STAGE		ANTIBIOTIC [*]
	I	Axial filament	
	II	Forespore septum	Pen, Cyclo
Enhanced Pen-binding capacity	III	Engulfment	Rif
	IV	Cortex development	Pen, Cyclo
	V	Coat development	
	VI	Maturation	
	VII	Spore release	

Fig. 6.2 Effect of antibiotics on the sporulation process. (For further information, see Fig. 1.5 in Chapter 1.) Pen, benzylpenicillin; Cyclo, D-cycloserine; Rif, rifampicin.
[*] Other antibiotics also inhibit the septation stage (see text).

Fig. 6.3 Effect of chemotherapeutic antibiotics on germination and outgrowth. PM, polymyxin; CMP, chloramphenicol; Tet, tetracyclines; Act-D, actinomycin D; Mit C, mitomycin C.

and 6.3 (effects on germination and outgrowth) summarize the current position.

Recent studies have shown (Vinter and Stastna, 1980) that polymyxins E (colistin) and B will induce an accelerated release of free spores from sporangia of *B. cereus* and *B. subtilis*.

IV. *Effects of Non-antibiotic Agents on Bacterial Spores*

A. Phenols and Cresols

Historical information on phenolic disinfectants has been provided by Hugo (1978, 1979, 1982) and details of phenolic derivatives reviewed by Hugo and Russell (1982).

Kronig and Paul (1897) carried out an investigation into the effect of various chemicals on *B. anthracis* spores, and their results could be represented by a straight line when $\log_{10}$ of survivors was plotted against time (Chick, 1908). A similar logarithmic order of death was obtained by Chick (1908) when anthrax spores were treated with 5% w/v phenol. However, this concentration of phenol is considerably higher than that concentration needed to kill vegetative bacteria. Spores are, in fact, considered as being resistant to phenols (Cook, 1960; Sykes, 1965; Rubbo and Gardner, 1965; Briggs and Yazdany, 1974). It has been shown (Lund, 1962; Loosemore and Russell, 1963; Russell and Loosemore, 1964) that high numbers of *B. subtilis* spores survive exposure to 2·5 and 5% w/v phenol after 100 h at 25°C or 37°C. The most highly phenol-resistant spores found by Briggs (1966) were those of *B. stearothermophilus*, which over a period of 175 h in 5% phenol at 37°C showed an approximately 3-fold increase in viable count. *Bacillus licheniformis* spores were also highly resistant to phenol, there being approximately 10% survivors after 175 h. *Bacillus pantothenticus* spores were the next in order, followed by spores of *B. subtilis*, *B. cereus* and *B. megaterium*, the last-named being the most sensitive, with just above 0·001% survivors after 50 h treatment. These periods of contact must, of course, be considered as being many times above the periods normally tested in disinfection studies. Hess (1965) has stated that whereas vegetative cells are more or less rapidly destroyed by phenols and cresols, the effect of these substances on bacterial spores is uncertain, and that more work would have to be carried out on this field before any final conclusions could be drawn. However, the results cited from this laboratory (Loosemore and Russell, 1963; Russell and Loosemore, 1964), those of Sykes (1958, 1966) and the more comprehensive ones of Briggs (1966) show without doubt that bacterial spores are highly resistant even to high concentrations of phenol.

Pre-treatment of the spores before their exposure to phenol may have an important influence on the susceptibility of the spores. Reddish (1950), for example, found that *B. cereus* suspensions heated at 80°C for 15 min to remove vegetative cells, before exposure to 5% phenol at 25°C were considerably more sensitive to the chemical than spores which had not been subjected to an initial pre-heating process. Presumably, these spores could be heat-activated, rendering them liable to germinate and thus increasing their sensitivity to phenol, as phenol is lethal to germinated spores (Fernelius, 1960). Spores which are not heat-activable show the same resistance to phenol whether or not they have received an initial heat treatment (Loosemore, 1964).

In contrast to its poor sporicidal activity, phenol is active in low concentrations in inhibiting the growth of spores in nutrient media. Cresol and chlorocresol (*p*-chloro-*m*-cresol), which also possess little sporicidal activity, are likewise potent sporostatic agents (Table 6.1). A comparison of the sporostatic concentrations and bacteriostatic concentrations of these substances (Table 6.1) shows that the values for a particular substance are of approximately the same order, against spores and vegetative cells.

The effectiveness of phenol as a general bactericidal agent is dependent on pH and temperature (Bennett, 1959; Russell, 1974, 1982; Marouchoc, 1979) and its activity against bacterial spores is also influenced by these variables. Phenol is more effective at acid pH, both as a sporostatic agent (Loosemore, 1964) and as a sporicidal substance (Sykes and Hooper, 1954). Sykes and Hooper (1964), for example, reported that whereas *B. subtilis* spores remained viable in 0·5% w/v phenol for 2 weeks at pH 7·5, they were killed within 8 days by 0·1% w/v phenol at pH 3 or 4. The sporicidal activity of chlorocresol (Berry *et al.*, 1937; Briggs and Yazdany, 1974) and of phenol (Berry *et al.*, 1937; Russell and Loosemore, 1964) is greatly accelerated when used at elevated temperatures. As a result of their findings with chlorocresol, Berry *et al.* (1937) recommended the use of this substance in certain injections, and proposed one method, still present in the British Pharmacopoeia (1980), of sterilizing these products by heating them at 98–100°C with either 0·2% w/v chlorocresol or 0·002% w/v phenylmercuric nitrate (PMN). Using a filtration technique, however, Davies and Davison (1947) found that relatively low numbers of *B. subtilis* spores could survive heating with chlorocresol, and subsequently, by the same procedure, heating with PMN (Davison, 1951). It is, however, far from clear whether their containers received the stated period at 98–100°C (Davison, 1951), and this is one possible reason for their results. A second is that the containers for their experiments consisted of screw-capped bottles closed with a rubber liner, for it is a well known fact (Sykes, 1958) that chlorocresol and, to a greater extent, PMN are absorbed into rubber. Confirmation of the results of Davies and Davison (1947) and of Davison (1951) has not been reported. Thus, it seems to be a reasonable conclusion that the phenol, chlorocresol, is sporicidal when used at elevated temperatures, and that, in consequence, the pharmacopoeial method of incorporating it into injections which are to be sterilized at 100°C is based on sound experimental evidence.

Dozier (1924) found that treatment of *Cl. botulinum* spores with phenol delayed their subsequent germination. Using *B. subtilis* spores, Lund (1962) showed that treatment with a high phenol concentration over a long period had little effect on their viability, and that over this period about 87% of the spores remained as bright spores. In contrast, spores exposed to moist heat lost their viability, but retained their refractility. During a 64 h period at 4°C, 5% w/v phenol has been observed to be highly effective in inducing the release of from 77 to 88% of the DPA from *B. megaterium* spores (Rode and Foster, 1960). The spores remained refractile, but Rode and Foster (1960) gave no account of any viability loss. Lund (1962) also found that 0·2% w/v phenol almost completely prevented germination (i.e. in which the spores lost their refractility, "bright" spores becoming "dark" spores), whereas 0·05% phenol retarded germination, those organisms which passed through this stage showing apparently normal outgrowth. It was pointed out that the concentration of phenol, 0·2%, required to inhibit germination was of the same order as that required to inhibit the growth of vegetative organisms in general. Loosemore (1964) and Loosemore and Russell (1964) studied the effect of different concentrations of phenol on the oxygen uptake of *B. subtilis* spores in glucose. An initial lag period of *ca.* 3 h in the control (phenol absent) corresponded to the time required for the complete loss of heat resistance when the spores were suspended in L-alanine + glucose; this lag period was followed by a rapid rate of O_2 uptake, which indicated that O_2 was only taken up when germination and/or subsequent reproduction of the germinated vegetative cells proceeded. Phenol concentrations in the range 0·25–5% prevented O_2 uptake over a period of 125 h at 37°C. Thus, these results indicated that phenol inhibits some stage in the overall germination process. Oxygen uptake becomes detectable during germination (Hitchins *et al.*, 1963), and these findings lend support to the conclusions reached by Lund (1962) that phenol inhibits germination.

Such an inhibition of germination would therefore explain the reason for the sporostatic activity of phenol itself, and, presumably for that of other phenols and of cresols. The inhibition of germination is not irreversible, since neutralization of chlorocresol or other phenolics allows normal germination and outgrowth to proceed (Parker and Bradley, 1968; Lewis and Jurd, 1972).

Sporulation temperature (Bell and Parker, 1975) and media (Purves and Parker, 1973) affect the degree of germination sensitivity to chlorocresol.

Development of resistance to phenol during sporulation appears to occur late in the process (Milhaud and Balassa, 1973; Balassa *et al.*, 1979a,b).

B. Parabens

The parabens (esters of *p*-hydroxybenzoic acid) are important food, cosmetic and pharmaceutical preservatives (Lueck, 1980). They inhibit the growth and toxin production of *Cl. botulinum* (Robach and Pierson, 1978), but it is not as yet clear as to whether they act on germination or outgrowth (or indeed on both processes) (Lewis and Jurd, 1972; Prasad, 1974; Robach and Pierson, 1978).

The phenols (Section IV.A), which they tend to resemble in several ways, inhibit the germination process, and it is thus likely that the parabens act at this stage also.

C. **Alcohols**

1. *Ethyl alcohol (ethanol)*

Ethanol is rapidly lethal to non-sporing bacteria, but in all concentrations is ineffective as a germicidal agent against spore-forming bacteria (Gershenfeld, 1938; Klarmann, 1957; Morton, 1977). Spaulding (1939) observed that 70% ethanol rapidly killed vegetative cells in the wet state and rather less rapidly in the dry state, whereas it did not kill *Cl. tetani* or *Cl. perfringens* in the wet or dry state, after 18 h exposure. However, although *B. anthracis* was not killed in the dry state, it was killed in the wet state within that period of time.

Despite its lack of sporicidal activity, ethanol will inhibit spore germination in *B. subtilis* (Curran and Knaysi, 1964; Trujillo and Laible, 1970; Yasuda-Yasaki *et al.*, 1978), *B. pumilus* (Trujillo and Laible, 1970) and *Clostridium* species (Johnston *et al.*, 1964; Koransky *et al.*, 1978). Heuzenroeder and Johnson (1958) reported that ethanol did not kill bacterial spores after a 24 h contact, and the selective action against vegetative cells as opposed to spores has been utilized to facilitate the isolation of the latter (Johnston *et al.*, 1964). Because of the effects of ethanol on germination noted above, the technique involves treating a mixture of vegetative cells and spores with an effective alcohol concentration (e.g. 50% v/v: Johnston *et al.*, 1964; Koransky *et al.*, 1978) sufficient to kill the non-sporing forms and then plating into an appropriate recovery agar. This effectively reduces the ethanol concentration below the level that inhibits spore germination. Ethanol has also been shown to inhibit sporulation in *B. subtilis* cultures (Bohim *et al.*, 1976).

Morton (1977) stated that the inability of ethanol to destroy bacterial spores made hazardous its use in sterilizing contaminated instruments, particularly when these were soiled with pus, blood or other body fluids. Nevertheless, ethanol can form part of a mixture that shows sporicidal activity. Coulthard and Sykes (1936) found that whereas ethanol was ineffective, even on prolonged exposure, against bacterial spores, the addition of 1% sodium or potassium hydroxide, or of various acids (hydrochloric, nitric, sulphuric or phosphoric), or of 10% amyl-*m*-cresol to 70% ethanol, gave a mixture which was capable of destroying the spores within a few hours. Unfortunately, no adequate controls appear to have been made on the additives themselves. More recently, Coates and Death (1978) showed that initial sporicidal activity of an ethanol-hypochlorite mixture was high, but decreased as the mixture aged.

2. *Methanol (methyl alcohol)*

Methanol possesses a weak antibacterial action, but is not sporicidal (Kolb *et al.*, 1952). The addition of various substances to a suitable concentration of methanol has been claimed (Coulthard and Sykes, 1936) to give a mixture effective against bacterial spores. More recent studies have confirmed this claim. Coates and Death (1978) and Death and Coates (1979) have shown that mixtures of methanol (15%) and hypochlorite have a low initial sporicidal activity which increases as the mixture ages, in contrast to hypochlorite and ethanol (above) or hypochlorite and propan-1-ol or propan-2-ol (below). Increasing the methanol concentration to 25% and (especially) 50% gives a rapid initial sporicidal action which can be maintained for at least 8 h after preparation.

3. *Propan-1-ol and propan-2-ol*

Propan-1-ol and propan-2-ol (isopropyl alcohol) are not sporicidal (Coulthard and Sykes, 1936; Coates and Death, 1978). When used at the same concentration, propan-2-ol is a more effective bactericidal agent against non-sporulating organisms than ethanol (Report, 1965). The addition of various substances to these alcohols has been claimed to produce a sporicidal mixture (Coulthard and Sykes, 1936). Freshly prepared mixtures of hypochlorite with either propan-1-ol or propan-2-ol are rapidly sporicidal, but activity decreases as the mixture ages (Coates and Death, 1978).

4. *Phenethyl alcohol (phenylethanol)*

Phenethyl alcohol inhibits sporulation and germination at much lower concentrations than those inhibiting growth and DNA synthesis in vegetative forms (Slepecky, 1963) and it completely inhibits the development of the spore septum and forespore membrane (Remsen *et al.*, 1966). Vegetative cells of *B. cereus* are highly sensitive to phenethyl alcohol, vegetative cells of *B. megaterium* moderately sensitive and *Streptococcus faecalis* cells fairly resistant; the alcohol affects the membrane at concentrations close to the minimum lethal concentrations (Silva *et al.*, 1976).

5. *Octanol*

Octanol is considered briefly in Chapter 1 and again towards the end of the present chapter. It inhibits germination (Halmann and Keynan, 1962), and studies with spore coat mutants of *B. cereus* have shown that these mutants are more sensitive to octanol than the parent strain (Aronson and Fitz-James, 1975). Oligosporogenous (Osp) mutants have been obtained which are DPA-less but are octanol-resistant (Coote, 1972).

6. *Mechanism of action against spores*

(a) Inhibition of germination. Ethanol and other alcohols (including octanol: Curran and Knaysi, 1961) will inhibit spore germination, the extent of inhibition depending on the alcohol concentration. The inhibition is, however, reversible since germination continues when the alcohol is removed from the cell environment. It is only at some later point in development, probably during vegetative cell development, that inhibition becomes irreversible.

(b) Potentiation of activity. Ethanol is not sporicidal, but it and other alcohols may inhibit spore development. Ethanol may also assist penetration of other agents into the mature spore, although how this is brought about remains unclear.

7. *Conclusions*

Bacterial spores are highly resistant to alcohols (Lamy and Flack, 1962; Rubbo and Gardner, 1965), but despite this these compounds may be useful in potentiating the sporicidal activity of other agents. The lack of sporicidal activity of ethanol also means that it can be employed as a procedure for isolating spores in mixed suspensions of spores and vegetative cells.

D. **Mercury Compounds**

Koch (1881) claimed that mercuric chloride had a rapid sporicidal action on the spores of *B. anthracis*. It was not then appreciated, however, that there was need for an appropriate neutralizing agent in the subculture medium. It was subsequently found (Geppert, 1889) that if the spores were placed in ammonium sulphide solution before being transferred to the recovery medium they grew during subsequent incubation of this medium, which demonstrated conclusively that the effect of mercuric chloride was sporostatic and not sporicidal. It has since been shown that the germination of spores (of *Cl. botulinum*) treated with mercuric chloride is delayed (Dozier, 1924).

However, other early reports (Scott *et al.*, 1929) appeared which claimed that mercury compounds were, in fact, sporicidal. Birkhaug (1933) showed that, in comparison to tincture of iodine and phenol, low concentrations of various mercury compounds (phenylmercuric nitrate (PMN), merthiolate, metaphen and mercurochromone) were needed to inhibit growth of spores of *B. subtilis* in nutrient media. Sporicidal tests were also made, in which loopfuls of the reaction mixture of mercury compound plus spores were transferred into a recovery medium without a neutralizing agent. According to these results, and to those of Weed and Ecker (1931, 1932) who used a similar technique, but who showed that the concentration of PMN in the subculture medium was not inhibitory, PMN and other mercury compounds could be considered as being rapidly sporicidal to *B. subtilis*. Certainly, it is likely that the amount of the mercury compound transferred by a loopful into the recovery medium gives a subinhibitory concentration of the compound in that medium. However, Clock (1933) found that the mercury compounds tested by him (metaphen, mercurochrome, mercurophen, merthiolate and potassium mercuric iodide) would not sterilize catgut sutures; it is noteworthy that in his experiments, the sutures were, after treatment with a mercury compound, incubated in sodium thioglycollate solution, to inactivate the mercury, before being transferred to a suitable recovery medium. Moreover, Berry (1951) has stated that organic mercury-treated bacteria would, if treated with a thiol compound, e.g. sodium thioglycollate, revive and multiply, and that it was important to appreciate the dual action of thioglycollate as an inactivator (i.e. when mixed with the mercury compound either prior to, or at the time of, contact with the organisms) and as a reviver of mercury-treated organisms. It must be pointed out here that thioglycollate itself will induce changes in *B. megaterium* spores, but such changes—which include loss of stainability, DPA, viability, heat stability and the capacity to germinate in glucose (Rowley and Levinson, 1967), as well as loss of lysozyme resistance (Gould and Hitchins, 1963)—occur only at a low pH, *ca.* 2·6–3. It would thus not be expected to influence the results of sporicidal experiments when it is used as a neutralizing agent in recovery media with a pH near neutrality. Thioglycollate may even stimulate germination of some spores (Roberts and Hobbs, 1968), although with certain *Clostridium* spp. an inhibition of germination may result (Hirsch and Grinsted, 1954; Mossel and Beerens, 1968; Hibbert and Spencer, 1968).

Sodium thioglycollate, but not cysteine, inhibits germination of *Cl. botulinum* spores (Treadwell *et al.*, 1958), and cysteine has been recommended for use in anaerobic culture in sterility testing (see Russell, 1980, for further information).

Brewer (1939) stated that no adequate tests had been made against sporulating organisms for the then recently marked mercurials. Later (Brewer, 1948), he reported that spores remained viable even though suspended in the market strength of these mercury compounds for more than 12 years, and attempted to show whether these compounds could prevent the germination of bacterial spores in the animal body. In his experiments (Brewer, 1950), spore suspensions of *Cl. tetani* were mixed with the antiseptic just prior to injection into mice; control animals received spores only. In the control series there was 80% protection over a period of 60 days. An alternative method, in which spores were injected first, followed at intervals by the mercury compound under test, showed that the organic mercury compounds could prevent infection even when administered 1 h after injection of the organisms. Taken as a whole, these results, together with those of Morton *et al.* (1948), who showed that spores and vegetative cells may still be infectious while in a state of bacteriostasis, indicate that the mercury compounds are sporostatic rather than sporicidal. Christensen (1963) found that <1 μg/ml (<0.0001%) of thiomersal inhibited growth of *B. cereus* in culture media; the minimal bactericidal concentration was between 1 and 10 μg/ml (0.0001 and 0.001%), but it is far from clear from the technique used whether spores or vegetative cells were used in these experiments.

Berry *et al.* (1937) showed that PMN at a concentration of 0.001% w/v was effective at 98–100°C in destroying the spores of a strain of *B. subtilis* and despite subsequent criticism (Davison, 1951) of this finding, this method is still used (British Pharmacopoeia, 1980) as a means of sterilizing some injections. The main use of organic mercury compounds is as antimicrobial agents in injections and other pharmaceutical products (Report, 1965) such as eye-drops (Russell *et al.*, 1967).

The sporostatic concentrations of PMN are listed in Table 6.1. For comparison, its bacteriostatic concentrations against various non-sporulating bacteria are also given in this table, which indicates that low concentrations are required to inhibit the growth of *Staph. aureus* and of

B. subtilis spores, and that higher concentrations are required to prevent the growth of *E. coli*.

The fact that mercury compounds are sporostatic and not sporicidal suggests that they can inhibit germination and/or outgrowth. Such indeed is the case, as mercuric chloride has been found to be a powerful inhibitor of the germination of spores of *Cl. botulinum* Type A (Ando, 1973) and of *Bacillus* spp. (Powell, 1950; Murty and Halvorson, 1957; Gould and Sale, 1970; Vinter, 1970). Mercuric chloride may inhibit some reactions in germination before the loss in heat resistance but not the subsequent release of peptidoglycan (Hsieh and Vary, 1975).

E. Aldehydes

The antimicrobial activity of several aldehydes has been studied (reviewed by Russell and Hopwood, 1976; Gorman *et al.*, 1980), and a summary is presented in Table 6.3. Of these aldehydes, two stand out in the context of sporicidal activity and these will thus be discussed in detail.

Table 6.3. Comparative sporicidal activities of some aldehydes[a]

Aldehyde	Chemical structure	Sporicidal activity
Formaldehyde (methanal)	$H.CHO$	Good
Glyoxal (ethanedial)	$CHO.CHO$	Good
Malonaldehyde (propanedial)	$CHO.CH_2.CHO$	Slightly active
Succinaldehyde (butanedial)	$CHO.(CH_2)_2.CHO$	Slightly active
Glutaraldehyde (pentanedial)	$CHO.(CH_2)_3.CHO$[b]	Excellent
Adipaldehyde (hexanedial)	$CHO.(CH_2)_4.CHO$	Slightly active

[a] From Gorman *et al.* (1980).
[b] In simplest form.

1. *Glutaraldehyde (pentanedial)*

Stonehill *et al.* (1963) and Borick *et al.* (1964) found that a 2% aqueous glutaraldehyde solution, buffered with sodium bicarbonate to pH 7·5–8·5, was effective in killing non-sporing bacteria within 2 min, spores of *Bacillus* and *Clostridium* species in 3 h, and *Mycobacterium tuberculosis*, fungi and viruses in 10 min. The solution was not corrosive and was moderately toxic to human tissues such as the skin and eyes. Surprisingly, in view of its highly reactive nature with proteins, its activity was not decreased to any marked extent in the presence of serum.

Pepper and Chandler (1963) used alcoholic solutions of glutaraldehyde, containing 1% of this substance, 0·3% sodium bicarbonate and 70% isopropanol, and found that these sterilized stainless steel penicylinders contaminated with standardized numbers of various spore-formers (*Cl. tetani, Cl. sporogenes, B. subtilis* or *B. pumilus* E601) in a shorter time than did commercially available 8% formaldehyde solution. Of the four organisms, *B. subtilis* was the most resistant, but the *D*-value here was only 7 min. Glutaraldehyde was ten times as active as the simplest dialdehyde, glyoxal, with succinaldehyde solution occupying an intermediate position as a sporicidal substance.

Rubbo and Gardner (1965) and Rubbo *et al.* (1967) showed that a 2% aqueous solution of glutaraldehyde was rapidly bactericidal and sporicidal, killing 99·99% of spores (Inactivation Factor, IF, is thus 10^4) of an avirulent strain of *B. anthracis, Cl. tetani, Cl. sporogenes* in 15, 30 and *ca.* 20 min respectively. *Clostridium bifermentans* was the most sensitive with an IF of 10^5 in 5 min and *B. pumilis* E601 was the most resistant with an IF of only 10^1 after 30 min. It was significant that the spores used were not pre-heated, as such a treatment increased their subsequent sensitivity to the dialdehyde. An agent, sodium metabisulphite, frequently used to neutralize glutaraldehyde carried over into recovery media has itself been shown to inhibit the later stages of outgrowth (Gould, 1964; Tompkin *et al.*, 1980).

(a) **Factors influencing sporicidal activity.** One of the most important factors affecting the sporicidal activity of glutaraldehyde is undoubtedly pH. At acid pH and ambient temperatures, glutaraldehyde is only slowly sporicidal, whereas at alkaline pH its activity is increased markedly (Stonehill *et al.*, 1963; Borick, 1968; Borick and Pepper, 1970; Kelsey *et al.*, 1974; Thomas and Russell, 1974a,b; Christensen, 1977; Babb *et al.*, 1980; Gorman *et al.*, 1980).

As the temperature is increased, however, differences in activity between acid and alkaline solutions diminish and eventually disappear (Sierra and Boucher, 1971; Thomas and Russell, 1974b).

Problems have arisen with the stability of glutaraldehyde at alkaline pH. The acid solution is stable for long periods but once activated to alkaline pH it tends to polymerize rapidly to give a corresponding loss of sporicidal activity on storage (Thomas and Russell, 1974b; Gorman and Scott, 1979a) and is related to a fall in concentration of free aldehyde.

(b) **Novel glutaraldehyde formulations.** Problems associated with the instability of glutaraldehyde at alkaline pH have prompted research and development into novel formulations. Some utilize the benefits of formulation in the lower alkaline range (*ca.* pH 7·5) where instability is reduced. A stabilized glutaraldehyde product, which makes use of this knowledge, also contains surface-active agents and is claimed to have the antimicrobial activity of the original glutaraldehyde formulation, "Cidex", but with an improved stability (Miner *et al.*, 1977).

Several new glutaraldehyde formulations are based on acid glutaraldehyde. These, however, are claimed to have improved sporicidal activity as compared with the original acid glutaraldehyde by means of the presence of anionic, cationic or non-ionic surfactants which have been found to act synergistically with the dialdehyde (Stonehill, 1966; Boucher, 1971; Gorman and Scott, 1979a,b). An acid glutaraldehyde formulation which was sporicidal by means of the addition of a mixture of non-ionic ethoxylates of isomeric linear alcohols is stable for extended periods (Masferrer and Marquez, 1977; Boucher, 1977), and optimal efficiency of this product is achieved at 60°C or in conjunction with high intensity ultrasonics (Sierra, 1971a,b; Boucher, 1972, 1974, 1975, 1978, 1979a,b; Boucher *et al.*, 1973).

The findings that divalent cations (Gorman and Scott, 1979b) and inorganic cation–anionic surfactant combinations (Gorman and Scott, 1979a) increase the sporicidal activity of acid glutaraldehyde solutions could have an important bearing on future developments in this field.

(c) **Mechanism of sporicidal action.** Despite several studies during the past decade, the exact mechanism whereby glutaraldehyde kills bacterial spores and other bacteria remains unclear, although much progress has been made.

The enhanced sporicidal activity of glutaraldehyde at alkaline pH results from an effect of pH on (i) the glutaraldehyde molecule in relation to polymerization, (ii) the outer layers of the cell, or (iii) both. Antibacterial activity is due to the presence of the two free aldehyde groups in the molecule. The effect of sodium bicarbonate, which is often used to render alkaline the acid glutaraldehyde, is likely to be on the bacterial cell rather than on the dialdehyde molecule (Munton and Russell, 1970; King *et al.*, 1974). Although the degree of polymerization of glutaraldehyde is extensive at alkaline pH, this is measured in weeks rather than in the short period in which sporicidal activity is determined (Gorman and Scott, 1977). Interestingly, low concentrations of sodium bicarbonate inhibit the germination of *Bacillus* spores (Cross *et al.*, 1973). Studies on the interaction of glutaraldehyde with proteins and enzymes indicate a reaction between the aldehyde and the α-amino groups of amino acids, the rate of reaction being pH-dependent and increasing considerably over the pH range 4 to 9 (Russell and Hopwood, 1976).

Low concentrations of glutaraldehyde inhibit germination of spores, whereas much higher concentrations are sporicidal (Thomas and Russell, 1974a, 1975). Interaction at acid and alkaline pH appears to occur to a considerable extent with the outer spore layers. Interaction with the spore coat has not, however, been correlated with the much greater sporicidal effect of the aldehyde at alkaline pH. Conceivably acid glutaraldehyde interacts with, and remains at, the spore surface, whereas alkaline glutaraldehyde penetrates into the spore. Support from this observation comes from measurements on electrophoretic mobilities (Munton and Russell, 1970).

Spores of *B. cereus* become heat-sensitive in the presence of high concentrations of salts, possibly because the cations interact with the loosely cross-linked and electronegative peptidoglycan peculiar to spores with collapse of the cortex (Gould and Dring, 1975). The replacement of mobile counterions and a consequent fall in the osmotic dehydration of the core leads to a reduction in resistance. In this context, replacement of bicarbonate as an "activator" for glutaraldehyde with divalent metal chlorides produces quite a rapid sporicidal effect (Gorman and Scott, 1979a,b). This finding may indicate a possible role for sodium bicarbonate in facilitating penetration and interaction of glutaraldehyde with the abundant protein, enzymes and peptidoglycan in the cortex, this interaction probably involving $-NH_2$ groups. Calcium (Ca)-form spores appear to be more sensitive than hydrogen (H)-form spores to alkaline glutaraldehyde (Thomas and Russel, 1975; McErlean *et al.*, 1980).

At alkaline pH, high (10%) aldehyde concentrations interact strongly with one or more layers of the spore coat to produce an extremely tough, sealed structure. At acid pH, this interaction is much slower (Thomas, 1977).

2. Formaldehyde (methanal)

According to some workers (Ortenzio *et al.*, 1953) formaldehyde solution is rapidly sporicidal to *B. subtilis* but not to *Cl. sporogenes* (which was not killed after 2 h) and borax-formalin and formaldehyde-alcohol have been found to destroy *B. anthracis*, *Cl. tetani* and *Cl. perfringens* regularly within 3 h, although in his studies on these, Spaulding (1939) did not use neutralizing agents in the subculture media. Failure to control sporostasis in these media has been pointed out by Klarmann (1956, 1959), who obtained survival of spores of various clostridia even after exposure for 8 h to formaldehyde solution, and who also found that *B. subtilis* spores survived a 4 h treatment with

8% formaldehyde. Similar lack of sporicidal activity of formaldehyde at this concentration has been noted by Pepper and Chandler (1963).

(a) **Factors influencing activity.** Rubbo and Gardner (1965) and Rubbo *et al.* (1967) observed that, irrespective of whether an aqueous or alcoholic formaldehyde solution was used, time–survival curves of treated bacterial spores generally showed an initial shoulder. This is not, however, apparent in the findings of Trujillo and David (1972). According to Willard and Alexander (1964) and Rubbo *et al.* (1967) various alcohols—methanol, ethanol and isopropyl alcohol (propan-2-ol)—reduce the sporicidal activity of formaldehyde.

The bactericidal activity of formaldehyde is influenced markedly by temperature (Tilley, 1945; Trujillo and David, 1972), with extensive spore inactivation at temperatures of 40°C and above (Trujillo and David, 1972).

(b) **Formaldehyde base and formaldehyde-releasing disinfectants.** Novel formaldehyde base disinfectants have been developed by Trujillo and Lindell (1973). Basically these consist of preparations of formaldehyde in organic liquids (ethylene or propylene glycol, glycerol) which although not sporicidal as such become actively so when dissolved in water. Importantly, these new formulations do not appear to possess the irritating vapours of formaldehyde. As with formaldehyde alone ((a) above), the sporicidal activity of these formaldehyde base disinfectants is markedly increased as the temperature rises (Trujillo and Lindell, 1973).

Formaldehyde-releasing agents have been described by Rossmore (1979) and Hugo and Russell (1982).

(c) **Mechanism of sporicidal action.** Formaldehyde interacts with protein to give intermolecular cross-links (reviewed by Russell and Hopwood, 1976). It is considered to be sporicidal because it can penetrate into the interior of the spore (Sykes, 1970) but evidence to support this view is sadly lacking.

Formaldehyde inhibits the germination of *B. subtilis* spores. This inhibition is concentration-dependent and is reversible (Trujillo and David, 1972).

Formaldehyde is an extremely reactive chemical (Walker, 1964) and reacts with protein, DNA or RNA *in vitro*. Its interaction with protein results from a combination with the primary amide as well as with the amino groups, although phenol groups bind little of the chemical (Fraenkel-Conrat *et al.*, 1945; Fraenkel-Conrat, 1961). It has been proposed that formaldehyde acts as a mutagenic agent (Loveless, 1951) and as an alkylating agent by reaction with $-COOH$, $-SH$ and $-OH$ groups (Phillips, 1952). Formaldehyde can also react extensively with nucleic acids (Staehelin, 1958), but the reasons for its sporicidal action remain obscure.

F. Chlorine and Chlorine Compounds

A review of early work on these compounds, going back to the first half of the nineteenth century, when the disinfecting properties of chloride of lime were first recognized has recently been made by Dychdala (1977). She uses the term "active chlorine compounds" to denote aqueous solutions of active chlorine compounds, consisting of a mixture of OCl^-, Cl_2, $HOCl$ and other active chlorine compounds. Hugo and Russell (1982) have described the activity, including sporicidal potency, of various chlorine-releasing agents, including hypochlorite, chloramine T and dichloramine T.

Spores are more resistant than vegetative bacteria to chlorine compounds. This is clearly shown in the studies of Phillips (1952), who investigated the effect of various substances on *B. globigii* spores, *Staphylococcus aureus* and *Escherichia coli*. His results are expressed as *Ct* values, in which *C* is the concentration at which the disinfectant is used, and *t* the length of time required to produce a given effect. On the basis of this value, the ratio of the resistance to sodium hypochlorite of the spore to the non-spore-formers is about 10^4. The pre-treatment of the spores, i.e. whether or not they are heated before being exposed to the chlorine disinfectant, is of particular importance, for Cousins and Allan (1967) have found that spores of strain NCDO (National Culture of Dairy Organisms) 1069 of *B. subtilis* were rendered increasingly sensitive to a chlorine compound if heated before treatment. Heat caused activation of these spores. Conversely, spores of *B. subtilis* NCDO 1919 and *B. cereus* NCDO 577, neither of which required heat activation for germination, were unaffected by preliminary heat treatment as regards their sensitivity to chlorine compounds. In determinations of survivors of chlorine treatment, sodium thiosulphate appears to be a suitable neutralizing agent, both for vegetative bacteria (Mudge and Smith, 1935) and for spores (Weber and Levine, 1944; Cousins and Allan, 1967; Dye and Mead, 1972; Kulikovsky *et al.*, 1975; Coates and Death, 1978; Death and Coates, 1979; see also Russell *et al.*, 1979).

Dakin (1916) pointed out that the commercial hypochlorites then in use had an unconstant composition, and described a method for overcoming this and of stabilizing the solutions, which (Dakin, 1916) contained free alkali and sometimes free chlorine, and were, therefore, irritating when applied to wounds. In his method, chloride of lime was decomposed with a slight excess of sodium carbonate solution, the solution of sodium hypochlorite was then filtered off, and was neutralized with boric acid. The solution could be kept for not more than one week. Dakin's Solution (Chlorinated Soda Solution, Surgical) is still an official preparation in Britain.

Details of the stability of free available chlorine in solution have been discussed by Trueman (1971) and Dychdala (1977), and the stability shown to be dependent on the chlorine concentration, the presence of catalysts, pH of the solution, temperature, the presence of organic matter, and light.

The main types of chlorine compounds used are described below.

1. *Hypochlorites*

These are cheap, convenient to use, with a wide antibacterial spectrum (Davis, 1963), but they are less effective against spores than against vegetative bacteria. Their antibacterial activity decreases with increasing pH (Bean, 1967; see also Tables 6.4 and 6.5). This has been shown with *Staph. aureus* (Weber, 1950), *Cl. botulinum* type E spores (Ito *et al.*, 1967; Table 6.4) and by Charlton and Levine (1937) with *B. metiens* (*B. cereus*) spores and calcium hypochlorite solutions. The last authors found that 100 parts/10^6 available chlorine exhibited about the same degree of kill of spores as a 1000 parts/10^6 solution at pH 11·3. Rudolph and Levine (1941) showed the effect of pH on 25 parts/10^6 available chlorine solution to produce a 99% kill of these spores. The times necessary to achieve this kill were: pH 6, 2·5 min; pH 7, 3·6 min; pH 8, 5 min; pH 9, 19·5 min; pH 9·35, 35·5 min; pH 10, 131 min; and pH 12·85, 465 min.

At constant pH, the times to kill spores of this organism depended on the concentration of available chlorine: 500 parts/10^6, 13·1 min; 100 parts/10^6, 53·5 min; and 25 parts/10^6, 121 min (Rudolph and Levine, 1941).

Tonney *et al.* (1930) showed that clostridial spores in general were more sensitive to chlorine than those of bacilli, and this finding has been borne out by Dye and Mead (1972).

Weber and Levine (1944) studied the survival curves of *B. cereus* spores exposed to chlorine, over the period necessary to produce a 99% kill, and found that there was a marked lag followed by a progressively increasing death rate. A drop of 10°C in the reaction temperature resulted in a 2-fold increase in the period of exposure necessary to bring about the same kill, although sporicidal activity at sub-zero temperatures has been claimed (Jones *et al.*, 1968).

Table 6.4. Effect of pH on sporicidal activity of chlorine[a,b]

pH	Time (min) to kill 99·99% of spores of *Cl. botulinum* type E
3·5	1·1
5·0	2·8
6·5	4·0
8·0	17·0
10·0	>30

[a] Effect of pH on lethal time of 4·5 parts/10^6 free available chlorine in phosphate buffer.
[b] Data of Ito *et al.* (1967).

Table 6.5. Effect of various halogen-releasing compounds on *B. cereus* spores [a]

Compound	Concn[b] (parts/10^6)	Time (min) at 21°C to kill 99% spores at	
		pH 6·5	pH 8
Sodium hypochlorite	50	3	—
	100	—	5
Sodium dichloroisocyanurate	50	3	—
	100	—	11
Dichlorodimethyl hydantoin	50	9	—
	100	—	68
Dibromodimethyl hydantoin	50	27	—
	100	—	25
Iodophor (Iosan D)	50	20	—

[a] Data of Cousins and Allan (1967).
[b] As average halogen content.

Cousins and Allan (1967) have shown that sodium hypochlorite was the most effective of five halogens against *B. cereus* spores (Table 6.5) and that *B. subtilis* spores were more resistant to all the substances. The sporicidal activity of sodium hypochlorite may be potentiated by various compounds, e.g. Weber and Levine (1944) found that 25 parts/10^6 available chlorine at pH 10 exerted no sporicidal activity over a 240 min period at 20°C, whereas almost 99·9% of the spores were killed after this period when 6 parts/10^6 of ammonia were added. Cousins and Allan (1967) found that mixtures of 1·5–4% sodium hydroxide with sodium hypochlorite (200 parts/10^6 of available chlorine) were much more rapidly sporicidal than either sodium hydroxide or sodium hypochlorite, at pH 9 or above, used alone. Freshly prepared hypochlorite solutions, buffered to *ca.* pH 7·6, have a very rapid sporicidal activity (Kelsey *et al.*, 1974; Babb *et al.*, 1980).

Potentiation of the sporicidal activity of hypochlorites is attained in the presence of methanol and other alcohols (Kelsey *et al.*, 1974; Coates and Death, 1978; Death and Coates, 1979), and buffering to pH 7·6–8·1 of alcohol–hypochlorite solutions or hypochlorite alone produces powerful sporicidal activity with optimum stability (Death and Coates, 1979). These solutions are, however, inactivated in the presence of organic matter.

2. Other chlorine compounds

Dakin *et al.* (1916) considered that chloramine-T had a powerful germicidal action. Weber and Levine (1944) determined the survival curves of *B. cereus* spores exposed to chloramine-T during the time necessary to achieve a 99% kill; there was a short lag, followed by a constant death rate. Doubling the concentration of available chlorine reduced the killing time by 40%. A drop of 10°C in the reaction temperature resulted in a 3–4-fold increase in the time necessary to achieve a 99% kill. The bactericidal and sporicidal activities of chloramine-T against, respectively, *Staph. aureus* (Weber, 1950) and bacterial spores (Charlton and Levine, 1935), are considerably higher at acid than at alkaline pH values.

Recent studies on the sporicidal activity of chloramine-T suggest that, at pH 9 and 10°C, it is less active than low concentrations of free available chlorine against clostridial spores (Dye and Mead, 1972).

The effects of other chlorine disinfectants on bacterial spores have been reviewed by Trueman (1971). The effect of pH on sporicidal activity is much more marked with 1,3-dichloro-5,5-dimethyl hydantoin (DDH) than with dichloro-isocyanuric acid (DCCA) or dibromo-dimethyl hydantoin (Cousins and Allan, 1967). Trichloro-isocyanuric acid (TCCA) is less sporicidal than sodium hypochlorite (Trueman, 1971).

3. Mechanism of sporicidal action

Some progress has been made in recent years in elucidating the nature of the sporicidal action of hypochlorites. This seems partly from the observations that hypochlorites solubilize the cell walls of Gram-positive bacteria, and that *B. megaterium* spores and "spore integuments" are lysed (Rode and Williams, 1966). During this treatment, the spores lose refractility and darken, there is a significant separation of spore coat from cortex, and eventually lysis occurs (Kulikovsky *et al.*, 1975).

Bacillus or clostridial spores exposed to hypochlorites leak DPA (Alderton and Holbrook, 1971; Dye and Mead, 1972; Kulikovsky *et al.*, 1975) which suggests an increase in spore permeability, although not all the spore Ca, RNA and DNA are released by this treatment. The spore coat appears to act to some extent as a permeability barrier to chlorine (Wyatt and Waites, 1973, 1975; Kulikovsky *et al.*, 1975). The removal of protein from spore coats does not affect spore viability but renders spores more sensitive to hypochlorites (Wyatt and Waites, 1975; Waites and Bayliss, 1979; Balyiss *et al.*, 1981; Waites, 1982). Chlorine will itself remove coat protein, and allows lysozyme to initiate germination (Wyatt and Waites, 1975).

Sodium hydroxide increases the permeability of bacterial spores to germinants (Wyatt and Waites, 1971, 1974) and the potention of hypochlorite action by sodium hydroxide (Cousins and Allan, 1967) may be the result of the effect of the alkali on spore coats from which protein is removed (Gould *et al.*, 1970; Wood, 1972; Kulikovsky *et al.*, 1975), although the cortex is alkali-resistant (Kulikovsky *et al.*, 1975).

Low concentrations of chlorine have only slight effects on germination and outgrowth, moderate concentrations markedly retard outgrowth whereas high concentrations prevent germination (Wyatt and Waites, 1975).

Pre-treatment of spores with sublethal concentrations of chlorine renders them more sensitive to heating (Dye and Mead, 1972). Waites *et al.* (1976) have concluded that chlorine treatment alters the spore cortex making it susceptible to heating.

There remains the unanswered question of the potentiation by methanol or other alcohols of the sporicidal activity of hypochlorites (Kelsey *et al.*, 1974; Coates and Death, 1978; Death and Coates, 1979). Coates and Death (1978) envisage an effect of an alcohol on the spore coats, which are thereby altered sufficiently to allow penetration by hypochlorite.

G. Iodine and Iodophors

Iodine in aqueous or alcohol solution is considered (Gershenfeld and Witlin, 1950; Gershenfeld, 1956; Report, 1965) to be a most effective germicide, which is rapidly lethal to vegetative bacteria and also to spores (Trueman, 1971). Spaulding (1968), however, considers that alcoholic iodine (0·5% iodine in 70% alcohol) possesses good activity against vegetative bacteria, including *Mycobacterium tuberculosis*, but none against bacterial spores.

Iodine is sparingly soluble in cold water, but more soluble in hot water. Stronger solutions can be made in potassium iodine solutions or in aqueous alcohol. Unfortunately, iodine solutions stain fabrics and tissues, and tend to be toxic. However, certain non-ionic surface-active agents can solubilize iodine to form compounds, the iodophors, which retain the germicidal action, but not the undesirable properties, of iodine. The uses of the iodophors as detergent-sterilizers have been considered in detail by Davis (1962, 1963) and by Blatt and Maloney (1961).

Johns (1954) found that the iodophors exerted a very marked inhibitory effect against *B. subtilis* spores, and attributed this action to the non-ionic constituents in the formulation, since the inhibitory action could be neutralized by 2% skim milk in the culture media. Lawrence *et al.* (1957) determined the sporicidal activity of an iodophor (Wescodyne) against *B. subtilis*; spores were impregnated on to silk suture loops and treated with various concentrations of the iodophor for various periods of time before being transferred to appropriate recovery media. It was found that 1000 parts/10^6 of available iodine destroyed the spores in 6 to 10 h, whereas at an available iodine concentration of 500 parts/10^6 the time for a lethal effect to be observed was 24 h. These authors also quoted a personal communication to show that certain iodophors, in concentrations of 500 to 600 parts/10^6 available iodine, were effective against pathogenic anaerobic spores such as *Cl. perfringens* and *Cl. tetani* when the solutions were allowed to act on spore-impregnated surgical loops for 10–12 h.

More recently, another iodophor, povidone-iodine, has received attention. Gershenfeld (1962) showed that this iodophor and Iodine

Table 6.6. Effect of pH on antibacterial activity of iodine[a]

Name	Chemical form	pH	Antibacterial activity
Diatomic iodine	I_2	Neutral	Very bactericidal
Hypoiodous acid	HOI	and acid	Less bactericidal
Hypoiodite ion	OI^-		Even less active
Iodate ion	IO_3^-	Alkaline	Inactive
Iodide ion	I^-	pH	Inactive
Triiodide ion	I_3^-		Inactive

[a] Based on Trueman (1971).

Tincture, U.S.P., both killed three strains of each of *B. subtilis*, *Cl. tetani* and *Cl. perfringens* within a period of 2·5 h and Lowbury *et al.* (1964) found that povidone-iodine reduced the viable counts of *B. globigii* and *Cl. perfringens* from *ca.* 4 million to <10 in this period, and that povidone-iodine compresses reduced the numbers of viable sporing *B. globigii* on the skin by 99·85% in 60 min. This is an interesting finding, since it suggests that this iodophor has a part to play in removing transient sporing organisms from operation sites.

Iodine is more effective as a germicide at acid than at alkaline pH values, but is less affected by acidity than chlorine (Davis, 1962). The nature of the lethal species of iodine is summarized in Table 6.6 (based on Trueman, 1971). The lethal effect of an iodophor (Iosan D) on *B. cereus* spores is unchanged within the pH range 2·3–6·4 (Cousins and Allan, 1967).

The spores of *B. subtilis* (Lawrence *et al.*, 1957; Bartlett and Schmidt, 1957; Cousins and Allan, 1967) are considerably more resistant to iodophors than are the spores of *B. cereus* (Cousins and Allan, 1967). Iosan D, for example, at a concentration of 800 parts/10^6 of free iodine at pH 2 does not kill *B. subtilis* after 240 min, whereas a concentration of 22 parts/10^6 available iodine has a >99% kill on *B. cereus* in 60 min and 50 parts/10^6 requires 20 min (Cousins and Allan, 1967). It is not possible to put forward, at present, a reason to account for this difference.

That it is the concentration of free iodine in an iodophor which is responsible for its bactericidal action was shown conclusively by Allawala and Riegelman (1953). They made a log–log plot of killing time, in minutes, against mg% free iodine, and found that the 99% killing time of spores of *B. cereus* was a function of the concentration of free iodine in the presence or absence of added surface-active agent.

The mode of action of iodine has, surprisingly, been little studied, but it is considered by some (see Sykes, 1965, 1970) to bind to bacterial protein. The reasons for its comparative effectiveness against bacterial spores are not known. When dried on to epoxy-coated penicylinders, *Cl. sporogenes* spores are resistant to iodophor (Wilson and Nelson, 1979) whereas hydrogen peroxide and iodophor in combination are sporicidal (Chung *et al.*, 1979).

H. Quaternary Ammonium Compounds

The quaternary ammonium compounds (QACs, quats, onium compounds) form an important group of antibacterial and antifungal substances (D'Arcy, 1971; Hugo and Russell, 1982). They are convenient to use, of low toxicity, with little odour or taste, are non-corrosive but are relatively expensive (Davis, 1963). They are more active against bacteria at alkaline pH values than at acid, are weak detergents themselves, and are incompatible with soaps and anionic detergents. Full details of their medical uses have been considered by D'Arcy and Taylor (1962).

Examples of QACs are cetrimide (cetyltrimethylammonium bromide, CTAB, Cetavlon), dequalinium chloride (Dequadin), pyridinium chloride and benzalkonium chloride (Roccal).

The early published work on the antibacterial activity of the QACs included studies on their sporicidal and sporostatic activity. Dunn (1937), for example, carried out germicidal tests by the FDA technique on a mixture of alkyldimethylbenzylammonium chlorides, and found that its germicidal activity on *B. subtilis* spores was greatest at alkaline pH values. Green and Burkeland (1941) claimed that Ceepryn killed the spores of various aerobic and anaerobic bacteria, and Du Bois and Dibblee (1946) put forward evidence to show that another QAC killed 60–75% of the spores of *B. cereus* almost immediately at 80°C, the remaining 25–40% not being killed even after 6 h. Heinemann (1937) found that spores of *B. subtilis* and of two types of fungi were destroyed in 5 min or less by Zephiran. These findings obviously suggest that the QACs possess a remarkable degree of sporicidal activity. However, subsequent studies have demonstrated the fallacy of this earlier conclusion. McCulloch *et al.* (1948) found that 2% hyamine induced no reduction in viable spores of *B. subtilis*; it is noteworthy that an attempt was made here to overcome errors caused by bacteriostasis. Likewise, Kivela *et al.* (1948) described experiments involving the gradual recovery of apparently dead spores of *B. subtilis* which had earlier been exposed to QAC. The most significant findings, however, were made by Davies (1949) who showed that, whilst 0·1% cetavlon was a powerful bactericide, 1% cetavlon did not kill spores of *B. subtilis* and other bacilli at room temperature even after 3 days. Similar findings were obtained with 1% solutions of Zephiran, Phemerol and Ceepryn. Suspensions of the spores were apparently sterilized after 1 h when no precautions were taken to prevent bacteriostasis; however, when Lubrol W was included in the recovery medium, the lack of sporicidal activity could be detected. These results again demonstrate how little the earlier workers appreciated the need for neutralization and revival techniques (Russell *et al.*, 1979) and how, therefore, they arrived at highly erroneous conclusions. Klarmann (1960) cites benzalkonium chloride as being effective as a sporostatic substance against various *Clostridium* spp. (see Table 6.1), and Klarmann and Wright (1950) stressed that the QACs were not capable of killing the spores of resistant *Clostridium* spp. and of *B. anthracis*, and that publications which put forward an opposite view were based upon failure to control adequately sporostasis in the subcultures (see also Russell *et al.*, 1979; Russell, 1980).

Thus, the QACs are sporostatic and not sporicidal (Briggs and Yazdamy, 1974). Cetrimide is retained by the spores, and only washing with a Lubrol W-lecithin solution removes the QAC (Chiori *et al.*, 1965). Cetrimide could either inhibit germination of the spore by virtue of its binding, or could inhibit vegetative growth which normally followed germination, with the likelihood that the latter process is operative. This could conform to the earlier finding of Lund (1962) that cetrimide allows germination to proceed, but inhibits outgrowth of *B. subtilis*. Thus, the sporostatic effect of cetrimide may tentatively be explained in terms of an inhibition of the latter process.

I. Hydrogen Peroxide

The bactericidal and sporicidal properties of the oxidising agent, hydrogen peroxide, have long been known, and have been reviewed by Curran *et al.* (1940), Luck (1956), Roundy (1958), Cerf and Hermier (1972), von Bockelmann and von Bockelmann (1972), Ito *et al.* (1973) and von Bockelmann (1974). Several of these authors have described its uses in the food and canning industries.

1. *Factors influencing activity*

The sporicidal properties of hydrogen peroxide are influenced by a variety of factors, notably concentration, temperature, pH, the type and condition of the organism under test, stability (including the presence of metallic cations) and recovery conditions.

(a) **Concentration.** Low concentrations (6% w/v, 20 vols) are rapidly bactericidal but only slowly sporicidal (Ahmed and Russell, 1975). As would be expected, an increase in peroxide concentration results in an increase in sporicidal activity. At 25°C and concentrations of between 10 and 20% the concentration exponent (η-value) is approximately 1·5 (calculated from the results of Swartling and Lindgren, 1968). Spores exposed to low concentrations of hydrogen peroxide frequently exhibit a distinct shoulder in death rate; this shoulder decreases with increasing concentration (Ito *et al.*, 1973; Toledo *et al.*, 1973).

A "tailing" of survivor curves of certain spores treated with peroxide has been noted by various authors (Cerf and Hermier, 1972; Ito *et al.*, 1973; Cerf, 1976, 1977; Cerf and Metro, 1977). This has been attributed to the formation of clumps during peroxide treatment and the associated spore catalase which would destroy hydrogen peroxide in the immediate vicinity.

(b) **Temperature.** Temperature exerts a marked effect on the sporicidal activity of hydrogen peroxide (Curran *et al.*, 1940; Swartling and Lindgren, 1968; Ito *et al.*, 1973; Toledo *et al.*, 1973; Smith and Brown, 1980). In their early paper, Curran *et al.* (1940) stated that, in the 40–70°C temperature range, the time required for the destruction of 50% of the spores by 1% peroxide decreased from one-half to one-third for each 10°C rise in temperature. From these figures, it is possible to deduce that the temperature coefficient per 10°C rise, θ^{10} (or Q_{10}) is between 2 and 3, which is rather higher than the Q_{10} value of $1 \cdot 6$ calculated by Swartling and Lindgren (1968) but compares favourably with the value ($2 \cdot 5$) obtained by Cerf and Metro (1977). At ambient temperatures, peroxide is only slowly sporicidal (Toledo, 1975).

(c) **pH.** Acidification at high temperatures increases the activity of hydrogen peroxide aginst some types (Cerf and Hermier, 1972; Smith and Brown, 1980) but not against all types (Cerf and Hermier, 1972) of spores. Curran *et al.* (1940) found that, generally, sporicidal activity was greatest at pH 3 and least at pH 9.

(d) **Type and condition of organism.** As would be expected, hydrogen peroxide is less active against higher numbers of spores than against small inocula (Curran *et al.*, 1940). Although findings to date are hardly comprehensive, there is evidence to suggest that *Clostridium* species, with the exception of *Cl. botulinum*, are much less resistant to peroxide than the most resistant aerobic spore-formers (Ito *et al.*, 1973). Of the *Cl. botulinum* strains, type B appear to be the most resistant (Ito *et al.*, 1973). Differences in susceptibility of wet and dry spores do not seem to be great, although more information is needed before definite conclusions can be reached.

(e) **Stability.** A factor that can influence the sporicidal activity of a disinfectant is its stability under conditions of use. At 80°C, the concentration remains more or less constant, but in the presence of spores at this temperature it decreases at a moderate rate (Cerf and Metro, 1977). It is also destroyed by catalase, but pasteurization of milk destroys most of this enzyme, so that peroxide has a better preserving action on pasteurized than on raw milk (Luck, 1956). The decomposition of peroxide is accelerated by the presence of certain inorganic salts, and the influence of Cu^{2+} and Fe^{2+} ions on sporicidal activity is considered in more detail later (p. 211).

(f) **Recovery conditions.** This will be considered briefly as it is again referred to in Chapter 10 (Section IV.A). In brief, it seems likely that the composition of the recovery medium can influence the numbers of survivors, and consequently the sporicidal activity of hydrogen peroxide may be less than originally thought (Wallen and Walker, 1979).

2. Mechanism of sporicidal action

Hydrogen peroxide removes protein (presumably from the coat) in *Cl. bifermentans*; removal of coat protein from spores by dithiothreitol before exposure to peroxide markedly increases the lethal effects of H_2O_2 against these spores (Bayliss and Waites, 1976, 1979) but to a much lesser extent against *B. cereus* (Waites and Bayliss, 1979). Thus, in *Cl. bifermentans*, the spore coat is likely to exert a protective effect against hydrogen peroxide, whereas this does not apply in *B. cereus*.

Like sublethal chlorine concentrations (Wyatt and Waites, 1973), sublethal levels of peroxide increase the germination rate in spores of *Cl. bifermentans*. Gould and Hitchins (1963) found that the lysis of spores by H_2O_2 increased in the presence of certain divalent metal ions, such as Cu^{2+} and Co^{2+}. In the presence of Cu^{2+} ions, the lethal effect and the inhibition of germination of H_2O_2 acting on *Cl. bifermentans* spores is enhanced markedly, whereas against other spores, activity of hydrogen peroxide is not increased significantly in the presence of Cu^{2+} (Bayliss and Waites, 1976; Waites *et al.*, 1979; Waites, 1982). Although *Cl. bifermentans* and *B. subtilis* var. *niger* spores take up Cu^{2+} at about the same rate, only the spore protoplasts of the former organisms bind these cations. The lethal effects of H_2O_2 in the presence of Cu^{2+} and Fe^{2+} ions were first noted by Dittmar *et al.* (1930) and the promotion of its decomposition and increase of its oxidizing properties described. Activation of peroxide to hydroxyl radicals is necessary for sporicidal action (King and Gould, 1969).

Exposure of H_2O_2-treated spores (which have lost peripheral refractility) to monovalent cations (Na, K, Li or, to a lesser extent, NH_4) or to increasing pH (tris buffer, pH 8) results in a loss of the remaining refractility or a decrease in turbidity; conversely, Ca^{2+} reduces the percentage of H_2O_2-treated spores that lose central refractility induced by NaCl (Waites *et al.*, 1976).

Overall, the findings above suggest that hydrogen peroxide removes protein from spores, and that spores of *Cl. bifermentans* are protected against it by virtue of their spore coat. Recent studies with spores of this organism produced by growth on different media have shown that different responses to H_2O_2 take place, and that these changes are related to spore structure (Waites and Wyatt, 1974b; Waites, 1982; Waites and Bayliss, 1980; Waites *et al.*, 1980; Bayliss *et al.*, 1981). The more resistant types of spores have a thicker cortex and smaller protoplast (Waites *et al.*, 1980). This is an important finding, and perhaps further experiments along the lines of Hodges *et al.* (1980), who recommended the use of spores produced in chemically defined media in the testing of sporicidal activity, could be made with a view to linking the various parameters.

J. Curing Agents

It has been known from ancient times that common salt is very useful in preserving meats. Nowadays, it is known that high concentrations of sodium chloride will inhibit the growth of many types of organisms, including the growth of bacterial spores (Tanner and Evans, 1933; Segner *et al.*, 1971; Roberts and Derrick, 1978; Cann and Taylor, 1979). More recently, the development of sodium nitrite has arisen, this being far more effective as an antibacterial agent than sodium nitrate. The sole or major purpose of the latter appears to be merely a source of nitrite (Roberts, 1975; Lechowich *et al.*, 1978).

Sodium nitrite is an important food preservative (Pivnick *et al.*, 1969). High concentrations are, however, needed to inhibit growth of bacterial vegetative and spore forms. Castellani and Niven (1955) found that sterilization of glucose and sodium nitrite together produced considerable inhibition of *Staph. aureus* and similar results were obtained against *Cl. perfringens* (Gough and Alford, 1965). These findings are the forerunners of what is today known as the "Perigo effect" (Ashworth *et al.*, 1975). When nitrite is heated in laboratory media at temperatures >90°C it is more inhibitory to clostridial spores than is nitrite alone, i.e. unheated in media (Perigo *et al.*, 1967; Perigo and Roberts, 1968; Ashworth and Spencer, 1972). This Perigo effect is not observed with aqueous heated solutions of sodium nitrite (Ingram and Robert, 1971). The inhibitory activity of heated nitrite in laboratory media is not stable indefinitely. Much higher concentrations of unheated nitrite are required to inhibit vegetative cells (Perigo and Roberts, 1968) and spores (Roberts and Smart, 1974) of various clostridia than of nitrite heated in the medium. In both instances, the inhibitory effect is more marked at pH 6 than at pH 7, but this is especially true with unheated nitrite. Not all bacterial strains are inhibited by heated nitrite, however, and *Salm. typhimurium*, some strains of streptococci and some of *Bacillus* are insensitive (Roberts and Ingram, 1973). The Perigo effect is likely to result from the formation of an inhibitory substance (Riha and Solberg,

1973, 1975), sometimes referred to as the Perigo factor; see Roberts and Garcia (1973).

The Perigo effect is not always observed, however. It was not demonstrated in commercially produced meat (Johnston *et al.*, 1969) and appears to be produced in some commercially produced media but not in others (Johnston and Loynes, 1971). It occurs in synthetic media (Moran *et al.*, 1975). The variation in the inhibitory effect of sodium nitrite has been attributed to possible differences in batches of meat (Rhodes and Jarvis, 1976). Although Perigo *et al.* (1967) reported that the Perigo effect occurred with nitrite heated in media at temperatures >90°C, Ashworth *et al.* (1973) observed the same effect at pasteurization temperatures in pork.

Critical ingredients in cured meats to prevent botulism are sodium nitrite (not nitrate) and sodium chloride (Roberts and Ingram, 1973; Rhodes and Jarvis, 1976). Various factors influence the activity of unheated, filter-sterilized nitrite (Riemann, 1963; Pivnick *et al.*, 1969; Riemann *et al.*, 1972) and the inhibition of growth is a result of the interaction between pH, a_w value (adjusted by the sodium chloride concentration) and nitrite (Roberts and Ingram, 1973; Roberts *et al.*, 1976). Sodium nitrite inhibits toxin production by *Cl. botulinum* (Christiansen *et al.*, 1973; Robach *et al.*, 1978).

The sodium chloride content of the recovery medium affects the colony counts of heated aerobic and anaerobic spores (Roberts and Ingram, 1966; Roberts *et al.*, 1966). The heating process renders the spores considerably more sensitive to subsequent inhibition by sodium chloride and nitrite (Roberts and Ingram, 1966; Ingram and Roberts, 1971). Sodium chloride may (Duncan and Foster, 1968a,b) or may not (Gould, 1964) allow germination of spores, lower concentrations acting at the point between alongation and cell division. Low concentrations of sodium nitrite allow emergence and alongation but block cell division; higher concentrations permit refractility loss and swelling but prevent emergence (Duncan and Foster, 1968a,b). Sodium nitrate, on the other hand, has no apparent effect, even at high concentrations, on the germination and outgrowth of PA 3679 spores. High concentrations of sodium nitrite stimulate germination of PA 3679 and *Cl. perfringens* spores (Duncan and Foster, 1968c; Labbe and Duncan, 1970) and it was suggested (Duncan and Foster, 1968c) that the presence of sodium nitrite during and after a heating process may induce spores to germinate, consequently rendering them sensitive to heat. Any spores surviving this process would then be blocked at the outgrowth stage by residual nitrite. It has subsequently been shown, however, that nitrite does indeed induce germination, but only at higher concentrations than

H

those permitted legally in foods (Labbe and Duncan, 1970; Duncan, 1971). Its mechanism of action cannot, in practice, therefore be ascribed to increasing the spore sensitivity to heat. Nitrite does not prevent the germination of the majority of heat-injured spores (Labbe and Duncan, 1970), but the outgrowth of these spores is considerably more sensitive than uninjured spores to nitrite inhibition (Labbe and Duncan, 1970). No evidence has been obtained that prior combination of nitrite with a component in heated medium will prevent germination of heat-injured spores.

The inhibitory effect of sodium nitrite in underprocessed meat suspensions (involving heating at 100°C, 5 min) is increased by the addition of reducing agents such as cysteine, thioglycollate and ascorbate (Johnston and Loynes, 1971). The presence of another strong reducing agent, isoascorbate (erythrobate, a stereoisomer of ascorbate) markedly enhances the efficacy of nitrite on *Cl. botulinum* spores in perishable canned cured meat (Tompkin *et al.*, 1977, 1978), although the addition of isoascorbate to pork shoulders in the presence of unheated nitrite has no effect on the recovery of these spores (Sauter *et al.*, 1977). Heating of mixtures of nitrite, cysteine and either ferrous sulphate or ferric chloride at 121°C produces a potent inhibitor against *Cl. perfringens* spores and vegetative cells (Moran *et al.*, 1975; Asan and Solberg, 1976).

The exact nature of the inhibitor is still unknown. It does not appear to be a nitrosamine (Fiddler *et al.*, 1972; Wasserman and Huhtanen, 1972; Ashworth *et al.*, 1973, 1974; Gray and Randall, 1979), but is similar to iron nitrosyl coordination complexes known as Roussin black salts (Ashworth *et al.*, 1974). Incze *et al.* (1974) have shown that S-nitrocysteine, which forms readily by interaction of nitrite and cysteine in an acid medium, may be more inhibitory than nitrite. It has also been suggested that sodium nitrite inhibition may involve an interaction of nitrite as nitrous acid with −SH-containing cell constituents (O'Leary and Solberg, 1976; Morris and Hansen, 1981).

It is also possible that the Perigo factor may, in fact, be a mixture of substances contributing to the overall effect. An excellent discussion of the role of nitrite in meat products is provided by Ingram (1976).

K. Other Agents

Antibacterial agents other than those described in detail in the preceding pages have been shown to have an inhibitory effect on the sporulation and/or germination/outgrowth processes. Ethidium bromide, a trypanocidal drug that inhibits DNA template function by virtue of its intercalating effect (Gale *et al.*, 1981) prevents sporulation of *B. subtilis* when added during stage 0 or the early part of stage 1, but not if added later. Spore formation is, in fact, stopped at a drug concentration lower than that inhibiting vegetative cell growth (Rogolsky and Nakamura, 1974; see also Hanlin *et al.*, 1981). Acridine orange, another intercalating agent (Albert, 1979) will also block spore formation at concentrations subinhibitory to vegetative growth (Burke and Spizizen, 1977). Another dye, methylene blue, is also an effective inhibitor, even when added at a late stage, of the sporulation process, but at the same concentration, it does not inhibit germination or outgrowth (Burke *et al.*, 1979).

Ethylenediamine tetraacetic acid (EDTA) is an important microbiological agent not only because it will kill *Pseudomonas aeruginosa* but also because it affects the permeability of the cell envelopes of Gram-negative bacteria (Wilkinson, 1975). EDTA inhibits germination and outgrowth of *Cl. botulinum* type A spores (Winarno *et al.*, 1971). Auto-oxidized ascorbic acid has been shown to be sporicidal against *Cl. bifermentans* and *Cl. sporogenes* PA 3679 spores and to a lesser extent against *Cl. botulinum* type B spores (Eller *et al.*, 1968).

Other agents that inhibit sporulation include (i) α-picolinic acid (Gollakota and Halvorson, 1960), (ii) benzeneboronic acid, which selectively inhibits sporulation (without having an appreciable effect on vegetative cell growth) even when added 6 h after the end of logarithmic growth (Davis-Mancini *et al.*, 1978), (iii) promethazine, which cures plasmids in Gram-negative bacteria and which blocks spore formation, but only when added up to 4 h after the end of exponential growth (Burke and Spizizen, 1977), (iv) L-malate (Ohne and Rutberg, 1976).

pH is an important factor in limiting the growth of *Cl. botulinum* spores in foods. Acetic (ethanoic) acid inhibits the outgrowth of these spores in pureed cucumbers at pH 4·8 but not pH 5 (Ito *et al.*, 1976). Type A spores are generally more tolerant to acid than type B (Townsend *et al.*, 1954). Ito and Chen (1978) have reviewed the effects of pH on the growth of *Cl. botulinum*, and have pointed out that pH values of <4·6 are generally inhibitory, although individual foods will have their own factors, including inoculum size and incubation temperature. Failures do occur, however, and *Cl. botulinum* type A and B spores can, in fact, survive for long periods at pH 4·2 in acid media (tomato juice or buffer) and can germinate and grow when the pH of the medium increases to a level >4·6 (Odlaug and Pflug, 1977).

L. **Conclusions**

Bacterial spores are more resistant to disinfectants than are non-

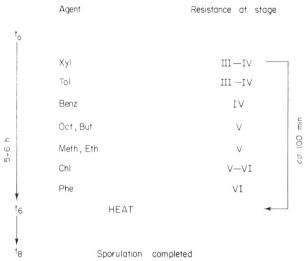

Fig. 6.4   Development* of spore resistance to antimicrobial agents. Xyl, xylene; Tol, toluene; Benz, benzene; Oct, octanol; But, butanol; Meth, methanol; Eth, ethanol; Chl, chloroform; Phe, phenol; Heat, 80°C for 10 min.
* Derived from the results of Milhaud and Balassa (1973) and Balassa *et al.* (1979b). Times are for 10^7 cells of *B. subtilis* to become resistant to each treatment.
t_0 is the time at which exponential growth slows down, t_6 is 5–6 h later, and t_8 is 8 h from t_0.
Further information on stages in sporulation can be obtained from Figs 1.5 and 6.2.

sporulating bacteria, the degree of resistance to some compounds being very marked. Nevertheless, several liquid-phase agents are sporicidal, notably chlorine-releasing agents, aldehydes (especially glutaraldehyde and formaldehyde) and hydrogen peroxide, all of which have important uses (see also Fig. 6.4). Conversely, many disinfectants show a distinct lack of sporicidal activity at normal temperatures, although low concentrations (equivalent to those that are inhibitory to non-sporulating bacteria) are effective inhibitors of germination and outgrowth. This is clearly demonstrated in Fig. 6.5, which depicts the site of action of several such compounds. Obviously, the changes that occur during germination and outgrowth (Chapter 1, Section IV) are sufficiently extensive to render, within a short period of time, a highly resistant form sensitive to a variety of chemical agents. These agents are, however, chemically diverse and do not share a common mechanism of action at the biochemical and molecular levels against vegetative bacteria (Hugo, 1976). In view of the occurrence of "superdormant" spores (Gould *et al.*, 1968) it is unlikely that initiation of germination can be used as a method of controlling spores.

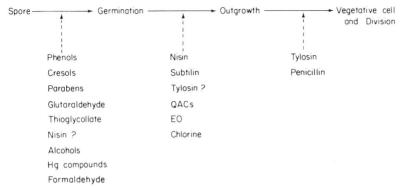

Fig. 6.5   Effect of some antimicrobial agents on germination and outgrowth. EO, ethylene oxide; QACs, quarternary ammonium compounds.

Thus, the finding that an antibacterial agent inhibits germination and/or outgrowth provides no information as to how and why that agent acts at these particular stages in the spore cycle. In other words, much additional information is needed at a more advanced level in order to probe any subtle effects induced by a chemical compound, possibly along the lines described by Dring and Gould (1974, 1975) with ionophorous antibiotics and uncoupling agents.

Some ten years ago, Russell (1971) opined the view that little information was available on the effects of bactericides at different stages in the sporulation process. There is ample evidence for a relationship between sporulation stage and the development of resistance to moist heat (Chapter 2), ionizing radiation (Chapter 4) or various antibiotics (present chapter, Section III) but less so for many disinfectant-type antibacterial agents. There is evidence from studies with "decadent" mutants that the sporulating cells become progressively resistant to chemicals, with butanol resistance closely following octanol resistance and resistance to chloroform, methanol and ethanol appearing at about the same time, and before the development of heat resistance (Fig 6.4) (Balassa and Yamamoto, 1970; Milhaud and Balassa, 1973; Sousa *et al.*, 1978; Balassa *et al.*, 1979a,b; see Fig. 6.4).

The information about the mechanisms of sporicidal action is still scanty, and reasons for the high resistance of spores to many agents are as yet imperfectly understood. Impermeability of the spore to many chemicals may well be the primary reason for this resistance, although this in itself is a rather meaningless statement, since it gives no indication of the site(s) on the spore responsible. Exposure of spores to agents that disrupt disulphide bonds renders the spores sensitive to lysozyme and hydrogen peroxide (Gould and Hitchins, 1963; Gould and King, 1969);

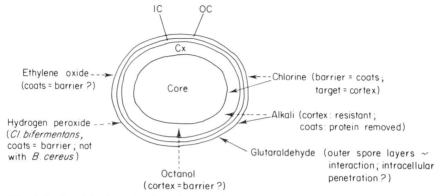

Fig. 6.6   Possible sites of action of non-antibiotic agents and spore barriers. The most important barriers are likely to be disulphide-rich protein, alkali-soluble protein and cortex. Cx, cortex; IC, inner spore coat; OC, outer spore coat; dotted arrow, barrier; full arrow, target.

when spores are treated with S–S disrupting agents and then with alkali, which solubilizes alkali-soluble protein from the spores, they are rendered even more sensitive to lysis by lysozyme and peroxide (Gould *et al.*, 1970). Alkali has been shown to alter the structure of the spore coat of various types of spores (Duncan *et al.*, 1972; Waites *et al.*, 1976), and thus these findings suggest that two defined spore components, viz. disulphide-rich protein and alkali-soluble protein, are involved in impermeability. A third factor, the cortex itself may also be implicated to some extent, since conditional cortex-less mutants of *B. sphaericus* containing a small amount of cortex are sensitive to octanol and xylene even though the spores contain normal spore coats (Imae and Strominger, 1976a,b; Imae *et al.*, 1978; see also Aronson and Fitz-James, 1975). It must also be borne in mind that a spore coat may exert a protective barrier in one spore-former but not in another (Bayliss and Waites, 1976; Waites and Bayliss, 1979).

Figures 6.4 and 6.5 summarize the effects of various agents on spore development and on germination and outgrowth, respectively.

Figure 6.6. is a diagrammatic representation of the possible sites of action of sporicides and also depicts possible resistance layers.

References

Ahmed, F. I. K. and Russell, C. (1975). *Journal of Applied Bacteriology* **39**, 31–40.
Albert, A. (1979). "Selective Toxicity", 6th edn. Chapman and Hall, London.
Alderton, A. and Holbrook, W. U. (1971). *Bacteriological Proceedings*, p. 12.

Allawalla, N. A. and Riegelman, S. (1953). *Journal of the American Pharmaceutical Association, Scientific Edition* **42**, 396–401.

Anderson, A. A. and Michener, H. D. (1950). *Food Technology* **4**, 188–189.

Ando, Y. (1973). *Journal of the Food and Hygiene Society of Japan* **14**, 462–466.

Anwar, R. A., Blumberg, P. M. and Strominger, J. L. (1974). *Journal of Bacteriology* **117**, 924–925.

AOAC (1975). "Official Methods of Analysis". AOAC, Washington.

Aronson, A. I. and del Valle, M. R. (1964). *Biochimica et Biophysica Acta* **87**, 267–276.

Aronson, A. I. and Fitz-James, P. C. (1975). *Journal of Bacteriology* **123**, 354–365.

Asan, T. and Solberg, M. (1976). *Applied and Environmental Microbiology* **31**, 49–52.

Ashworth, J. and Spencer, R. (1972). *Journal of Food Technology* **7**, 111–124.

Ashworth, J., Hargreaves, L. and Jarvis, B. (1973). *Journal of Food Technology* **8**, 477–484.

Ashworth, J., Didcock, A., Hargreaves, L. L., Jarvis, B., Walters, C. L. and Farkworthy, L. F. (1974). *Journal of General Microbiology* **84**, 403–408.

Ashworth, J., Hargreaves, L., Rosser, A. and Jarvis, B. (1975). *In* "Some Methods for Microbiological Assay" (R. G. Board and D. W. Lovelock, eds), pp. 76–90. Society for Applied Bacteriology Technical Series No. 8. Academic Press, London and New York.

Ayliffe, G. A. J. and Collins, B. (1982). *In* "Principles and practice of Disinfection, Preservation and Sterilization" (A. D. Russell, W. B. Hugo and G. A. J. Ayliffe, eds), pp. 244–261. Blackwell Scientific Publications, Oxford.

Babb, J. R., Bradley, C. R. and Ayliffe, G. A. J. (1980). *Journal of Hospital Infection* **1**, 63–75.

Balassa, G. (1963). *Biochimica et Biophysica Acta* **76**, 410–416.

Balassa, G. and Yamomoto, T. (1970). *Microbios* **5**, 73–76.

Balassa, G., Milhaud, P., Raulet, E., Silva, M. T. and Sousa, J. C. F. (1979a). *Journal of General Microbiology* **110**, 365–379.

Balassa, G., Milhaud, P., Sousa, J. C. F. and Silva, M. T. (1979b). *Journal of General Microbiology* **110**, 381–392.

Bartlett, P. G. and Schmidt, W. (1957). *Applied Microbiology* **5**, 355.

Bayliss, C. E. and Waites, W. M. (1976). *Journal of General Microbiology* **96**, 401–407.

Bayliss, C. E. and Waites, W. M. (1979). *FEMS Microbiology Letters* **5**, 331–333.

Bayliss, C. E., Waites, W. M. and King, N. R. (1981). *Journal of Applied Bacteriology* **50**, 379–390.

Bean, H. S. (1967). *Journal of Applied Bacteriology* **30**, 6–16.

Bell, N. D. S. and Parker, M. S. (1975). *Journal of Applied Bacteriology* **38**, 295–299.

Bennett, E. O. (1959). *Advances in Applied Microbiology* **1**, 123–140.

Berry, H. (1951). *Journal of Pharmacy and Pharmacology* **3**, 689–699.

Berry, H., Jensen, E. and Silliker, F. K. (1937). *Quarterly Journal of Pharmacy and Pharmacology* **11**, 729–735.

Birkhaug, K. E. (1933). *Journal of Infectious Diseases* **53**, 250–261.

Bittner, J. and Voinescu, V. (1965). *Archives Roumaines de Pathologie experimentale et de Microbiologie* **24**, 93–98. *Via Chemical Abstracts 1965* **63**, 12023d.

Blatt, R. and Moloney, J. V. (1961). *Surgery, Gynecology and Obstretrics* **113**, 699–704.

Board, R. G. and Lovelock, D. W. (1975) (Eds). "Some Methods for Microbiological Assay". Society for Applied Bacteriology Technical Series No. 8. Academic Press, London and New York.

Bohin, J. P., Rigomier, D. and Schaeffer, P. (1976). *Journal of Bacteriology* **127**, 934–840.

Borick, P. M. (1968). *Advances in Applied Microbiology* **10**, 291–312.
Borick, P. M. and Pepper, R. E. (1970). *In* Disinfection" (M. A. Benarde, ed.), pp. 85–102. Marcel Dekker Inc., New York.
Borick, P. M., Dondershine, F. H. and Chandler, V. L. (1964). *Journal of Pharmaceutical Sciences* **53**, 1273–1275.
Boucher, R. M. G. (1971). *U.S. Patent Application* No. 155, 233.
Boucher, R. M. G. (1972). *American Journal of Hospital Pharmacy* **29**, 660–672.
Boucher, R. M. G. (1974). *American Journal of Hospital Pharmacy* **31**, 546–557.
Boucher, R. M. G. (1975). *Canadian Journal of Pharmaceutical Sciences* **10**, 1–7.
Boucher, R. M. G. (1977). *Respiratory Care* **22**, 790.
Boucher, R. M. G. (1978). *Respiratory Care* **23**, 1063–1072.
Boucher, R. M. G. (1979a). *British Medical Journal* **2**, 444.
Boucher, R. M. G. (1979b). *Canadian Journal of Pharmaceutical Sciences* **14**, 1–12.
Boucher, R. M. G., Last, A. I. and Smith, G. K. (1973). *Proceedings of the Western Pharmacological Society* **16**, 282–288.
Brewer, J. H. (1939). *Journal of the American Medical Association* **112**, 2009–2018.
Brewer, J. H. (1948). *Journal of the American Medical Association* **137**, 858–863.
Brewer, J. H. (1950). *Annals of the New York Academy of Sciences* **53**, 211–219.
Briggs, A. (1966). *Journal of Applied Bacteriology* **29**, 490–504.
Briggs, A. and Yazdany, Z. Z. (1974). *Journal of Applied Bacteriology* **37**, 623–631.
British Pharmacopoeia (1980). Pharmaceutical Press, London.
Brock, T. D. (1962). *Nature, London* **195**, 309.
Burke, W. F. Jr. and Spizizen, J. (1977). *Journal of Bacteriology* **129**, 1215–1221.
Burke, W. F. Jr., Pietuch, T. J. and Yee, S. A. (1979). *Current Microbiology* **2**, 227–231.
Busta, F. F. and Speck, M. L. (1965). *Applied Microbiology* **13**, 1043–1044.
Campbell, L. L. and Sniff, E. E. (1959). *Journal of Bacteriology* **77**, 766–770.
Cann, D. C. and Taylor, L. Y. (1979). *Journal of Food Technology* **14**, 123–129.
Castellani, A. G. and Niven, C. F., Jr. (1955). *Applied Microbiology* **3**, 154–159.
Cerf, O. (1976). *Revue Laitière Francaise* **340**, 149–156.
Cerf, O. (1977). *Journal of Applied Bacteriology* **42**, 1–19.
Cerf, O. and Hermier, J. (1972). *Le Lait* **52**, 1–20.
Cerf, O. and Metro, F. (1977). *Journal of Applied Bacteriology* **42**, 405–415.
Charlton, D. B. and Levine, M. (1937). *Iowa Engineering and Experimental Station Bulletin* **No. 132**. Iowa, U.S.A.
Chick, H. (1908). *Journal of Hygiene, Cambridge* **8**, 92–158.
Chiori, C. O., Hambleton, R. and Rigby, G. J. (1965). *Journal of Applied Bacteriology* **28**, 322–330.
Christiansen, L. N., Johnston, R. W., Kautter, D. A., Howard, J. W. and Aunan, W. J. (1973). *Applied Microbiology* **25**, 357–362.
Christensen, P. E. (1963). *Acta Pathologica et Microbiologica Scandinavica* **61**, 483–486.
Christensen, R. P. (1977). *Journal of Dental Research* **56**, 822–826.
Chung, K.-T., Rice, S. L., Wilson, P. W. and Nelson, P. E. (1979). *Journal of Food Technology* **44**, 1261–1262.
Clock, R. O. (1933). *Surgery, Gynecology and Obstretrics* **56**, 149–161.
Coates, D. and Death, J. E. (1978). *Journal of Clinical Pathology* **31**, 148–152.
Cook, A. M. (1959). *Pharmaceutical Journal* **183**, 333–335.
Cook, A. M. (1960). *Journal of Pharmacy and Pharmacology* **12**, 19T–28T.
Coote, J. G. (1972). *Journal of General Microbiology* **71**, 1–15.

Coote, J. G., Wood, D. A. and Mandelstam, J. (1973). *Biochemical Journal* **134**, 263–270.

Coulthard, C. E. and Sykes, G. (1936). *Pharmaceutical Journal* **139**, 79–81.

Cousins, C. M. and Allan, C. D. (1967). *Journal of Applied Bacteriology* **30**, 168–174.

Cross, G., Wolf, J. and Barker, A. N. (1974). *In* "Spore Research 1973" (A. N. Barker, G. W. Gould and J. Wolf, eds), pp. 199–204. Academic Press, London and New York.

Curran, H. R. and Evans, F. R. (1945). *Journal of Bacteriology* **49**, 335–346.

Curran, H. R. and Knaysi, G. (1961). *Journal of Bacteriology* **82**, 793–797.

Curran, H. R., Evans, F. R. and Leviton, A. (1940). *Journal of Bacteriology* **40**, 423–434.

Dakin, H. D. (1916). *British Medical Journal* **2**, 318–320.

Dakin, H. D., Cohen, J. B. and Kenyon, J. (1916). *British Medical Journal* **1**, 160–162.

Danders, W. and Marahiel, M. A. (1981). *FEMS Microbiology Letters* **10**, 277–283.

D'Arcy, P. F. (1971). *In* "Inhibition and Destruction of the Microbial Cell" (W. B. Hugo, ed.), pp. 613–686. Academic Press, London and New York.

D'Arcy, P. F. and Taylor, E. P. (1962). *Journal of Pharmacy and Pharmacology* **14**, 129–146.

Davies, G. E. (1949). *Journal of Hygiene, Cambridge* **47**, 271–277.

Davies, G. E. and Davison, J. E. (1947). *Quarterly Journal of Pharmacy and Pharmacology* **20**, 212–218.

Davies, G. E. and Fishburn, A. G. (1946). *Quarterly Journal of Pharmacy and Pharmacology* **19**, 365–372.

Davis, J. G. (1962). *Journal of Applied Bacteriology* **25**, 195–201.

Davis, J. G. (1963). *The Sanitarian*, October issue, pp. 3–11.

Davis-Mancini, K., Lopez, I. P. and Hageman, J. H. (1978). *Journal of Bacteriology* **136**, 625–630.

Davison, J. E. (1951). *Journal of Pharmacy and Pharmacology* **3**, 734–738.

Death, J. E. and Coates, D. (1979). *Journal of Clinical Pathology* **32**, 148–153.

Denny, C. B. and Bohrer, C. W. (1959). *Food Research* **24**, 247–252.

Denny, C. B., Sharpe, L. E. and Bohrer, C. W. (1961a). *Applied Microbiology* **9**, 108–110.

Denny, C. B., Reed, J. M. and Bohrer, C. W. (1961b). *Food Technology* **15**, 338–340.

Dittmar, H. R., Baldwin, I. L. and Miller, S. B. (1930). *Journal of Bacteriology* **19**, 203–211.

Doi, R. H., Brown, L. R., Rodgers, G. and Hsu, Y. (1970). *Proceedings of the National Academy of Sciences, U.S.* **66**, 404–410.

Dozier, C. C. (1924). *Journal of Infectious Diseases* **35**, 156–176.

Dring, G. J. and Gould, G. W. (1974). *In* "Spore Research 1973" (A. N. Barker, G. W. Gould and J. Wolf eds), pp. 139–152. Academic Press, London and New York.

Dring, G. J. and Gould, G. W. (1975). *In* "Spores VI" (P. Gerhardt, R. N. Costilow and H. Sadoff, eds), pp. 488–494. American Society for Microbiology, Washington D.C.

Du Bois, A. S. and Diblee, D. (1946). *Science, New York* **103**, 734.

Duncan, C. L. (1970). *Journal of Applied Bacteriology* **33**, 60–73.

Duncan, C. L. and Foster, E. M. (1968a). *Applied Microbiology* **16**, 401–405.

Duncan, C. L. and Foster, E. M. (1968b). *Applied Microbiology* **16**, 406–411.

Duncan, C. L. and Foster, E. M. (1968c). *Applied Microbiology* **16**, 412–416.

Duncan, C. L., Labbe, R. G. and Reich, R. (1972). *Journal of Bacteriology* **109**, 550–559.

Dunn, C. G. (1937). *American Journal of Hygiene* **26**, 46–52.
Dychdala, G. R. (1977). *In* "Disinfection, Sterilization and Preservation" (S. S. Block, ed.), 2nd edn., pp. 167–195. Lea and Febiger, Philadelphia.
Dye, M. and Mead, G. C. (1972). *Journal of Food Technology* **7**, 173–181.
Eastoe, J. E. and Long, J. E. (1959). *Journal of Applied Bacteriology* **22**, 1–7.
Eller, C., Edwards, F. F. and Wynn, E. S. (1968). *Applied Microbiology* **16**, 349–354.
European Pharmacopoeia (1978). Maisonneuve SA, France.
Farkas, J., Kiss, I. and Andrassy, E. (1967). *In* "Radiosterilization of Medical Products", pp. 123–131. Proceedings of a Symposium, International Atomic Energy Agency, Vienna.
Fernelius, A. L. (1960). *Journal of Bacteriology* **79**, 755.
Fiddler, W., Piotrowski, E. G., Pensabene, J. W., Doerr, R. C. and Wasserman, A. E. (1972). *Journal of Food Science* **37**, 668–670.
Fitz-James, P. C. (1963). *Colloques Internationaux du Centre National de la Recherche Scientifique* **124**, 529–544.
Forsyth, M. P. (1975). *Developments in Industrial Microbiology* **16**, 37–47.
Fortnagel, P. (1973). *Colloques Internationaux du Centre National de la Recherche Scientifique* **227**, 2113–2114.
Fortnagel, P. and Bergman, R. (1973). *Biochimica et Biophysica Acta* **299**, 136–141.
Fortnagel, P. and Freese, E. B. (1977). *Journal of General Microbiology* **101**, 299–306.
Fowler, G. G., Jarvis, B. and Tramer, J. (1975). *In* "Some Methods for Microbiological Assay" (R. G. Board and D. W. Lovelock, eds), pp. 91–105. Society for Applied Bacteriology Technical Series No. 8. Academic Press, London and New York.
Fraenkel-Conrat, H. (1961). *Biochimica et Biophysica Acta* **49**, 169–180.
Fraenkel-Conrat, H., Cooper, M. and Olcott, H. S. (1945). *Journal of the American Chemical Society* **67**, 950–954.
Franklin, T. J. and Snow, G. A. (1981). "Biochemistry of Antibiotic Action", 3rd edn. Chapman and Hall, London.
Friedl, J. L. (1955). *Journal of the Association of Official Agricultural Chemists* **38**, 280–287.
Friedl, J. L. (1957). *Journal of the Association of Official Agricultural Chemists* **40**, 759–763.
Friedl, J. L. (1960). *Journal of the Association of Official Agricultural Chemists* **43**, 386–387.
Gale, E. F., Cundliffe, E., Reynolds, P. E., Richmond, M. H. and Waring, M. J. (1981). "The Molecular Basis of Antibiotic Action" 2nd edn. John Wiley and Sons, London.
Galizzi, A., Cacco, G., Siccardi, A. G. and Mazza, G. (1975). *Antimicrobial Agents and Chemotherapy* **8**, 366–369.
Gardner, A. D. (1945). *Lancet* **1**, 658–659.
Geppert, J. (1889). *Berliner Klinische Wochenschrift* **26**, 789.
Gershenfeld, L. (1938). *American Journal of Medical Sciences* **195**, 358–361.
Gershenfeld, L. (1956). *American Journal of Pharmacy* **138**, 335–339.
Gershenfeld, L. (1962). *American Journal of Pharmacy* **134**, 78–81.
Gershenfeld, L. and Witlin, B. (1950). *Annals of the New York Academy of Sciences* **53**, 172–182.
Gillespie, W. A. (1961). *Journal of Clinical Pathology* **14**, 26–31.
Gollakota, K. G. and Halvorson, H. O. (1960). *Journal of Bacteriology* **79**, 1–8.
Gorman, S. P. and Scott, E. M. (1977). *Microbios Letters* **6**, 39–44.

Gorman, S. P. and Scott, E. M. (1979a). *International Journal of Pharmaceutics* **4**, 57–65.

Gorman, S. P. and Scott, E. M. (1979b). *Journal of Applied Bacteriology* **47**, 463–468.

Gorman, S. P., Scott, E. M. and Russell, A. D. (1980). *Journal of Applied Bacteriology* **48**, 161–190.

Gough, B. J. and Alford, J. A. (1965). *Journal of Food Science* **30**, 1025–1028.

Gould, G. W. (1964). *4th International Symposium of Food Microbiology* pp. 17–24. SIK, Göteborg, Sweden.

Gould, G. W. (1971). *In* "Methods in Microbiology" (J. R. Norris and D. W. Ribbons, eds), Vol. 6A, pp. 327–381. Academic Press, London and New York.

Gould, G. W. and Dring, G. J. (1975). *Nature, London* **258**, 402–405.

Gould, G. W. and Hitchins, A. D. (1963). *Nature, London* **200**, 385.

Gould, G. W. and King, W. L. (1969). *In* "Spores IV" (L. L. Campbell, ed.), pp. 276–286. American Society of Microbiology, Washington, D.C.

Gould, G. W. and Sale, A. J. H. (1970). *Journal of General Microbiology* **60**, 335–346.

Gould, G. W., Jones, A. and Wrighton, C. (1968). *Journal of Applied Bacteriology* **31**, 357–366.

Gould, G. W., Stubbs, J. M. and King, W. L. (1970). *Journal of General Microbiology* **60**, 347–355.

Gray, J. I. and Randall, C. J. (1979). *Journal of Food Protection* **42**, 168–179.

Green, T. W. and Burkeland, J. M. (1941). *Journal of Bacteriology* **41**, 34.

Greenberg, R. A. and Silliker, J. H. (1962). *Journal of Food Science* **27**, 64–68.

Halman, M. and Keynan, A. (1962). *Journal of Bacteriology* **84**, 1187–1193.

Halvorson, H. O. and Szulmajster, J. (1973). *In* "Biochemistry of Bacterial Growth" (J. Mandelstan and K. McQuillen, eds), 2nd edn, pp. 494–516. Blackwell Scientific Publications, Oxford.

Hanlin, J. H., Cloutier, M. J. and Slepecky, R. A. (1981). *Applied and Environmental Microbiology* **42**, 79–82.

Hansen, J. N., Spiegelman, G. and Halvorson, H. O. (1970). *Science, New York* **168**, 1291–1298.

Hare, R., Raik, E. and Gash, S. (1963). *British Medical Journal* **2**, 496–500.

Hawirko, R. Z., Chung, K. L. and Magnusson, A. J. C. (1976). *Journal of General Microbiology* **92**, 81–88.

Heinemann, P. G. (1937). *Journal of the American Pharmaceutical Association, Scientific Edition* **26**, 711–717.

Hess, H. (1965). *Pharmaceutisch Weekblad Voor Nederland* **100**, 764–774.

Heuzenroeder, M. and Johnston, K. D. (1958). *Australasian Journal of Pharmacy* **40**, 944–948.

Hibbert, H. R. and Spencer, R. (1970). *Journal of Hygiene, Cambridge* **68**, 131–135.

Hirsch, A. and Grinsted, E. (1954). *Journal of Dairy Research* **21**, 101–110.

Hirsch, A., Grinsted, E., Chapman, H. R. and Mattick, A. T. R. (1951). *Journal of Dairy Research* **18**, 205.

Hitchins, A. D. and Slepecky, R. A. (1969). *Journal of Bacteriology* **97**, 1513–1515.

Hitchins, A. D., Gould, G. W. and Hurst, A. (1963). *Journal of General Microbiology* **30**, 445–453.

Hodges, N. A., Melling, J. and Parker, S. J. (1980). *Journal of Pharmacy and Pharmacology* **32**, 126–130.

Holdowsky, S. (1957). *Antibiotics and Chemotherapy* **7**, 49–54.

Hsieh, L. K. and Vary, J. C. (1975). *Journal of Bacteriology* **123**, 463–470.

Hugo, W. B. (1976). *In* "The Survival of Vegetative Microbes", 26th Symposium of the Society for General Microbiology (T. R. G. Gray and J. R. Postgate, eds), pp. 383–413. Cambridge University Press, Cambridge.

Hugo, W. B. (1978). *Journal of Antimicrobial Chemotherapy* **4**, 489–494.

Hugo, W. B. (1979). *Microbios* **23**, 83–85.

Hugo, W. B. (1982). *In* "Principles and Practice of Disinfection, Preservation and Sterilization" (A. D. Russell, W. B. Hugo and G. A. J. Ayliffe, eds), pp. 3–7. Blackwell Scientific Publications, Oxford.

Hugo, W. B. and Russell, A. D. (1982). *In* "Principles and practice of Disinfection Preservation and Sterilization" (A. D. Russell, W. B. Hugo and A. D. Russell, eds), pp. 8–106. Blackwell Scientific Publications, Oxford.

Imae, Y. and Strominger, J. L. (1976a). *Journal of Bacteriology* **126**, 907–913.

Imae, Y. and Strominger, J. L. (1976b). *Journal of Bacteriology* **126**, 914–918.

Imae, Y., Strominger, M. B. and Strominger, J. L. (1978). *In* "Spores VII" (G. Chambliss and J. C. Vary, eds), pp. 62–66. American Society for Microbiology, Washington D.C.

Incze, K., Farkas, J., Mihalyi, V. and Zukal, E. (1974). *Applied Microbiology* **27**, 202–205.

Ingram, M. (1976). *In* "Microbiology in Agriculture, Fisheries and Food". Society for Applied Bacteriology Symposium Series No. 4 (F. A. Skinner and J. G. Carr, eds), pp. 1–18. Academic Press, London and New York.

Ingram, M. and Roberts, T. A. (1971). *Journal of Food Technology* **6**, 21–28.

Ito, K. A. and Chen, J. K. (1978). *Food Technology* **32**, 71–72, 76.

Ito, K. A., Seslar, D. J. and Mercer, W. A. (1967). *In* "Botulism 1966" (M. Ingram and T. A. Roberts, eds), pp. 108–122. Chapman and Hall, London.

Ito, K. A., Denny, C. B., Brown, C. K., Yao, M. and Seeger, M. L. (1973). *Food Technology* **27**, 58–66.

Ito, K. A., Chen, J. K., Lerke, P. A., Seeger, M. L. and Unverferth, J. A. (1976). *Applied and Environmental Microbiology* **32**, 121–124.

Johns, C. K. (1954). *Canadian Journal of Technology* **32**, 71.

Johnston, M. A. and Loynes, R. (1971). *Canadian Institute of Food Technology Journal* **4**, 179–184.

Johnston, M. A., Pivnick, H. and Samson, J. M. (1969). *Canadian Institute of Food Technology Journal* **2**, 52–55.

Johnston, R., Harmon, S. and Kautter, D. (1964). *Journal of Bacteriology* **88**, 1521–1522.

Jones, L. A. Jr., Hoffman, R. K. and Phillips, C. R. (1968). *Applied Microbiology* **16**, 787–791.

Kavanagh, F. (1975). "Analytical Microbiology", 2nd edn. Academic Press, London and New York.

Kelsey, J. C. and Maurer, I. M. (1974). *Pharmaceutical Journal* **207**, 528–530.

Kelsey, J. C., Mackinnon, I. H. and Maurer, I. M. (1974). *Journal of Clinical Pathology* **27**, 632–638.

Kenney, D. S., Grundy, W. E. and Otto, R. H. (1964). *Bulletin of the Parenteral Drug Association* **18**, 10–19.

Keynan, A. and Halvorson, H. (1965). *In* "Spores III" (L. L. Campbell and H. O. Halvorson, eds), pp. 174–179. American Society for Microbiology, Washington D.C.

Keynan, A., Berns, A. A., Dunn, G., Young, M. and Mandestan, J. (1976). *Journal of Bacteriology* **128**, 8–14.

King, J. A., Woodside, W. and McGucken, P. V. (1974). *Journal of Pharmaceutical Sciences* **63**, 804–805.

King, W. L. and Gould, G. W. (1969). *Journal of Applied Bacteriology* **32**, 481–490.

Kivela, E. W., Mallmann, W. L. and Churchill, E. S. (1948). *Journal of Bacteriology* **55**, 565–572.

Klarmann, E. G. (1956). *American Journal of Pharmacy* **128**, 4–18.

Klarmann, E. G. (1957). *American Journal of Pharmacy* **129**, 42–45.

Klarmann, E. G. (1959). *American Journal of Pharmacy* **131**, 86–90.

Klarmann, E. G. (1960). *In* "Medicinal Chemistry", 2nd edn (A. Burger, ed.), p. 1109. Interscience Publishers Inc.

Klarmann, E. G. and Wright, E. S. (1950). *American Journal of Pharmacy* **122**, 330–336.

Koch, R. (1881). *Arbeiten aus dem K. Gesundheitsamte* **1**, 1–49.

Kolb, R. W., Schnitzer, R., Floyd, E. and Byers, D. H. (1952). *Archives of International Hygiene and Occupational Medicine* **5**, 354–364.

Koransky, J. R., Allen, S. D. and Dowell, V. R. (1978). *Applied and Environmental Microbiology* **35**, 762–765.

Korch, C. T. and Doi, R. H. (1971). *Journal of Bacteriology* **105**, 1110–1118.

Kornberg, A., Spudich, J. A., Nelson, D. L. and Deutscher, M. P. (1968). *Annual Review of Biochemistry* **37**, 51–78.

Kronig, B. and Paul, Th. (1897). *Zentralblatt für Hygiene und Infektionskrankheiten* **25**, 1–112.

Kulikovsky, A., Pankratz, H. S. and Sadoff, H. L. (1975). *Journal of Applied Bacteriology* **38**, 39–46.

Labbe, R. G. and Duncan, C. L. (1970). *Applied Microbiology* **19**, 353–359.

Labbe, R. G. and Duncan, C. L. (1976). *Journal of Bacteriology* **125**, 444–452.

Labbe, R. G. and Duncan, C. L. (1977). *Journal of Bacteriology* **129**, 843–849.

Lamy, P. P. and Flack, H. L. (1965). *American Journal of Hospital Pharmacy* **19**, 473–480.

Lawrence, C. A., Carpenter, C. M. and Naylor-Foote, A. W. C. (1957). *Journal of the American Pharmaceutical Association, Scientific Edition* **46**, 500–505.

Lawrence, P. J. (1974). *Antimicrobial Agents and Chemotherapy* **6**, 815–820.

Lawrence, P. J., Rogolsky, M. and Hanh, V. T. (1971). *Journal of Bacteriology* **108**, 662–667.

Lechowich, R. V., Brown, R. L., Deibel, R. H. and Somers, I. I. (1978). *Food Technology* **32**(5), 45–58.

Leighton, T. J. and Doi, R. H. (1971). *Journal of Biological Chemistry* **246**, 3189–3195.

Lewis, J. C. and Jurd, L. (1972). *In* "Spores V" (H. O. Halvorson, R. Hanson and L. L. Campbell, eds), pp. 384–389. American Society of Microbiology, Washington D.C.

Lewis, J. C., Michener, H. D., Stumbo, C. R. and Titus, D. S. (1954). *Journal of Agricultural and Food Chemistry* **2**, 298–302.

Lightbown, J. W. (1961). *Proceedings of the 7th International Congress of Microbiological Standardization, London 1961*. E. and S. Livingstone, Edinburgh.

Loosemore, M. (1964). M. Pharm. Thesis, University of Wales.

Loosemore, M. and Russell, A. D. (1963). *Journal of Pharmacy and Pharmacology* **15**, 558.

Loveless, A. (1951). *Nature, London* **167**, 338–342.

Lowbury, E. J. L., Lilly, H. A. and Bull, J. P. (1964). *British Medical Journal* **2**, 531–536.

Luck, H. (1956). *Dairy Science Abstracts* **18**, 365–386.

Lueck, E. (1980). "Antimicrobial Food Preservatives". Springer-Verlag, Berlin.

Lund, B. M. (1962). Ph.D. Thesis, University of London.

Marouchoc, S. R. (1979). *Developments in Industrial Microbiology* **20**, 15–24.

Masferrer, R. and Marquez, R. (1977). *Respiratory Care* **22**, 257–262.

McCulloch, E. C., Hauge, S. and Migaki, H. (1948). *Journal of the American Veterinary Medical Association* **112**, 283–290.

McErlean, E. P., Gorman, S. P. and Scott, E. M. (1980). *Journal of Pharmacy and Pharmacology* **32**, 32p.

McLintoch, M., Serres, L., Marzolf, J. J., Hirsch, A. and Mocquot, G. (1952). *Journal of Dairy Research* **19**, 187.

Michener, H. D. (1955). *Journal of Bacteriology* **70**, 192–200.

Michener, H. D., Thompson, P. A. and Lewis, J. C. (1959a). *Applied Microbiology* **7**, 166–173.

Michener, H. D., Thompson, P. A. and Lewis, J. C. (1959b). *Agricultural Research Service*, ARS-74-11. United States Department of Agriculture.

Mikolajcik, F. M., Reeves, C. B. and Harper, W. J. (1965). *Journal of Dairy Science* **48**, 1522–1524.

Milhaud, P. and Balassa, G. (1973). *Molecular and General Genetics* **125**, 241–250.

Miner, N. A., McDowell, J. W., Willcockson, G. W., Bruckner, N. I., Stark, R. L. and Whitmore, E. J. (1977). *American Journal of Hospital Pharmacy* **34**, 376–382.

Moran, D. M., Tannebaum, R. and Archer, M. C. (1975). *Applied Microbiology* **30**, 838–843.

Morris, S. L. and Hansen, J. N. (1981). *Journal of Bacteriology* **148**, 465–471.

Morton, H. E. (1977). *In* "Disinfection, Sterilization and Preservation" (S. S. Block, ed.), 2nd end, pp. 301–318. Lea and Febiger, Philadelphia.

Morton, H. E., North, L. L. and Engley, F. B. (1948). *Journal of the American Medical Association* **136**, 36–41.

Mossel, D. A. A. (1963). *Laboratory Practice* **12**, 898–899.

Mossel, D. A. A. and Beerens, H. (1968). *Journal of Hygiene, Cambridge* **66**, 269–272.

Mudge, C. S. and Smith, F. R. (1935). *American Journal of Public Health* **25**, 442–447.

Munton, T. J. and Russell, A. D. (1970). *Journal of Applied Bacteriology* **33**, 410–419.

Murrell, W. G. (1967). *Advances in Microbial Physiology* **1**, 133–251.

Murrell, W. G. and Warth, A. D. (1965). *In* "Spores III" (L. L. Campbell and H. O. Halvorson, eds), pp. 1–24. American Society for Microbiology, Washington D.C.

Murty, G. G. K. and Halvorson, H. D. (1957). *Journal of Bacteriology* **73**, 230–240.

Nakayama, T., Kurogi, Y. and Matsuo, H. (1980). *Journal of Biochemistry* **87**, 1619–1624.

O'Brien, R. T., Titus, D. S., Devlin, K. A., Stumbo, C. R. and Lewis, J. C. (1956). *Food Technology* **10**, 353–355.

Odlaug, T. E. and Pflug, I. J. (1977). *Applied and Environmental Microbiology* **34**, 30–33.

Ohne, M. and Rutberg, B. (1976). *Journal of Bacteriology* **125**, 453–460.

O'Leary, V. and Solberg, M. (1976). *Applied and Environmental Microbiology* **31**, 208–212.

Ortenzio, L. F. (1966). *Journal of the Association of Official Agricultural Chemists* **49**, 721–726.

Ortenzio, L. F., Stuart, L. S. and Friedl, J. L. (1953). *Journal of the Association of Official Agricultural Chemists* **36**, 480–484.

Parker, M. S. (1969). *Journal of Applied Bacteriology* **32**, 322–328.
Parker, M. S. and Bradley, T. J. (1968). *Canadian Journal of Microbiology* **14**, 745–746.
Pearce, S. M. and Fitz-James, P. C. (1971a). *Journal of Bacteriology* **105**, 339–348.
Pearce, S. M. and Fitz-James, P. C. (1971b). *Journal of Bacteriology* **107**, 337–344.
Pepper, R. E. and Chandler, V. L. (1963). *Applied Microbiology* **11**, 384–388.
Perigo, J. A. and Roberts, T. A. (1968). *Journal of Food Technology* **3**, 91–94.
Perigo, J. W., Whiting, E. and Bashford, T. E. (1967). *Journal of Food Technology* **2**, 377–397.
Phillips, C. R. (1952). *Bacteriological Reviews* **16**, 135–138.
Pivnick, H., Barnett, H. W., Nordin, H. R. and Rubin, L. J. (1969). *Canadian Institute of Food Technology Journal* **2**, 141–148.
Powell, J. F. (1950). *Journal of General Microbiology* **4**, 330–338.
Prasad, C. (1974). *Journal of Bacteriology* **119**, 805–810.
Purves, J. and Parker, M. S. (1973). *Journal of Applied Bacteriology* **36**, 39–45.
Ramseier, H. R. (1960). *Archiv für Mikrobiologie* **37**, 57–94.
Reddish, C. F. (1950). Cited by Schmidt, C. F. (1955). *Annual Review of Microbiology* **9**, 387–400.
Remsen, C. C., Lundgren, D. G. and Slepecky, R. A. (1966). *Journal of Bacteriology* **91**, 324–331.
Report (1965). Use of Disinfectants in Hospitals. *British Medical Journal* **1**, 408–413.
Reybrouck, G. (1982) *In* "Principles and Practice of Disinfection, Preservation and Sterilization" (A. D. Russell, W. B. Hugo and G. A. J. Ayliffe, eds) pp. 134–157. Blackwell Scientific Publications, Oxford.
Rhodes, A. C. and Jarvis, B. (1976). *Journal of Food Technology* **11**, 13–23.
Riemann, H. (1963). *Food Technology* **17**, 39–49.
Riemann, H., Lee, W. H. and Genigeorgis, C. (1972). *Journal of Milk and Food Technology* **35**, 514–523.
Riha, W. E. and Solberg, M. (1973). *Journal of Food Science* **38**, 1–3.
Riha, W. E. and Solberg, M. (1975). *Journal of Food Science* **40**, 439–442.
Robach, M. C. and Pierson, M. D. (1978). *Journal of Food Science* **43**, 787–792.
Robach, M. C., Ivey, F. J. and Hickey, C. S. (1978). *Applied and Environmental Microbiology* **36**, 210–211.
Roberts, T. A. (1975). *Journal of the Science of Food and Agriculture* **26**, 1755–1760.
Roberts, T. A. and Derrick, C. M. (1978). *Journal of Food Technology* **13**, 349–353.
Roberts, T. A. and Garcia, C. E. (1973). *Journal of Food Technology* **8**, 463–466.
Roberts, T. A. and Hobbs, G. (1968). *Journal of Applied Bacteriology* **31**, 75–88.
Roberts, T. A. and Ingram, M. (1973). *Journal of Food Technology* **8**, 467–475.
Roberts, T. A. and Smart, J. L. (1974). *Journal of Applied Bacteriology* **37**, 261–264.
Roberts, T. A., Gilbert, R. J. and Ingram, M. (1966). *Journal of Food Technology* **1**, 227–235.
Rode, L. J. and Foster, J. W. (1960). *Journal of Bacteriology* **79**, 1772–1778.
Rode, L. J. and Williams, M. G. (1966). *Journal of Bacteriology* **92**, 1771–1778.
ɹgolsky, M. and Nakamura, H. T. (1974). *Journal of Bacteriology* **111**, 57–61.
Rogolsky, M., Lawrence, P. J. and Hanh, V. T. (1973). *Journal of Bacteriology* **114**, 220–227.
Rossmore, H. W. (1979). *Developments in Industrial Microbiology* **23**, 41–71.
Roundy, Z. D. (1958). *Journal of Dairy Science* **41**, 1460–1465.
Rowley, D. B. and Levinson, H. S. (1967). *Journal of Bacteriology* **93**, 1017–1022.
Rubbo, S. D. and Gardner, J. F. (1965). "A Review of Sterilization and Disinfection". Lloyd-Luke, London.

Rubbo, S. D., Gardner, J. F. and Webb, R. L. (1967). *Journal of Applied Bacteriology* **30**, 78–87.

Rudolph, A. S. and Levine, M. (1941). *Iowa Engineering and Experimental Station Bulletin* **No. 150**. Iowa, U.S.A.

Russell, A. D. (1967). Unpublished data.

Russell, A. D. (1971). *In* "Inhibition and Destruction of the Microbial Cell" (W. B. Hugo, ed.), pp. 451–612. Academic Press, London and New York.

Russell, A. D. (1974). *Microbios* **10**, 151–174.

Russell, A. D. (1980). *In* "Pharmaceutical Microbiology" (W. B. Hugo and A. D. Russell, eds), 2nd end, pp. 317–324. Blackwell Scientific Publications, Oxford.

Russell, A. D. (1982). *In* "Principles and Practice of Disinfection, Preservation and Sterilization" (A. D. Russell, W. B. Hugo and G. A. J. Ayliffe, eds), pp. 107–133. Blackwell Scientific Publications, Oxford.

Russell, A. D. and Hopwood, D. (1976). *Progress in Medicinal Chemistry* **13**, 271–301.

Russell, A. D. and Loosemore, M. (1964). *Applied Microbiology* **12**, 403–406.

Russell, A. D., Jenkins, J. and Harrison, I. H. (1967). *Advances in Applied Microbiology* **9**, 1–38.

Russell, A. D., Ahonkhai, I. and Rogers, D. T. (1979). *Journal of Applied Bacteriology* **46**, 207–244.

Sauter, E. A., Kemp, J. D. and Langlois, B. E. (1977). *Journal of Food Science* **42**, 1678–1679.

Scheibel, I. and Lennert-Petersen, O. (1955). *Acta Pathologica et Microbiologica Scandinavica* **44**, 232–238.

Scott, V. N. and Taylor, S. L. (1981a). *Journal of Food Science* **46**, 117–120.

Scott, V. N. and Taylor, S. L. (1981b). *Journal of Food Science* **46**, 121–126.

Scott, W. W., Hill, J. H. and Ellis, M. G. (1929). *Journal of the American Medical Association* **92**, 111–116.

Segmiller, J. L., Xezones, H. and Hutchings, I. J. (1965). *Journal of Food Science* **30**, 166–171.

Segner, W. P., Schmidt, C. F. and Boltz, J. K. (1971). *Applied Microbiology* **22**, 1025–1029.

Shaner, E. D. (1964). *Journal of the Acoustics Society of America* **36**, 2238–2239.

Sierra, G. (1971a). *Canadian Patent No.* 865, 913.

Sierra, G. (1971b). *Canadian Patent No.* 874, 713.

Sierra, G. and Boucher, R. M. G. (1971). *Applied Microbiology* **22**, 160–164.

Silva, M. T., Sousa, J. C. F., Macedo, M. A. E., Polonia, J. and Parente, A. M. (1976). *Journal of Bacteriology* **127**, 1359–1369.

Slepecky, R. A. (1963). *Biochemical and Biophysical Research Communications* **12**, 369–373.

Smith, Q. J. and Brown, K. L. (1980). *Journal of Food Technology* **15**, 169–179.

Snyder, R. W. and Cheadle, E. L. (1965). *American Journal of Hospital Pharmacy* **22**, 321–327.

Sofos, J. N., Busta, F. F., Bhothipaksa, K. and Allen, C. E. (1979). *Journal of Food Science* **44**, 668–675.

Somers, E. B. and Taylor, S. L. (1981). *Journal of Food Sciences* **46**, 1972–1973.

Sousa, J. C. F., Silva, M. T. and Balassa, G. (1978). *Annales de Microbiologie (Institut Pasteur)* **129B**, 377–390.

Spaulding, E. H. (1939). *Surgery, Gynecology and Obstetrics* **69**, 738–744.

Spaulding, E. H. (1968). *In* "Disinfection, Sterilization and Preservation" (C. A. Lawrence and S. S. Block, eds), pp. 517–531. Lea and Febiger, Philadelphia.

Spaulding, E. H., Cundy, K. R. and Turner, F. J. (1977). *In* "Disinfection, Steriliza-
tion and Preservation" (S. S. Block, ed.), 2nd edn, pp. 654–684. Lea and Febiger,
Philadelphia.
Staehelin, M. (1958). *Biochimica et Biophysica Acta* **29**, 410–417.
Stark, R. L., Ferguson, P., Garza, P. and Miner, N. A. (1975). *Developments in
Industrial Microbiology* **16**, 31–36.
Steinberg, W. and Halvorson, H. O. (1968a). *Journal of Bacteriology* **95**, 469–478.
Steinberg, W. and Halvorson, H. O. (1968b). *Journal of Bacteriology* **95**, 479–489.
Steinberg, W., Halvorson, H. O., Keynan, A. and Weinberg, E. (1965). *Nature,
London* **208**, 710–711.
Sterlini, J. M. and Mandelstam, J. (1969). *Biochemical Journal* **113**, 29–37.
Stonehill, A. A. (1966). *U.S. Patent No.* 3, 282, 775.
Stonehill, A. A., Krop, S. and Borick, P. M. (1963). *American Journal of Hospital
Pharmacy* **20**, 458–465.
Stuart, L. S. (1967). *Journal of the Association of Official Agricultural Chemists* **50**,
763–764.
Swartling, P. and Lindgren, B. (1968). *Journal of Dairy Research* **35**, 423–428.
Sykes, G. (1958). *Journal of Pharmacy and Pharmacology* **10**, 40T–45T.
Sykes, G. (1962). *Journal of Applied Bacteriology* **25**, 1–11.
Sykes, G. (1963). *Chemistry and Industry* 885–893.
Sykes, G. (1965). "Disinfection and Sterilization", 2nd edn. Spon, London.
Sykes, G. (1966). *Process Biochemistry* August issue, pp. 1–5.
Sykes, G. (1970). *Journal of Applied Bacteriology* **33**, 147–156.
Sykes, G. and Hooper, M. C. (1954). *Journal of Pharmacy and Pharmacology* **6**,
552–557.
Sykes, G. and Hooper, M. C. (1959). *Journal of Pharmacy and Pharmacology* **11**,
235T–239T.
Szulmajster, J., Canfield, R. E. and Blicharske, J. (1963). *C.R. Academie des Sciences*
256, 2057–2060.
Takahashi, I. (1980). *Current Microbiology* **4**, 159–161.
Tanner, F. W. and Evans, F. L. (1938). *Zentralblatt für* **88**, Abt. II, 44–54.
Thomas, S. (1977). *Microbios Letters* **5**, 199–204.
Thomas, S. and Russell, A. D. (1974a). *Journal of Applied Bacteriology* **37**, 83–92.
Thomas, S. and Russell, A. D. (1974b). *Applied Microbiology* **28**, 331–335.
Thomas, S. and Russell, A. D. (1975). *Journal of Applied Bacteriology* **38**, 315–317.
Thorpe, R. H. (1960). *Journal of Applied Bacteriology* **23**, 136–145.
Tilley, F. W. (1945). *Journal of Bacteriology* **50**, 469–473.
Toledo, R. T. (1975). *Food Technology* **29**, 102–112.
Toledo, R. T., Escher, F. E. and Ayres, J. C. (1973). *Applied Microbiology* **26**, 592–597.
Tompkin, R. B., Christiansen, L. N. and Shaparis, A. B. (1977). *Journal of Food
Science* **42**, 1046–1048.
Tompkin, R. B., Christiansen, L. N. and Shaparis, A. B. (1978). *Applied and Environ-
mental Microbiology* **35**, 59–61.
Tompkin, R. B., Christiansen, L. N. and Shaparis, A. B. (1980). *Applied and Environ-
mental Microbiology* **39**, 1096–1099.
Tonney, F. O., Greer, F. E. and Leibig, G. F., Jr. (1930). *American Journal of Public
Health* **20**, 503–508.
Townsend, C. T., Yee, L. and Mercer, W. A. (1954). *Food Research* **19**, 536–542.
Tramer, J. (1964). *4th International Symposium on Food Microbiology* pp. 25–33. SIK,
Göteborg, Sweden.

Treadwell, P. E., Jann, G. J. and Salle, A. J. (1958). *Journal of Bacteriology* **76**, 549–555.

Trueman, J. R. (1971). *In* "Inhibition and Destruction of the Microbial Cell" (W. B. Hugo, ed.), pp. 137–183. Academic Press, London and New York.

Trujillo, R. and David, T. J. (1972). *Applied Microbiology* **23**, 618–622.

Trujillo, R. and Laible, N. (1970). *Applied Microbiology* **20**, 620–623.

Trujillo, R. and Lindell, K. F. (1973). *Applied Microbiology* **26**, 106–110.

Underwood, E. (1982). *In* "Principles and Practice of Disinfection, Preservation and Sterilization" (A. D. Russell, W. B. Hugo, and G. A. J. Ayliffe, eds) pp. 221–243. Blackwell Scientific Publications, Oxford.

Vinter, V. (1964). *Folia Microbiologica* **9**, 58–72.

Vinter, V. (1965a). *Folia Microbiologica* **10**, 280–287.

Vinter, V. (1965b). *In* "Spores III" (L. L. Campbell and H. O. Halvorson, eds), pp. 25–37. American Society of Microbiology, Washington D.C.

Vinter, V. (1965c). *Folia Microbiologica* **10**, 288–298.

Vinter, V. (1970). *Journal of Applied Bacteriology* **33**, 50–59.

Vinter, V. and Stastna, J. (1980). *Journal of Applied Bacteriology* **49**, 155–164.

von Beckelmann, I. (1974). *The Sporicidal Action of Chemical Disinfectants. SIK Rapport* No. 359.

von Beckelmann, I. and von Beckelmann, B. (1972). *Lebensmittelwissenschaft ünd Technologie* **5**, 221–225.

Waites, W. M. (1982). *In* "Principles and Practice of Disinfection, Preservation and Sterilization" (A. D. Russell, W. B. Hugo and G. A. J. Ayliffe, eds), pp. 207–220. Blackwell Scientific Publications, Oxford.

Waites, W. M. and Bayliss, C. E. (1979). *Journal of Applied Biochemistry* **1**, 71–76.

Waites, W. M. and Bayliss, C. E. (1980). *In* "Microbial Growth and Survival in Extremes of Environment" (G. E. Gould and J. E. L. Corry, eds), pp. 169–172. Symposium for Applied Bacteriology Technical Series No. 15. Academic Press, London and New York.

Waites, W. M. and Wyatt, L. R. (1974a). *In* "Spore Research 1973" (A. N. Barker, G. W. Gould and J. Wolf, eds) pp. 177–184. Academic Press, London and New York.

Waites, W. M. and Wyatt, L. R. (1974b). *Journal of General Microbiology* **80**, 253–258.

Waites, W. M., Wyatt, L. R., King, N. R. and Bayliss, C. E. (1976). *Journal of General Microbiology* **93**, 388–396.

Waites, W. M., Bayliss, C. E., King, N. R. and Davies, A. M. C. (1979). *Journal of General Microbiology* **112**, 225–233.

Waites, W. M., Bayliss, C. E. and King, N. R. (1980). *Journal of General Microbiology* **116**, 271–276.

Walker, H. W. (1964). *Journal of Food Science* **29**, 360–365.

Wallen, S. E. and Walker, H. W. (1979). *Journal of Food Science* **44**, 560–563.

Warth, A. D. and Strominger, J. L. (1969). *Proceedings of the National Academy of Sciences, U.S.* **64**, 528–535.

Wasserman, A. E. and Hutanen, C. N. (1972). *Journal of Food Science* **37**, 785–786.

Weber, G. R. (1950). *Public Health Reports* **65**, 503–512.

Weber, G. R. and Levine, M. (1944). *American Journal of Public Health* **34**, 719–728.

Weed, L. A. and Ecker, E. E. (1931). *Journal of Infectious Diseases* **49**, 440–449.

Weed, L. A. and Ecker, E. E. (1932). *Journal of Infectious Diseases* **51**, 309–314.

Wilkinson, G. S. (1975). *In* "Resistance of *Pseudomonas aeruginosa*" (M. R. W. Brown, ed.), pp. 145–188. John Wiley and Son, Chichester.

Willard, M. and Alexander, A. (1964). *Applied Microbiology* **12**, 229–233.

Wilson, P. W. and Nelson, P. E. (1979). *Journal of Food Science* **44**, 251–253.

Winarno, F. G., Stumbo, C. R. and Hayes, K. M. (1971). *Journal of Food Science* **36**, 781–785.

Wood, D. A. (1972). *Biochemimcal Journal* **130**, 505–514.

Wyatt, L. R. and Waites, W. M. (1971). *In* "Spore Research 1971" (A. N. Barker, G. W. Gould and J. Wolf, eds), pp. 121–131. Academic Press, London and New York.

Wyatt, L. R. and Waites, W. M. (1973). *Journal of General Microbiology* **78**, 383–385.

Wyatt, L. R. and Waites, W. M. (1974). *Journal of General Microbiology* **84**, 391–394.

Wyatt, L. R. and Waites, W. M. (1975). *Journal of General Microbiology* **89**, 337–344.

Wynne, E. S. and Harrell, K. (1951). *Antibiotics and Chemotherapy* **1**, 198–202.

Wynne, E. S., Collier, R. E. and Mehl, D. A. (1952). *Journal of Bacteriology* **64**, 883–886.

Yasuda-Yasuki, Y., Namiki-Kanie, S. and Hachisaka, Y. (1978). *In* "Spores VII" (G. Chambliss and J. C. Vary, eds), pp. 113–116. American Society for Microbiology, Washington D.C.

Young, M. (1976). *Journal of Bacteriology* **126**, 928–936.

7

Effect of Vapour Phase Bactericides on Bacterial Spores

I. *Introduction*

The previous chapter considered the effects of liquid phase antibacterial agents on bacterial spores. This chapter deals with vapour phase bactericides.

Although gases of one type or another have been employed for many years for the purpose of killing bacteria, we owe much of our present knowledge of gaseous sterilization to the early studies of Griffith and Hall (1938) and particularly to those of Phillips, Kaye and their associates. The publications of the latter group have led to an increased interest into the possible use of ethylene oxide as a means of sterilizing certain medical products. Subsequently, research has been directed towards assessing the value of other gases as sterilizing agents, and these will be discussed where appropriate.

A summary of the chemical and physical properties of the more important gaseous disinfectants is provided in Table 7.1, and their chemical structures are presented in Fig. 7.1.

Table 7.1. Properties of the most commonly used gaseous disinfectants

Gaseous disinfectant	Molecular weight	Boiling point (°C)	Solubility in water	Sterilizing concn (mg/l)	RH requirement (%)	Penetration of materials	Microbicidal activity[a]	Best application as gaseous disinfectant
Ethylene oxide	44	10·4	Complete	400–1000	Non-desiccated 30–50; large loads 60	Moderate	Moderate	Sterilization of plastic medical supplies
Propylene oxide	58	34	Good	800–2000	Non-desiccated 30–60	Fair	Fair	Decontamination
Formaldehyde	30	90°/Formalin[b]	Good	3–10	75	None (surface sterilant)	Excellent	Surface sterilant for rooms
β-Propiolactone	72	162	Moderate	2–5	>70	None (surface sterilant)	Excellent	Surface sterilant for rooms
Methyl bromide	95	4·6	Slight	3500	30–50	Excellent	Poor	Decontamination

[a] Based on an equimolar comparison.
[b] Formalin contains formaldehyde plus methanol.

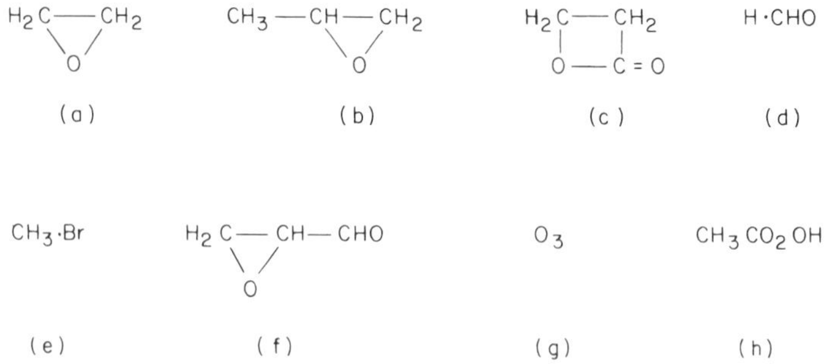

Fig. 7.1   Ethylene oxide and other gaseous disinfectants. (a) Ethylene oxide; (b) propylene oxide; (c) β-propiolactone; (d) formaldehyde; (e) methyl bromide; (f) glycidaldehyde; (g) ozone; (h) peracetic acid.

Because bacterial spores are more resistant to chemical and physical agents (Roberts and Hitchins, 1969; Russell, 1971), it is not surprising that most of the studies on gaseous bactericides have been directed towards their sporicidal activity. The destruction of spores by such agents has been the subject of several reviews, notably those by Phillips (1952, 1961, 1968, 1977, Bruch (1961a,b, 1973), Kelsey (1967), Kereluk and Lloyd (1969), Roberts and Hitchins (1969), Bruch and Bruch (1970), Hoffman (1971), Russell (1971), Ernst (1968, 1973, 1974) and Christensen and Kristensen (1981). Kereluk (1971) has dealth with lesser known gases, and Russell (1976) has discussed the inactivation of non-sporing bacteria by gaseous disinfectants.

II. *Types of Gaseous Bactericides*

A. Ethylene Oxide

1. *Properties*

Ethylene oxide (EO) exists normally as a gas, which is soluble in water, oils, rubber and most organic solvents. It is inflammable when in contact with air, but this inflammability can be overcome by using mixtures of EO with carbon dioxide (Phillips and Kaye, 1949) or with fluorocarbon compounds (Barwell and Freeman, 1959; Freeman and Barwell, 1960). The use of 100% EO has been reviewed by Alguire (1963). It is freely diffusible, and penetrates paper, cellophane, cardboard, fabrics and some plastics, e.g. polyvinyl chloride, but less rapidly through polythene. The rate of diffusion of various gases,

including EO, may be predicted from physical and chemical considerations (Opfell *et al.*, 1964). It cannot penetrate many solid materials,
particularly crystalline materials (this point is discussed more fully
later).

EO gas, but not liquid, has an irritant effect upon the skin. Both
cause smarting of the eyes, headaches, nausea and vomiting (Sutaria
and Williams, 1961).

2. *Antibacterial activity*

The most important of the earlier papers on ethylene oxide were those
published by Phillips (1949), Phillips and Kaye (1949), Kaye (1949,
1950), Kaye and Phillips (1949) and Kaye *et al.* (1952). The first paper
in this series (Phillips and Kaye, 1949) reviewed the work on ethylene
oxide up to 1949. The other papers were concerned with a reappraisal of
its antimicrobial activity, and with studies of the effect of time, temperature, concentration and relative humidity (RH) on its bactericidal
efficiency. Since these early studies, several other papers have considered these aspects, with the result that much is now known about the
factors which influence EO activity. Various articles in which several of
these points have been dealt with have been published by Phillips and
Warshowsky (1958), Thomas (1960), Bruch (1961a), Phillips (1961,
1968), Sutaria and Williams (1961), Russell (1965), Kelsey (1961,
1967), Ernst and Doyle (1968a,b), Doyle *et al.* (1970), Kereluk *et al.*
(1970a,b,c,d) and Ernst (1973, 1974, 1975, 1977).

Several factors influence the antibacterial activity of EO and these are
discussed below.

(a) **Concentration.** The concentration of the gas is expressed as milli-
grams per litre (mg/l). The "effective concentration" is the actual
amount of EO present in the sterilizer, and does not refer to the amount
of EO present in carbon dioxide.

As would be expected, the higher the concentration of EO, the more
rapid is the rate at which microorganisms are killed (Kereluk *et al.*,
1970c). This is also shown in Table 7.2, which is based on the results of
Phillips (1949) who evaluated the effect of EO on *B. globigii* spores
affixed to cotton cloth, for five different gas concentrations and three
different temperatures, for sufficient time to achieve sterilization at
various combinations. In this table, k is the reciprocal of the time
required to kill 90% of the spores. Thus, if N_0 represents the original
number of spores, and N the number viable at the end of time t, log
$N_0/N = Kt_{90\%}$ becomes $t_{90\%} = 1/k$. The death rate was found to be
logarithmic during the sterilization period so that k could be calculated

Table 7.2. Effect of concentration on the sporicidal activity of ethylene oxide[a,b]

Concentration of EO (mg/l)	1/k
22	7·2
44	3·3
88	1·6
442	0·5
884	0·35

[a] At 25°C against *B. globigii* spores dried on cloth.
[b] Based on the data of Phillips (1949).
   1/k is the time required (in hours) to kill 90% of the spores.

Table 7.3. Effect of temperature on the sporicidal activity of ethylene oxide against *B. subtilis*[a]

Spores on:	Temperature (°C)	D-value (min)
Paper discs[b]	40	14·7
	50	9·6
	60	2·8
	70	1·8
	80	0·7
Glass discs[b]	40	15·5
	50	9·9
	60	3·0
	70	2·0
	80	0·7

[a] Derived from the data of Liu *et al.* (1968).
[b] RH during sample exposure to EO . . . 33 ± 2%.

from the slope of the straight line produced when surviving fraction was plotted against time, or more simply the time could be read from the graph for the number of spores to fall by 90%. As the concentration of EO increased, $t_{90\%}$ decreased. However, the conclusion of Phillips that Ct_{90} values (concentration × time for 90% kill) are reasonably constant would appear to apply only to the range of EO concentrations of 22–884 mg/l and to temperatures of 5–37°C (Ernst and Shull, 1962a: see also Chapter 9).

(b) **Time of exposure.** As the concentration of EO increases, the time to kill spores and other bacteria decreases. This is clearly shown in Table 7.2, and as described above, Phillips (1949) has pointed out the reasonably constant figures of the Ct_{90} values. Table 7.3 indicates that at a given EO concentration, the time to kill depends on the temperature at which the spores are treated, an increase in temperature shortening the time for a 90% kill to be achieved, and on the relative humidity. The latter aspect is considered in greater detail later.

However, the results indicate that the gas is only slowly lethal to bacteria, e.g. in Table 7.2 it can be seen that even a high concentration of EO takes approximately 20 min to kill 90%, i.e. to reduce the viable numbers by one log cycle, of *B. globigii* spores at 25°C. This slow rate of kill is an obvious disadvantage of the gas, and is one which is taken into account in assessing suitable conditions whereby sterilization of certain equipment may be achieved.

(c) **Temperature.** With *B. globigii* spores, EO has a temperature co-efficient of 2·74 for each 10°C rise in temperature (Phillips, 1949). Thus, an increase in temperature considerably reduces the time necessary to achieve a specified degree of kill. The British Pharmacopoeia (1980) recommends that EO may be used as one of four methods for sterilizing powders, and stipulates that the temperature during treatment be 60°C. The sporicidal activity of the gas will thus be increased even further under such conditions, so decreasing the period necessary for sterilization to be complete. Perkins and Lloyd (1961), in their studies, recommended a temperature of 54°C. When tested by the Association of Official Agricultural Chemists (A.O.A.C.) sporicide test, EO was sporicidal to various *Bacillus* and *Clostridium* spp. at 20°C (Friedl *et al.*, 1956).

(d) **Type of organism.** Griffith and Hall (1938) patented the use of EO as a means of killing bacteria and their spores, moulds, yeasts and their spores. In contrast to various disinfectants which may be several thousand-fold more active against vegetative cells than they are against spores, the resistance of spores to EO may be only twice (Toth, 1959), and certainly not more than five to ten times (Phillips, 1968) that of vegetative bacteria. Spores of *B. stearothermophilus* were found by Freeman and Barwell (1960) to be less resistant than some vegetative bacteria, and although *B. subtilis* spores were the most resistant, sterilization was still achieved within 4 h. A similar resistance to spore of organisms such as *Staph. aureus* (Thomas *et al.*, 1959) or *M. radiodurans* or *Strep. faecalis* (Kereluk *et al.*, 1970b) has also been noted. The recent paper by Dadd and Daley (1980) should be consulted for its broad comparison of EO sensitivity of various species of sporing and non-sporing organisms.

(e) **Type of sterilizer.** The type of EO sterilizer may sometimes influence the degree of bacterial inactivation. Walter and Kundsin

(1959) described experiments with a table model sterilizer, and found that sterility, in terms of killing of the test spores (*B. subtilis* and *Cl. sporogenes* spores), did not invariably result when the manufacturer's directions were followed. Similar findings with unnamed *Bacillus* were reported by Taguchi *et al*. (1963). Beeby and Whitehouse (1965) tested *B. subtilis* spores in an EO laboratory apparatus and in a commercial EO sterilizer. Spores dried from saline could not be killed in either apparatus, and spores dried from serum and from nutrient broth showed differing responses in the machine and laboratory apparatus.

These results demonstrate that caution may sometimes be needed in assessing the findings obtained by different workers using different types of apparatus, although present-day equipment is generally of a much higher standard than that used in the earlier years.

(f) **Relative Humidity (RH).** The initial studies on the effects of RH on EO activity against *B. globigii* spores were made by Kaye and Phillips (1949), who showed that EO was more bactericidal in relatively dry air than in an atmosphere of higher RH. However, when EO was allowed to act upon these spores in highly evacuated systems from which almost all the air and moisture had been removed before the admission of EO vapour, sterilization became more difficult (Schley *et al*., 1960). At 28% RH the action of the gas was about four times as rapid as at 65% RH and about ten times as rapid as at 97% RH. The optimum RH is considered to be about 28–33% (Phillips, 1961, 1968, 1977; Rubbo and Gardner, 1965). The creation of a vacuum before admission of EO to the sterilization chamber could cause marked desiccation of any contaminating organisms, and pre-humidification of the chamber is necessary (Halowell *et al*., 1958; Ernst and Shull, 1962b).

However, this RH effect is more complex than appears at first sight, and a considerable amount of data has accumulated as a result of the efforts of Phillips and his colleagues (Phillips, 1961; Gilbert *et al*., 1964), Perkins and Lloyd (1961) and Mayr (1961). The findings of Phillips (1961) are of particular interest in this respect, and his results, which he presented in graphical form, are summarized in Table 7.4. Further results along these lines have been published by Gilbert *et al*. (1964) and Kereluk *et al*. (1970c). The moisture content of microorganisms varies with the RH of the atmosphere and the conditions prevailing at the time of sterilization. *Bacillis globigii* spores dehydrated beyond a critical point no longer react uniformly to EO sterilization, a small percentage of resistant cells being obtained, even when the actual EO exposure is carried out at 33%. Gilbert *et al*. (1964) also found that, to overcome this resistance to EO produced by dehydration, the cells must

Table 7.4. Effect of relative humidity (RH) on the sporicidal activity of ethylene oxide[a,b]

% RH dried	% RH conditioned	% RH exposed	Approx. time (h) for sterility (IF of 10^8)	Shape of time–survivor curve
33	33	33	7	Linear
50	50	50	11	Linear
75	75	75	16	Linear
98	98	98	16	Linear
33	33	33	7	Linear
22	22	22	Not sterilized	Non-linear
11	11	11	Not sterilized	Non-linear
<1	<1	<1	Not sterilized	Non-linear
33		33	7	Linear
1 for 1 h		33	Not sterilized	Non-linear
1 for 4 h		33	Not sterilized	Non-linear
1 for 24 h		33	Not sterilized	Non-linear
33	33	33	7	Linear
1	33	33	Not sterilized	Non-linear
1	1 for 12 h	33	Not sterilized	Non-linear
1	1 for 12 h	33	Not sterilized	Non-linear

[a] Concentration 120 mg/l, at 25°C, against *B. globigii* spores on cotton patches.
[b] From the data of Phillips (1961).

be actually wetted, and that merely equilibrating to a high RH (*ca.* 75–98%) requires 4–6 days to break the effect. This is probably due to the fact that there is less water in bacterial cells that have been desiccated and then equilibrated to successively high RH values (up to 100%) than in cells which have not been desiccated, but instead allowed to dry naturally until equilibrated to the same RH values. Perkins and Lloyd (1961) have also shown that the "normal" humidification of a sterilizing chamber to a RH of 20–40% at 54°C is not sufficient to render organisms on surfaces of a solid nature, e.g. glass or metal, susceptible to EO, whereas during a "dwell" period of 60 min at an RH of 55–60%, following the introduction of moisture into the chamber, the surfaces would adsorb sufficient moisture to render the contaminants susceptible to EO. The moisture content (a_w) of the atmosphere surrounding the organisms (the "microenvironment") is more important in determining spore resistance than is the overall RH (Kereluk *et al.*, 1970c).

A reverse effect of RH on the lethal activity of EO on spores in dry earth was noted by Mayr (1961), e.g. at 90%, the lethal effect took 2 h; at 60%, 4 h; and at 30%, 9 h. According to Mayr's hypothesis, when the atmosphere has a high RH, the spore membrane swells and becomes permeable to EO, this "pre-moistening" or " acclimitization" thus reducing the exposure time. Whitbourne and Reich (1979) have demonstrated that spores or other bacteria dried on to filter paper carriers are more resistant to EO at low RH values.

Winge-Heden (1963) found that freshly prepared test "slips" of *B. brevis, Staph. aureus* and *Strep. faecalis* are considerably easier to sterilize than "slips" which have been stored dry for a period of time; the latter probably represents the desiccation effect of Phillips described above. Complete sterility was obtained if the test "slips" were kept in open dishes during the sterilization or moistened prior to sterilization.

Ernst (1973, 1974, 1975, 1977) has explained the paradoxical RH effects by characterizing spores with respect to their immediate environment and relative moisture content.

(g) **Condition of the organism.** By this is meant the influence of various drying conditions, of supporting surfaces and of powders, and of the use of aerosols, in determining the sensitivity of spores to EO.

Thus, those factors which affect the sensitivity of bacterial spores to EO gas are:

(i) *Spores in aerosol form.* Kaye (1949) determined the effect of EO and other gases on the viability of bacterial aerosols, consisting of *B. globigii* spores, and found that aerosols were disinfected 1·5 times more rapidly than the same organisms on cloth. This finding would be expected, as in the aerosol form the spores are freely exposed to the gas as compared to organisms partially protected by resting against a solid object.

(ii) *Drying of spores from various media.* Organisms dried from salt solutions are more difficult to sterilize than those dried from water (Kaye and Phillips, 1949). Royce and Bowler (1961) found that with *B. subtilis* spores in saline, wet films were readily sterilized, whereas dry films showed about 1% survivors after treatment with EO. *Bacillus subtilis* spores dried from broth are more resistant to EO than those dried from water (Gilbert *et al.*, 1964). Beeby and Whitehouse (1965) examined the possible uses of aluminium foil strips carrying various numbers of spores of *B. subtilis* (camp Detrick strain) dried from water, 90% v/v methanol, 5 and 20% serum, nutrient broth and isotonic saline, as test pieces for the control of EO sterilization. Spores dried from water or methanol were more susceptible than those dried from saline, serum or broth; those dried from saline could not be killed by EO.

Perkins and Lloyd (1961) were unable to sterilize porous surfaces contaminated with more than 10^5 spores per 0·15 ml of *Cl. sporogenes* when the spores were produced in a pork infusion medium, but sterilization was achieved with 10^6–10^7 spores of this organism obtained from a synthetic medium and dried on solid surfaces.

Drying itself renders spores more resistant; wet films from *B. subtilis* and *Cl. sporogenes* are readily sterilized, whereas dried spores are not (Royce and Bowler, 1961; Friedl *et al.*, 1956).

(iii) *Surface on which spores are dried.* Opfell *et al.* (1959) used *B. globigii* ATCC 9372 dried on several types of surfaces, and then exposed to EO. Significant effects were produced by the presence of the hygroscopic materials, glycerin and filter paper; the absence of hygroscopic substances appeared to increase the resistance of the spores to the gas. *Bacillus brevis* spores dried on aluminium foil are far more resistant to EO than spores dried on filter paper (Winge-Heden, 1963) and sterilization of *B. subtilis* spores is more difficult to achieve on impervious substances, such as glass, than on cotton cloth or Whatman No. 5 filter paper (Gilbert *et al.*, 1964). This effect of impermeable surfaces can be partially overcome by increasing the RH at which the organisms were dried and exposed to EO, e.g. on glass, spores dried and conditioned at 33% RH and exposed to EO gas at 33% RH were not sterilized after 24 h (IF = 10^6), whereas dried and conditioned at 75% RH and exposed at 50% RH the spores were sterilized after 12 h (IF = 10^8) (Gilbert *et al.*, 1964). A similar finding has been made by Perkins and Lloyd (1961) who describe the necessity of a "dwell" period of 60 min following the introduction of moisture into the sterilizing chamber. Bacterial spores or non-sporing organisms dried on hygroscopic surfaces are less resistant than those on non-hygroscopic ones (Kereluk *et al.*, 1970b).

(iv) *Presence of powders and crystals.* The most important early findings here were made by Abbott *et al.* (1956), Royce (1959) and Royce and Bowler (1959, 1961). In the experiments of Abbott *et al.*, sterile powders and crystals of Rochelle salt dusted with freeze-dried spores, crystals grown from contaminated liquor and powder crystallized from contaminated liquor were all exposed to EO gas. The maximum period of exposure to EO was insufficient to sterilize surface-contaminated material, but there was a reduction in the viable count. With the large crystals and the crystalline powder prepared from contaminated mother liquors, the number of viable spores remained quite high. Royce (1959) and Royce and Bowler (1961) contaminated glucose monohydrate with an aqueous suspension of *B. subtilis* spores, and air-dried the mixture, which was then further dried to remove most of the water of crystallization. Some of the anhydrous material was partly rehydrated with 5% water, and some more than fully rehydrated by adding 12% water. The various products were then exposed to EO gas, and the results demonstrated that organisms included in the crystals were protected from EO action. These and other findings led Royce and Bowler (1961) to state that if organisms were enclosed within crystals of insoluble materials, no equilibration at any RH would effect them and they remained unsterilizable. EO cannot penetrate crystalline materials (Opfell and Miller, 1965; Hess *et al.*, (1973). However, Ernst (1977) has stated that bacteria occluded in crystals do not, in fact, pose the severe problems once attributed to them, and that sodium chloride-occluded spores will be killed by EO at elevated temperatures and relatively high RH. Apparently, the crystals of sodium chloride dissolve and subsequently re-form, but this allows sufficient time of exposure for destruction of the spores.

(h) **Conclusions.** The factors which have been described indicate that the sterilizing efficiency of EO depends on time, temperature of treatment and concentration of the gas. These are obviously important factors, but need not be considered further here, since they would, from the wealth of data available on disinfection, be expected to influence the sporicidal and bactericidal activity of the gas. The outstanding discoveries, therefore, concern the effect of RH, the medium from which the organisms have been dried, and the surface on to which they are dried. Organisms dried on to hard surfaces are more difficult to sterilize than those on absorbent surfaces. Powders, too, can influence the lethal activity of the gas, and whereas within soluble substances, washing with water can liberate "protected" organisms, in the case of slightly soluble substances washing can "convert a surface contamination, which could be eliminated by EO, into an internal one that cannot" (Royce and Bowler, 1961). This is no longer, however, the insuperable problem that once appeared likely (Ernst, 1974, 1977).

3. Mode of action

EO is an alkylating agent, and it has been proposed (Phillips, 1949, 1952, 1961, 1977; Kelsey, 1967; Bruch and Bruch, 1970; Hoffman, 1971) that it inactivates bacteria or their spores by combining with the amino, carboxyl, sulphydryl and hydroxyl groups of proteins (Fig. 7.2). The general activity of similar substances parallels their activity as alkylating agents (Fig. 7.3). Thus, cyclopropane and 1,4-dioxane (which are not alkylating agents) have no bactericidal activity, EO and ethylene sulphide have the same activity, and epichlorohydrin and ethylene imine possess greater activity than EO. Alkylation is itself defined (Price, 1958) as the conversion:

$$H–X \rightarrow R–X$$

where R is an alkyl group. The biological activity of the alkylating

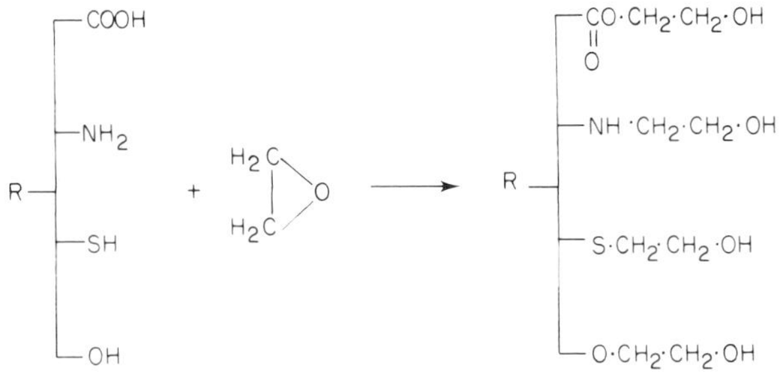

Fig. 7.2   Interaction of ethylene oxide with protein groups.

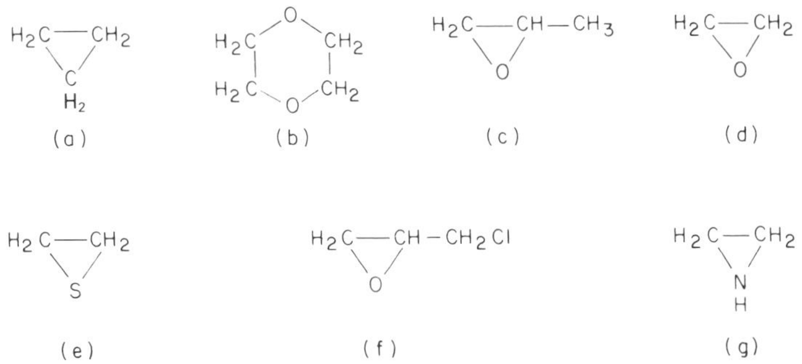

Fig. 7.3   Ethylene oxide and related substances: their antibacterial activity relative to that of ethylene oxide.
No bactericidal activity: (a) Cyclopropane, (b) 1,4-Dioxane. *Less bactericidal activity:* (c) Propylene oxide. *Equal bactericidal activity:* (d) Ethylene oxide, (e) Ethylene sulphide. *Greater bactericidal activity:* (f) Epichlorohydrin, (g) Ethylene imine.

agents is indicated by reaction with nucleophilic groups (Stacey, *et al.*, 1958; Smith and Spencer, 1975).

It has frequently been observed that bacterial spores are only a few times more resistant than non-sporulating bacteria to EO (Kaye and Phillips, 1949; Toth, 1959; Blake and Stumbo, 1970; Russell, 1971, 1976; Phillips, 1977) in contrast to liquid disinfectants where the difference in resistance may be several thousand-fold (Roberts and Hitchins, 1969; Russell, 1971). This appears to be a general property of the alkylating agents.

The effect of RH on the bactericidal activity of EO has been explained in terms that alkylation is prevented when insufficient water is present, whereas too much water causes hydrolysis of EO to ethylene glycol (Kelsey, 1967), which is considerably less active than EO (Wilson and Bruno, 1950). Thus, the bactericidal action of EO is not due to its conversion, on contact with water, to ethylene glycol. Thomas

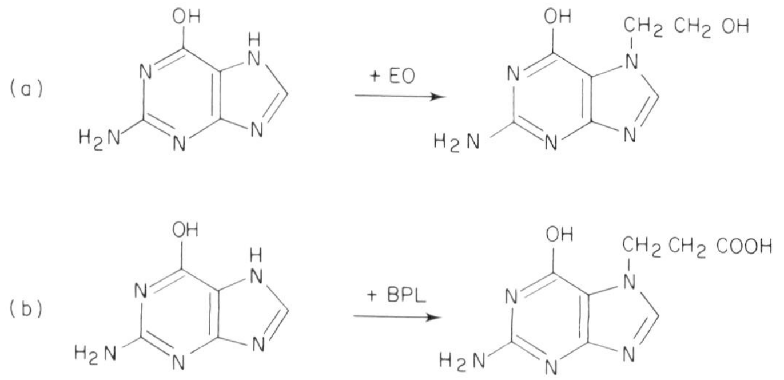

Fig. 7.4   Interaction with guanine of (a) ethylene oxide, (b) β-propiolactone.

(1959) pointed out that EO would react with many substances of biological importance, including amino acids, proteins and nucleoproteins, even under mild conditions, and thus concluded that EO would cause a general disruption of biological processes.

Research in biological systems other than bacteria has described interaction of epoxides (including EO) with proteins and amino acids (Ross, 1958). EO causes hydroxyethylation of amino acids (Starbuck and Busch, 1963) and also interacts with nucleic acids, e.g. with the phosphate group to form a triester (Alexander and Stacey, 1958) and with guanine to produce 7-(2'-hydroxyethyl) guanine (Fig. 7.4; Brooks and Lawley, 1964). Alkylating agents have a principal site of interaction at N–7 of guanine moieties in DNA, the second most reactive site being at N–3 of adenine moieties (Brooks and Lawley, 1964). EO gas hydroxyethylates tertiary heterocyclic N atoms in adenosine and adenosine triphosphate (Windemueller and Kaplan, 1961) and EO reacts almost exclusively with guanine residues of RNA from tobacco mosaic virus (Fraenkel-Conrat, 1961).

The significance of these findings in relation to the mechanism of the sporicidal and bactericidal actions of EO has yet to be fully realized, although studies with *Salmonella senftenberg* and *Escherichia coli* have suggested that alkalyation by EO of phosphated guanine is primarily responsible for the lethal effect of the gas (Michael and Stumbo, 1970). Differences in response of bacteria to alkylating agents may be the result of variations in enzymatic DNA repair processes that allow recovery of damaged cells (Lawley and Brooks, 1963). *Bacillus subtilis* spores exposed to EO release considerably greater quantities of DNA, RNA, protein and dipicolinic acid (DPA) than untreated spores, and pre-treatment of spores with thioglycollic acid plus urea alters their response to EO (Marletta and Stumbo, 1970), suggesting that the spore coat plays a part in resistance (Fig 6.6, p. 218). Sublethal concentrations of EO inhibit outgrowth, but not germinaton, of spores (Reich, 1980).

Bruch (1961) considered that the radiomimetic properties (i.e. those resembling ionizing radiations in their biological effects) of alkylating agents accounted for their high microbicidal activity, and that such agents were mutagenic, in that they damaged the cytoplasm and nuclei of rapidly growing cells and caused injury to the chromosomal mechanism of dividing cells. Liquid sulphur mustard, a known alkylating agent with a mutagenic effect, induces abnormal colony formation in bacteria exposed to it (Gilbert *et al.*, 1964). However, mutations do not occur with EO-treated tobacco mosaic virus (Fraenkel-Conrat, 1961) or with EO-treated bacteria or their spores (Gilbert *et al.*, 1964; Hoffman, 1971; Savage and Stumbo, 1971; see also Bruch and Bruch, 1970), although a consequence of N–7 alkylation of purines could be anomalous base pairing leading to mutation and ultimately defective proteins and thereby cell death (Roxon, 1973).

The reaction(s) responsible for the death of EO-treated spores and non-sporulating bacteria thus cannot be stated with any degree of certainty. Death could result from a general poisoning of the cell involving alkylation of nucleic acid and/or proteins, or from a single reaction with a vital site in the DNA or RNA molecule (Hoffman, 1971). Bacterial spores with defective coats are not less resistant to EO than are "normal" spores (Dadd and Daley, 1980): cf. above and Fig. 6.6 (p. 218).

4. Indicators for ethylene oxide sterilization

Since bacterial spores are somewhat more resistant to EO than vegetative bacteria, it is evident that logically the former would be used as indicators for sterilization by this gas. The exposure of various organisms to EO showed that *B. subtilis* var. *niger* (*B. globigii*) was probably the most resistant, and it was generally assumed that this organism would then be used as a test for adequate sterilization (Kelsey, 1961). Kelsey (1961) also stated that all that could at that time be usefully said was that the presentation of spores should resemble the load to be sterilized, e.g. contaminated plastic surfaces as a test for disposable items. Later, *B. subtilis* strain Camp Derrick (NCTC 10073; formerly *B. glogibii*), a pigmented strain, was shown to be convenient to use and to present a reasonable challenge to EO. It is obviously unrealistic to present too severe a challenge to EO gas (Beeby and Whitehouse, 1965). There are, in fact, several types of *Bacillus* species, the spores of which are more resistant to EO (Dadd and Daley, 1980).

Spores of strain NCTC 10073 survive well in 90% methanol, and also when dried from this on to aluminium foil, and show little variation in resistance to EO over a period of several months (Beeby and White-house, 1965). Because of the various parameters that affect EO ster-ilization (Macek, 1973) a suitable biological indicator (BI) must be chosen with care. Spores of *B. brevis* and vegetative cells of *Staph. aureus* and *Strep. faecalis* are more resistant to EO when dried on aluminium foil than when dried on to filter paper (Winge-Heden, 1963) and may thus be considered a more suitable means of testing the sterilization process. *Bacillus subtilis* spores dried from saline are almost, if not entirely, impossible to sterilize (Royce and Bowler, 1961; Beeby and Whitehouse, 1965; see earlier, also, and Ernst, 1973), and aluminium foils containing such spores cannot be used as a test piece (Beeby and Whitehouse, 1965). Spores of this organism dried on to aluminium foil from a 90% methanol suspension are considered to be a suitable method for testing an EO sterilization process (Beeby and Whitehouse, 1965).

Whitbourne and Reich (1979) have demonstrated the need for a precisely defined, industrially accepted testing protocol. Gillis *et al.* (1976) have compared BIs from various manufacturers and have sug-gested survival and lethal times for various concentrations of EO at an RH of 65 ($\pm$15)% and a temperature of 55°C (Table 7.5; see also Reich, 1980; Myers *et al.*, 1981).

Table 7.5. *B. subtilis* var. *globigii* as a biological indicator for ethylene oxide[a]

Concn (mg/l) of ethylene oxide[b]	Survivors[c] after exposure for (min)	No survivors[c] after exposure for (min)
300 ± 50	20	50
600 ± 50	15	45
900 ± 50	7·5	30

[a] Derived from data of Gillis *et al.* (1976).
[b] Relative humidity 65 ± 15%; temperature 55°C.
[c] Initial numbers of spores per test piece ranged from $5·9 \times 10^5$ to $2·1 \times 10^6$.

The recovery and revival of spores damaged but not killed by EO is a factor that must be considered in designing a test for any BI. This aspect is discussed more fully in Chapter 10.

5. *Uses of ethylene oxide*

This section would on EO not be complete without a brief description of its industrial uses. Suitable employment of EO as an industrial ster-ilization method have been described in a comprehensive paper by Ernst (1973).

EO has been used to sterilize the following products:

(i) · Various ophthalmic instruments, without damage to such equipment (Skeehan *et al.*, 1956). Tests were made against bacterial spores and *Ps. aeruginosa*.

(ii) Anaesthetic equipment (Snow *et al.*, 1962). Tests were carried out against *B. subtilis, Cl. sporogenes, Staph. aureus* and *Ps. aeruginosa*.

(iii) Heart–lung machines (Bracken *et al.*, 1960). *B. stearothermophilus* was used as test organism.

(iv) Sterilization of penicillin and streptomycin (Kaye *et al.*, 1952). Penicillin could be sterilized by exposure of the dry powder to EO vapour, or by adding EO to solutions of the antibiotic. No loss of potency or increase in toxicity occurred. With streptomycin–calcium chloride, there was no increase in toxicity, but a 35% loss of potency, when this antibiotic was treated with EO vapour. The killing of *B. subtilis* spores and *E. coli* was used as an indication of sterilization.

(v) Disposable syringes. Here, the paper of Rubbo and Gardner (1968) must be borne in mind. In this it was shown, with *B. globigii* as test organism, that the rate of failure in sterilization was related to syringe design, as well as to the number of spores initially present.

(vi) Hospital blankets. Kaye (1950) showed that hospital blankets and linens were completely sterilized by EO. *Bacillus globigii* was used as test organism.

(vii) Microbial culture media. Hansen and Snyder (1947) showed that, following EO sterilization, microbial culture media supported growth of bacteria.

In addition to the sterilization uses listed, EO has also been recommended as a decontamination procedure for articles handled by tuberculous patients.

B. β-Propiolactone

1. *Properties*

β-Propiolactone (BPL) exists as a colourless liquid at room temperature (Table 7.1). It boils at 163°C and is vaporized in a special atomizer, it is non-inflammable, its penetrating powers are low and it has been stated to be carcinogenic (Kelsey, 1967). It hydrolyses readily in water to form hydracrylic acid (β-hydroxypropionic acid), the rate of hydrolysis increasing with an increase in temperature (Hoffman and Warshowsky,

1958). The half-life of a 1% aqueous solution is 3–4 h at room temperature. BPL is soluble in water to the extent of 37% by volume at 25°C.

2. *Antibacterial activity*

BPL exerts a strong bactericidal action on surfaces of objects immersed in aqueous solutions of it, or exposed to its vapour phase (Allen and Murphy, 1960). Its antimicrobial activity is a direct function of its concentration and the temperatures and the RH at which it is used (Spiner and Hoffman, 1960). Of bacteria, viruses and fungi, bacterial spores are the most resistant to BPL solutions (Trafas *et al.*, 1954; LoGrippo *et al.*, 1955; Hazeu and Bueck, 1965), although spores are only some 4–5 times more resistant to BPL vapour than are some strains of *Staph. aureus* (Hoffman and Warshowsky, 1958; Allen and Murphy, 1960; Hoffman, 1971).

Under suitable conditions, BPL rapidly kills bacterial spores (Curran and Evans, 1956), and the majority of spores of *B. subtilis* were found to be more resistant to BPL than those of *Cl. botulinum* and *B. stearothermophilus* strain 1518 (Curran and Evans, 1956). The death rate of various organisms, for a 99% plus destruction to occur, is essentially linear, although Curran and Evans (1956) used BPL in water, milk and nutrient broth and found that a period of contact beyond 2 h had little influence on the final result, as by this time hydrolysis of BPL was practically complete. They also noted, however, that a small proportion of certain spore populations was more resistant than the majority, and survived low or medium concentrations of the drug, whereas relatively high concentrations of BPL rapidly sterilized nutrient broth containing 10^6 spores/ml.

At constant temperature and RH, the time required to kill bacteria depends on the concentration of BPL. The sporicidal activity of BPL vapour and liquid increases with increasing temperature. For optimum activity of BPL vapour, the temperature must be kept above 24°C (Spiner and Hoffman, 1960). For each 10°C change in temperature in the range of -10 to $+25$°C, the temperature coefficient for BPL-treated spores is 2–3 (Hoffman and Warshowsky, 1958).

Important though these factors are, however, the single most important property determine bacterial response to BPL vapour is RH. For optimum activity of BPL vapour, the RH should be kept above 70–75% (Hoffman and Warshowsky, 1958; Spiner and Hoffman, 1960; Hoffman, 1968, 1971) as a high RH is required for rapid sporicidal activity. The activity of BPL against *B. globigii* spores is much less at 60% than at 75%, and at 50% RH there is only a 90% kill after 6 h exposure of the spores (Hoffman and Warshowsky, 1958). Moreover, the shape of the time–survivor curve changes from a straight line response at RH values of 75% and above to a non-linear graph at 60% and below. It is not necessarily the atmospheric RH which is the important factor in BPL sterilization, however, but the moisture content and location of water in the bacterial cell. *Bacillus globigii* spores equilibrated to 98% RH are readily killed by BPL at an RH of 45% to which the spores are not normally susceptible; however, only 99% of spores equilibrated to 75% RH are killed by BPL at 45% RH, and a small percentage of spores pre-conditioned at 1% RH are thereafter very resistant to BPL at 75% RH (Hoffman, 1968).

3. *Mode of action of β-propiolactone*

BPL is a highly reactive chemical, although it owes this reactivity to the highly strained structure of the β-lactone rather than to the presence of an unsaturated bond in the lactone ring (Dickens, 1964). It reacts with various cellular groups and is considered (Hoffman and Warshowsky, 1958; Hoffman, 1971; Phillips, 1977) to be an alkylating agent which combines with $-NH_2$, $-COOH$, $-OH$ and $-SH$ groups, although it is far from clear which (if any) such reaction is responsible for inactivation of bacteria and their spores. It reacts *in vitro* with guanosine, deoxyguanylic acid and RNA (Roberts and Warwick, 1963) and with the N–7 guanine position (Fig. 7.4) in nucleic acids extracted from BPL-treated *E. coli* (Ichikawa *et al.*, 1967; cited by Hoffman, 1971) and in DNA *in vitro* (Troll *et al.*, 1969).

BPL causes no increase in the irreversibility of the heat denaturation of calf thymus DNA *in vitro*, but brings about a much higher degree of guanine alkylation than propylene oxide (Walles, 1974). The former finding is indicative of a lack of single-strand DNA breaks and suggests that BPL does not alkylate the phosphate groups of DNA, since phosphate alkylation induce breaks more rapidly than base alkylation (Rhaese and Freese, 1969).

Unlike EO and propylene oxide (cf. below also) BPL induces mutations in non-sporulating bacteria (Iyer and Szybalski, 1958). Although the reaction between BPL and guanine might prove to occur less readily than that between BPL and $-SH$ groups in protein, it might provide a mechanism for its interference with nucleic acid metabolism (Dickens, 1964) in vegetative bacteria and thus with the genetic material of the cell, since BPL is known to be carcinogenic (Walpole *et al.*, 1954).

The reasons for the sporicidal activity of BPL are even less apparent.

C. **Propylene Oxide**

1. *Properties*

Propylene oxide (PO) has a boiling point above room temperature (Table 7.1) and so is not readily dispersed or removed; it is usual to raise the temperature to assist volatilization (Sykes, 1965). PO hydrolyzes to the non-toxic propylene glycol, and unlike EO is allowed to be used in the foodstuff industry. Nevertheless, recent studies (Rosenkranz *et al.*, 1975) have shown that non-volatile residual chloropropanols (1-chloro-2-propanol and 2-chloro-1-propanol) are mutagenic, and possibly carcinogenic also.

2. *Antibacterial activity*

Bruch (1961a), in a review of gaseous sterilizing agents, reported that PO was less microbicidal than EO. Bruch and Koesterer (1961) studied the effect of PO on spore strips of *B. globigii* under different conditions of temperature and RH, and in the presence and absence of food (cereal). Their results demonstrate that the time required for a 90% kill decreases as the concentration of PO gas increases; if the concentration of gas is doubled, the time for a 90% kill is approximately halved. The presence of food in the sterilizing system can alter the time/concentration values for the destruction of the spores by PO; an increase in RH reduces the lethal efficiency of PO against the spores.

The reverse effect of RH on the activity of PO against a wide range of non-sporing and sporing bacteria has been observed by Himmelfarb *et al.* (1962). Of the organisms which they tested, *B. subtilis* spores were the most resistant, whereas *B. stearothermophilus* spores were less resistant than certain non-sporing organisms. Himmelfarb *et al.* (1962) desiccated their samples prior to admitting water vapour, so that a similar type of effect could be obtained to that observed with EO (Phillips, 1961, 1977; Gilbert *et al.*, 1964).

3. *Mode of action of propylene oxide*

There have been no significant studies at the molecular level on the effects of PO on sporing and non-sporing bacteria. It is generally believed, however, to act as an alkylating agent in a similar manner to EO (Hoffman, 1971; Kereluk, 1971; Lawley and Jarman, 1972). PO causes an increased irreversibility of heat denaturation, the extent of which depends on the degree of alkylation. This is indicative of single-strand DNA breaks caused predominantly by phosphate alkylation, breaks caused by guanine alkylation also occurring but at a slower rate (Rhaese and Freese, 1969).

D. **Formaldehyde (methanal)**

1. *Properties*

Formaldehyde is a gas at ordinary temperatures, and has a pungent smell. Commercially, it is employed as a 40% aqueous solution (formalin). Formaldehyde shows a remarkable tendency to polymerize. The vapour may be obtained by evaporating appropriate dilutions of standardized batches of commercial formalin, i.e. a 40% solution of formaldehyde in water with 10% methanol added to prevent polymerization from taking place (Report, 1958).

2. *Antibacterial activity*

Bacterial spores and non-sporulating bacteria are fairly readily killed by formaldehyde gas (Sykes, 1965), the degree of resistance being only some 2–3 times (Report, 1958) or 2–15 times (Phillips, 1952) that of non-sporing bacteria.

There is a linear relationship between the concentration of formaldehyde and the killing rate (Report, 1958), but little effect on disinfection rate from variation in temperature over the range 0–30°C has been observed (Report, 1958). However, Nordgren (1939) noted that the rate of disinfection of spores exposed to formaldehyde vapour increased as the temperature was increased in the range 10–70°C. The addition of formaldehyde vapour to steam under subatmospheric pressure at temperatures below 90°C greatly increases the sporicidal activity of the steam (Devrill and Cripps, 1981), with deep penetration into fabrics (Alder *et al.*, 1966; Alder and Simpson, 1982). Organic matter as blood, sputum or soil reduces the rate of formaldehyde-induced bacterial inactivation (Nordgren, 1939). As is the case with ethylene oxide, spores are protected from formaldehyde by their inclusion within a crystal mass (Abbott *et al.*, 1956).

As with other vapour phase disinfectants, the antibacterial activity of formaldehyde depends on RH. Various RH levels for optimum activity of formaldehyde have been proposed. An optimum RH of 80–90% but with no great increase in disinfection rate above 58% has been mentioned (Report, 1958; Baird-Parker and Holbrook, 1971). A somewhat similar conclusion was reached by Nordgren (1939) who observed an increase in the rate of kill as the RH was raised to 50% but little increase thereafter. According to Spaulding *et al.* (1977), however, there is no bactericidal effect of formaldehyde unless the RH is 70% or above. Rather confusingly, Hoffman (1971) has reported that formaldehyde is quite effective even at RH values below 50%, and that formaldehyde generated from paraformaldehyde (see below) was more active than an equivalent amount generated from formalin solution. Increasing the RH causes an increasing adsorption of formaldehyde on to surfaces (Braswell *et al.*, 1970).

Although paraformaldehyde was originally considered to be of little practical use because of its slow volatilization (Nordgren, 1939) this is no longer a valid opinion. Paraformaldehyde, a polymer of formaldehyde with the formula $HO.(CH_2)_n.H$, where $n = 8$–100, is a flake or a fine or coarse powder and is produced by evaporating aqueous solutions of formaldehyde. When heated, paraformaldehyde depolymerizes rapidly to give formaldehyde, and this is the basis of the process used by C. Kaitz (cited by Taylor *et al.*, 1969) for disseminating formaldehyde gas.

More recently, an interesting paper by Tulis (1973) has drawn attention to the fact that certain organic resins and polymers, when exposed to elevated temperatures, release potentially sterilizing amounts of gaseous formaldehyde. This evolution of formaldehyde is such that the rate of release is a function of time and temperature. Examples of such products are melamine formaldehyde and urea formaldehyde products (a mixture of mono-methylol urea and di-methylol urea). Paraformaldehyde-produced formaldehyde gas is lethal to spores and other bacteria (Taylor *et al.*, 1969; Tulis, 1973) and is considerably more effective as a sporicidal agent than the formaldehyde-releasing resins. The inactivation process is strictly a function of the available formaldehyde gas, and at various temperatures the percentage loss of formaldehyde from paraformaldehyde is much greater than from the resins (Tulis, 1973).

3. Mechanism of action

The mechanism of action of liquid formaldehyde has been discussed in Chapter 6 (Section IV.E). Since formaldehyde vapour is likely to act in a similar or identical manner, it will not be considered further.

4. Uses

A comprehensive discussion on the uses of formaldehyde vapour is outside the scope of this book. Briefly, it is used in combination with water vapour in the sterilization of heat-sensitive medical devices and supplies (Christensen and Kristensen, 1982).

E. Others

1. *Methyl bromide*

Methyl bromide kills sporing and non-sporing bacteria, but is considerably less active than EO (see Table 7.1; Kolb and Schneiter, 1950; Kelsey, 1967; Bruch and Bruch, 1970; Kereluk, 1971) or even PO (Kelsey, 1967). *Bacillus subtilis* spores in the dry state are, however, completely resistant to methyl bromide (Harry *et al.*, 1972).

Mixtures of EO and methyl bromide may be more effective than each single agent acting alone (Kereluk, 1971).

There is very little information as to its mechanism of sporicidal and bactericidal action, although Phillips (1977) considers that it is likely to act as an alkylating agent.

2. *Ozone*

Ozone has bactericidal and sporicidal properties (Hoffman, 1971; Russell, 1976). However, it is unstable, toxic and corrosive and thus finds little application as a gaseous disinfectant (Hoffman, 1971).

3. *Hydrochloric acid*

It has recently been shown (Tuynenburg Muys *et al.*, 1978) that hydrogen chloride (hydrochloric acid gas) is an effective sterilizing agent at ambient temperatures. A detailed examination of the parameters that influence its sporicidal activity has been conducted by Lelieveld and van Eljk (1979). Further investigations are undoubtedly necessary, but this gas might well have important industrial applications.

Gaseous hydrogen chloride inactivates spores, which collapse possibly by the rupture of disulphide bonds and the neutralization of carboxyl groups in cortex peptidoglycan (Lelieveld, 1980).

4. *Peracetic acid vapour*

Peracetic acid is used mainly in the liquid form (Jones *et al.*, 1967). It is, however, sporicidal when used in the vapour phase, with an optimum activity at 80% RH (Portner and Hoffman, 1968; Hoffman, 1971).

References

Abbott, C. F., Cockton, J. and Jones, W. (1956). *Journal of Pharmacy and Pharmacology* **8**, 709–719.

Alder, V. G., Brown, A. M. and Gillespie, W. A. (1966). *Journal of Clinical Pathology* **19**, 83–89.

Alder, V. G. and Simpson, R. (1982). *In* "Principles and Practice of Disinfection, Preservation and Sterilization" (A. D. Russell, W. B. Hugo and G. A. J. Ayliffe, eds), pp. 433–463. Blackwell Scientific Publications, Oxford.

Alexander, P. and Stacey, K. A. (1958). *Annals of the New York Academy of Sciences* **68**, 1225–1237.

Alguire, D. E. (1963). *Bulletin of the Parenteral Drug Association* **17**, 1–8.

Allen, H. F. and Murphy, J. T. (1960). *Journal of the American Medical Association* **172**, 1759–1763.

Baird-Parker, A. C. and Holbrook, R. (1971). *In* "Inhibition and Destruction of the Microbial Cell" (W. B. Hugo, ed.), pp. 369–397. Academic Press, London and New York.

Barwell, C. F. and Freeman, M. A. R. (1959). *Lancet* **1**, 917–918.

Beeby, M. W. and Whitehouse, C. E. (1965). *Journal of Applied Bacteriology* **28**, 349–360.

Blake, D. F. and Stumbo, C. R. (1970). *Journal of Food Science* **35**, 26–29.

Bracken, A., Wilton-Davies, C. C., Weale, F. F. and Kelsey, J. C. (1966). *Guy's Hospital Reports* **109**, 75–80.

Braswell, J. R., Spiner, D. R. and Hoffman, R. K. (1970). *Applied Microbiology* **20**, 765–769.

British Pharmacopoeia (1980). Pharmaceutical Press, London.

Brooks, P. and Lawley, P. D. (1964). *British Medical Bulletin* **20**, 91–95.

Bruch, C. W. (1961a). *Annual Review of Microbiology* **15**, 245–262.

Bruch, C. W. (1961b). *American Journal of Hygiene* **73**, 1–9.

Bruch, C. W. (1973). *In* "Industrial Sterilization: International Symposium, Amsterdam, 1972" (G. B. Phillips and W. S. Miller, eds), pp. 119–123. Duke University Press, North Carolina.

Bruch, C. W. and Bruch, M. K. (1970). *In* "Disinfection" (M. A. Benarde, ed.), pp. 141–206. Marcel Dekker, New York.

Bruch, C. W. and Koesterer, M. G. (1961). *Journal of Food Science* **26**, 428–435.

Christensen, E. A. and Kristensen, H. (1982). *In* "Principles and Practice of Disinfection, Preservation and Sterilization" (A. D. Russell, W. B. Hugo and G. A. Ayliffe, eds), pp. 548–568. Blackwell Scientific Publications, Oxford.

Curran, H. R. and Evans, F. R. (1956). *Journal of Infectious Diseases* **99**, 212–218.

Dadd, A. H. and Daley, G. M. (1980). *Journal of Applied Bacteriology* **49**, 89–101.

Deverill, C. E. A. and Cripps, N. F. (1981). *Journal of Hospital Infection* **2**, 175–180.

Dickens, F. (1964). *British Medical Bulletin* **20**, 96–101.

Doyle, J. E., McDaniel, A. W., West, K. L., Whitbourne, J. G. and Ernst, R. R. (1970). *Applied Microbiology* **26**, 793–797.

Ernst, R. R. (1968). *In* "Disinfection, Sterilization and Preservation" (C. A. Lawrence and S. S. Block, eds), pp. 703–740. Lea and Febiger, Philadelphia.

Ernst, R. R. (1973). *In* "Industrial Sterilization: International Symposium, Amsterdam, 1972" (G. B. Phillips and W. S. Miller, eds), pp. 181–208. Duke University Press, North Carolina.

Ernst, R. R. (1974). *Biotechnology and Bioengineering Symposium* **No. 4**, pp. 865–878.

Ernst, R. R. (1975). *Acta Pharmaceutica Suecica* **12** (Supplement), 44–64.

Ernst, R. R. (1977). *Developments in Industrial Microbiology* **18**, 363–372.

Ernst, R. R. and Doyle, J. E. (1968a). *Biotechnology and Bioengineering* **10**, 1–31.

Ernst, R. R. and Doyle, J. E. (1968b). *Developments in Industrial Microbiology* **9**, 293–296.

Ernst, R. R. and Shull, J. J. (1962a). *Applied Microbiology* **10**, 337–341.

Ernst, R. R.and Shull, J. J. (1962b). *Applied Microbiology* **10**, 342–346.

Fraenkel-Conrat, H. (1961). *Biochemica et Biophysica Acta* **49**, 169–180.

Freeman, M. A. R. and Barwell, C. F. (1960). *Journal of Hygiene, Cambridge* **58**, 337–345.

Friedl, J. L., Ortenzio, L. F. and Stuart, L. S. (1956). *Journal of the Association of Official Agricultural Chemists* **39**, 480–483.

Gilbert, G. L., Gambill, V. M., Spiner, D. R., Hoffman, R. K. and Phillips, C. R. (1964). *Applied Microbiology* **12**, 496–503.

Gillis, J. R., Woodrow, J. R., Powell, K. A. and Halleck, F. E. (1976). *Developments in Industrial Microbiology* **17**, 417–430.

Griffith, C. L. and Hall, L. A. (1938). *U.S. Patent* **2**, 189, 947.

Halowell, P., Murphy, J. T. and Mangiaracine, A. B. (1958). *Anaesthesiology* **19**, 665–670.

Hansen, N. H. and Snyder, W. C. (1947). *Phytopathology* **37**, 369–371.

Harry, E. G., Brown, W. B. and Goodship, G. (1972). *Journal of Applied Bacteriology* **35**, 485–491.

Hazeu, W. and Hueck, J. (1965). *Antonie van Leeuwenhoek* **31**, 295–300.

Hess, H., Geller, L. and Buhlmann, X. (1973). *In* "Industrial Sterilization: International Symposium, Amsterdam, 1972" (G. B. Phillips and W. S. Miller, eds), pp. 283–296. Duke University Press, North Carolina.

Himmelfarb, P., Read, R. B. and Litsky, W. (1962). *Applied Microbiology* **9**, 534–537.

Hoffman, R. K. (1968). *Applied Microbiology* **16**, 641–644.

Hoffman, R. K. (1971). *In* "Inhibition and Destruction of the Microbial Cell" (W. B. Hugo, ed.), pp. 225–258. Academic Press, London and New York.

Hoffman, R. K. and Warshowsky, B. (1958). *Applied Microbiology* **6**, 358–362.

Iyer, V. N. and Szybalski, W. (1958). *Applied Microbiology* **6**, 23–29.

Jones, L. A., Hoffman, R. K. and Phillips, C. R. (1967). *Applied Microbiology* **15**, 357–362.

Kaye, S. (1949). *American Journal of Hygiene* **50**, 289–295.

Kaye, S. (1950). *Journal of Laboratory and Clinical Medicine* **35**, 823–828.

Kaye, S. and Phillips, C. R. (1949). *American Journal of Hygiene* **50**, 296–305.

Kaye, S., Irminger, H. F. and Phillips, C. R. (1952). *Journal of Laboratory and Clinical Medicine* **40**, 67–72.

Kelsey, J. C. (1961). *Journal of Clinical Pathology* **14**, 59–62.

Kelsey, J. C. (1967). *Journal of Applied Bacteriology* **30**, 92–100.

Kereluk, K. (1971). *Progress in Industrial Microbiology* **10**, 105–128.

Kereluk, K. and Lloyd, R. S. (1969). *Journal of Hospital Research* **7**, 7–75.

Kereluk, K., Gammon, R. A. and Lloyd, R. S. (1970a). *Applied Microbiology* **19**, 146–151.

Kereluk, K., Gammon, R. A. and Lloyd, R. S. (1970b). *Applied Microbiology* **19**, 152–156.

Kereluk, K., Gammon, R. A. and Lloyd, R. S. (1970c). *Applied Microbiology* **19**, 157–162.

Kereluk, K., Gammon, R. A. and Lloyd, R. S. (1970d). *Applied Microbiology* **19**, 163–165.

Kolb, R. W. and Schneiter, R. (1950). *Journal of Bacteriology* **59**, 401–411.

Lawley, P. D. and Brooks, P. (1963). *Biochemical Journal* **89**, 127–128.

Lawley, P. D. and Jarman, M. (1972). *Biochemical Journal* **126**, 893–900.
Lelieveld, H. L. M. (1980). *Journal of Applied Bacteriology* **48**, 59–61.
Lelieveld, H. L. M. and van Eljk, H. M. J. (1979). *Journal of Applied Bacteriology* **47**, 121–134.
Liu, T., Howard, G. L. and Stumbo, C. R. (1968). *Food Technology* **22**, 86–89.
LoGrippo, G. A., Overhulse, P. R., Szilagyi, D. E. and Hartman, F. W. (1955). *Laboratory Investigation* **4**, 217–231.
Macek, T. J. (1973). *In* "Industrial Sterilization" (G. B. Phillips and W. S. Miller, eds), pp. 19–34. Duke University Press, Durham, North Carolina.
Marletta, J. and Stumbo, C. R. (1970). *Journal of Food Science* **35**, 627–631.
Mayr, G. (1961). *In* "Recent Developments in the Sterilization of Surgical Materials", pp. 90–97. Report of a Symposium. Pharmaceutical Press, London.
Michael, G. T. and Stumbo, C. R. (1970). *Journal of Food Science* **35**, 631–634.
Myers, T., Lipstein, M., Troppoli, K. and Chrai, S. (1981). *Journal of Parenteral Science and Technology* **35**, 98–99.
Nordgren, G. (1939). *Acta Pathologica et Microbiologica Scandinavica, Supplement* **No. 40**, pp. 1–165.
Opfell J. B. and Miller, C. E. (1965). *Advances in Applied Microbiology* **7**, 81–102.
Opfell, J. B., Hohmann, J. P. and Latharn, A. B. (1959). *Journal of the American Pharmaceutical Association, Scientific Edition* **48**, 617–619.
Opfell, J. B., Wang, Y. L., Louderback, A. L. and Miller, C. E. (1964). *Applied Microbiology* **12**, 27–31.
Perkins, J. J. and Lloyd, R. S. (1961). *In* "Recent Developments in the Sterilization of Surgical Materials", pp. 76–90. Report of a Symposium. Pharmaceutical Press, London.
Phillips, C. R. (1949). *American Journal of Hygiene* **50**, 280–288.
Phillips, C. R. (1952). *Bacteriological Reviews* **15**, 135–138.
Phillips, C. R. (1961). *In* "Recent Developments in the Sterilization of Surgical Materials", pp. 59–75. Report of a Symposium. Pharmaceutical Press, London.
Phillips, C. R. (1968). *In* "Disinfection, Sterilization and Preservation" (C. A. Lawrence and S. S. Block, eds), pp. 669–685. Lea and Febiger, Philadelphia.
Phillips, C. R. (1977). *In* "Disinfection, Sterilization and Preservation" (S. S. Block, ed.), 2nd edn, pp. 592–610. Lea and Febiger, Philadelphia.
Phillips, C. R. and Kaye, S. (1949). *American Journal of Hygiene* **50**, 270–279.
Phillips, C. R. and Warshowsky, B. (1958). *Annual Review of Microbiology* **12**, 525–550.
Portner, D. M. and Hoffman, R. K. (1968). *Applied Microbiology* **16**, 1782–1785.
Price, C. C. (1958). *Annals of the New York Academy of Sciences* **68**, 663–668.
Reich, R. (1980). *Journal of the Parenteral Drug Association* **34**, 200–211.
Report (1958). Disinfection of Fabrics with Gaseous Formaldehyde. Report by the Committee on Formaldehyde Disinfection. *Journal of Hygiene, Cambridge* **56**, 488–515.
Rhaese, H. J. and Freese, E. (1969). *Biochimica et Biophysica Acta* **190**, 418–433.
Roberts, J. J. and Warwick, G. P. (1963). *Biochemical Pharmacology* **12**, 1441–1442.
Roberts, T. A. and Hitchins, A. D. (1969). *In* "The Bacterial Spore" (G. W. Gould and A. Hurst, eds), pp. 611–670. Academic Press, London and New York.
Rosenkranz, H. S., Wlodkowski, T. J. and Bodine, S. R. (1975). *Mutation Research* **30**, 303–304.
Ross, W. J. C. (1958). *Annals of the New York Academy of Sciences* **68**, 669–681.
Roxon, J. J. (1973). *Australian Journal of Pharmaceutical Sciences* **NS2**, 65–76.

Royce, A. (1959). *Public Pharmacist* **16**, 245–241.
Royce, A. and Bowler, C. (1959). *Journal of Pharmacy and Pharmacology* **11**, 294T–298T.
Royce, A. and Bowler, C. (1961). *Journal of Pharmacy and Pharmacology* **13**, 87T–94T.
Rubbo, S. D. and Gardner, J. F. (1965). "A Review of Sterilization and Disinfection". Lloyd-Luke, London.
Rubbo, S. D. and Gardner, J. F. (1968). *Journal of Applied Bacteriology* **31**, 164–169.
Russell, A. D. (1965). *Manufacturing Chemist and Aerosol News* **36**, 38–45.
Russell, A. D. (1971). *In* "Inhibition and Destruction of the Microbial Cell" (W. B. Hugo, ed.), pp. 451–612. Academic Press, London and New York.
Russell, A. D. (1976). *In* "Inactivation of Vegetative Microbes" (F. A. Skinner and W. B. Hugo, eds). Symposium No. 5, Society for Applied Bacteriology, pp. 61–88. Academic Press, London and New York.
Savage, R. A. and Stumbo, C. R. (1970). *Journal of Food Science* **36**, 182–184.
Schley, D. G., Hoffman, R. K. and Phillips, C. R. (1960). *Applied Microbiology* **8**, 15–19.
Skeehan, R. A., King, J. H. and Kaye, S. (1956). *American Journal of Ophthalmology* **42**, 424–430.
Smith, H. J. and Spencer, P. S. J. (1978). *Manufacturing Chemist and Aerosol News* **46**(9) 57–61, (10) 43–48.
Snow, J. C., Mangiaracine, A. B. and Anderson, M. L. (1962). *New England Journal of Medicine* **266**, 443–446.
Spaulding, E. H., Grundy, K. R. and Turner, F. J. (1977). *In* "Disinfection, Sterilization and Preservation" (S. S. Block, ed.), 2nd edn, pp. 654–684. Lea and Febiger, Philadelphia.
Spiner, D. R. and Hoffman, R. K. (1960). *Applied Microbiology* **8**, 152–155.
Stacey, K. A., Cobb, M., Cousens, S. F. and Alexander, P. (1958). *Annals of the New York Academy of Sciences* **68**, 682–701.
Starbuck, W. C. and Busch, H. (1963). *Biochimica et Biophysica Acta* **78**, 594–605.
Sutaria, R. H. and Williams, F. H. (1961). *Pharmaceutical Journal* **186**, 311–314.
Sykes, G. (1965). "Disinfection and Sterilization", 2nd edn. Spon, London.
Taguchi, J. T., Edmonds, P. and Harmon, G. A. (1963). *American Journal of Medical Sciences* **245**, 299–303.
Taylor, L. A., Barbeito, M. S. and Gremillion, G. (1969). *Applied Microbiology* **17**, 614–618.
Thomas, C. G. A. (1960). *Guy's Hospital Reports* **109**, 57–74.
Thomas, C. G. A., West, B. and Besser, H. (1959). *Guy's Hospital Reports* **108**, 446–463.
Toth, L. Z. J. (1959). *Archiv für Mikrobiologie* **32**, 409–410.
Trafas, P. C., Carlson, R. E., LoGrippo, G. A. and Lam, C. R. (1954). *Archives of Surgery* **69**, 415–424.
Troll, W., Rinde, E. and Day, P. (1969). *Biochimica et Biophysica Acta* **174**, 211–219.
Tulis, J. J. (1973). *In* "Industrial Sterilization: International Symposium, Amsterdam, 1972" (G. B. Phillips and W. S. Miller, eds), pp. 209–238. Duke University Press, North Carolina.
Tuynenburg Muys, G., van Rhee, R. and Lelieveld, H. L. M. (1978). *Journal of Applied Bacteriology* **45**, 213–217.
Walles, S. A. (1974). *Chemico-Biological Interactions* **9**, 97–103.
Walpole, A. L., Roberts, D. C., Rose, F. L., Hendry, J. A. and Homer, R. F. (1954). *British Journal of Pharmacology* **9**, 306–323.

Walter, C. W. and Kundsin, R. B. (1959). *Journal of the American Medical Association* **170**, 1543–1544.

Whitbourne, J. E. and Reich, R. R. (1979). *Journal of the Parenteral Drug Association* **33**, 132–143.

Wilson, A. R. and Bruno, P. (1950). *Journal of Experimental Medicine* **91**, 449–458.

Windemueller, H. G. and Kaplan, N. D. (1961). *Journal of Biological Chemistry* **236**, 2716–2726.

Winge-Heden, K. (1963). *Acta Pathologica et Microbiologica Scandinavica* **58**, 225–244.

8

Inactivation of Bacterial Spores by Hydrostatic Pressure

I. *Introduction*

The term "hydrostatics" refers to that branch of science that deals with the mechanical properties and behaviour of fluids which are not in motion. Hydrostatic pressure deals with the effects of high pressure exerted by liquids on (in the present context) microorganisms, and especially bacterial spores. Organisms can exist, for example, at the bottom of deep oceans, where they are subjected to very high hydrostatic pressure (Dring, 1976).

The effects of pressure on spores and other microorganisms have been reviewed by, respectively, Gould and Sale (1972) and Dring (1976) and Marquis and Matsumara (1978). Zimmerman (1970) presents a detailed account of the effects of pressure on cellular processes. Knaysi and Curran (1961) have described the effects of some mechanical factors on *B. subtilis* spores: see also Rode and Foster (1960) and Zobell and Johnson (1949).

II. *Bacterial Sensitivity*

Early workers (reviewed by Heden, 1964) showed, not surprisingly, that bacterial spores were more resistant to hydrostatic pressure than non-sporulating bacteria. It was, in fact, found that even pressures as high as 12 000 atmospheres did not kill spores.

Reinvestigations of these findings have confirmed that spores are more resistant to hydrostatic pressure, but have also produced some interesting and rather unexpected results.

Table 8.1 compares the sensitivites of non-sporing and sporing bacteria to hydrostatic pressure. The following conclusions may be made: bacterial spores are much more resistant to hydrostatic pressure than are germinated spores or non-sporulating bacteria; vegetative cells of *Clostridium* and *Bacillus* species have the same order of sensitivity to hydrostatic pressure.

Table 8.1. Comparative sensitivites of sporing and non-sporing bacteria and yeasts to hydrostatic pressure

Group of organisms	Lethal hydrostatic pressure (atm)
Gram-negative rods	500–600
Gram-positive cocci	500–600
Mycobacteria	500–600
Yeasts	400
Bacterial spores	*ca.* 2000[a][b]
Germinated spores	500–600

[a] At much higher pressures, rate of inactivation may decrease: see Table 8.2.
[b] Depends markedly on treatment temperature: see Table 8.3.
1 atm ≈ 101 kPa.

III. *Factors Influencing Sensitivity of Bacterial Spores*

A. Lethal Effects of Different Pressures

It would logically be expected that an increase in pressure would bring about an increased lethal effect on the spores. This simple relationship

Table 8.2. Lethal effects of different pressures[a,b]

Spore	Increasing rate of kill over (atm)	Decreasing rate of kill over (atm)
B. cereus NCTC 8035	1000–1500	2000–4000[c]
B. cereus PX	1000–2000	2500–4000[c]
B. subtilis var. niger	1000–2500	3000–8000
B. polymyxa	1000–2500	3000–6000[c]

[a] Range tested: 1000–8000 atm at 20°C for 1 h.
[b] Based on the data of Sale et al. (1970) and Wills (1974).
[c] At pressure in excess of the maximum figure, a greater inactivation was again observed.

Table 8.3. Effect of temperature on the lethal effect of hydrostatic pressure on bacterial spores

Pressure (atm)	Treatment temp. (°C)	Approx. reduction of log cycles[a] following No post-treatment heating	Post-treatment heating[b]
1000	25	0·2	0·5
	45	1	2
	55	2	2·8
	65	3	3·6
2000	25	1	2
	45	1·2	3
	55	3·5	4
	65	4·5	5·8
3000	25	1·3	2
	45	3	5·9
	55	4·5	7·7
	65	7	—
4000	25	0·5	1·7
	45	2·8	7
	55	5·1	—
	65	—[c]	—
8000	25	0	0·2
	45	1	5·1
	55	4·9	—

[a] Calculated from the graphical data presented by Gould and Sale (1972).
[b] 70°C, 30 min.
[c] Not possible to calculate a value.

does not, in fact, hold true. Within a certain range of pressures, which may vary with different spores, the number of survivors after a fixed period of treatment decreases as pressure increases. Above this range, however, increasing pressure has a reduced effect, although with at least some strains of spores still further increases leads to an increased lethal effect (Table 8.2, based on the data of Sale *et al.* (1970) and Wills (1974)).

The sporicidal effect of a range of pressures is also related to the temperature of treatment as considered below and summarized in Table 8.3. This table also demonstrates that a post-treatment heating period may increase the effect of a particular pressure, and that at least some of the spores become sensitive to a subsequent mild heat treatment. Interestingly, at exposure temperatures above 55°C (no subsequent heat treatment at 70°C) or above 45°C (with subsequent heat treatment at 70°C), an increase in hydrostatic pressure does not have a reduced lethal effect in contrast to that noted above.

B. Effect of pH

Pressure-induced inactivation of bacterial spores is dependent on the treatment pH, although the composition of buffer appears to be of minor importance. With *B. coagulans* spores, inactivation is greatest in the pH range of 7–9, but survival counts are higher at pH 11 and highest at pH 3 (Sale *et al.*, 1970).

C. Effect of Temperature

Contrary to the earlier suggestions of Johnson and Zobell (1949), temperature has a profound effect on bacterial sensitivity to hydrostatic pressure (Clouston and Wills, 1969, 1970; Gould, 1970, 1973; Sale *et al.*, 1970; Murrell and Wills, 1977), and this applies to both *Bacillus* and *Clostridium* species. The rate of inactivation increases as the temperature increases, e.g. over the range 25–75°C for *B. coagulans* (Gould, 1970, 1973; Sale *et al.*, 1970). This combined effect of temperature and hydrostatic pressure can be further potentiated if an additional heat treatment is given after pressurization (Gould, 1970; Sale *et al.*, 1970). This means that a proportion of the spores has been heat-sensitized, but not inactivated, by the pressure. This is an important point in the context of understanding the mechanism whereby hydrostatic pressure exerts its effect on spores (see Section IV). A comparison of the effects of hydrostatic pressure with or without a post-treatment heating period, based on the findings of Gould and Sale (1972), is presented in Table

8.3. Murrell and Wills (1973) showed that the rate at which the fraction of spores stained (i.e. extent of germination) by a given pressure increased markedly with a rise in temperature over a specified temperature range.

D. **Pressure and Germinants**

Hydrostatic pressure can induce germination of spores held in water or buffer. Combinations of pressure with physiological germinants such as L-alanine give a synergistic response (Gould, 1970; Gould and Sale, 1972). It is known that D-alanine at 1 atm is an inhibitor of L-alanine-induced germination (Gould and Sale, 1970). However, pressure plus D-alanine also gives a synergistic response in the context of spore germination. The likely reason for this apparent discrepancy is the acceleration induced by hydrostatic pressure of the racemization of D-alanine to L-alanine. Support for this is obtained from the finding that an inhibitor (O-carbamyl-D-serine, OCDS) of alanine racemase antagonizes the potentiating action of D-alanine and increases the potentiating action of L-alanine (Gould and Sale, 1970).

E. **Effect of Solutes**

When spores are pressurized in solutions of known a_w value, the inactivation depends more on the nature of the solute than on the actual a_w. Thus, non-ionic solutes (such as glycerol and sucrose) at low a_w values do not affect the inactivation of spores by pressure; in contrast, ionic solutes (such as NaCl and, especially, $CaCl_2$) at low a_w decrease the inactivation by pressure (Sale *et al.*, 1970).

IV. *Mechanism of Action*

Heden (1964) found that the melting temperature (T_m) of DNA from *B. subtilis* was 86–92°C, above this temperature the biological activity disappearing rapidly. T_m was, however, increased at a pressure of 2700 atm, which protected the biological activity of the DNA against thermal inactivation. Timson and Short (1965) discuss the mechanism of the lethal effects of hydrostatic pressure, and suggest that the primary mechanism is the ionization and concomitant precipitation of protein complexes, and point out that bacterial spores are more resistant to pressure than vegetative cells because the spore proteins are protected against solvation and excessive ionization by DPA.

Two stages are involved in the inactivation of spores by hydrostatic pressure (approximately 2000 atm):

(a) induction of germination;
(b) inactivation of the germinated forms.

Sublethal pressures (a few hundred atm) will induce (a), but are too low to achieve (b) (Gould and Sale, 1970). Germination is likely to occur by the initiation of biochemical reactions within the spore itself rather than by physical distortion of the spore (Gould, 1970). Pressure-induced transformation of a dormant to a germinating spore could involve either core hydration or a decrease in core viscosity (Murrell and Wills, 1977). Mercuric chloride, an inhibitor of germination initiated by physiological germinants (Fig. 6.5, p. 217), also inhibits the germination induced by hydrostatic pressure (Gould and Sale, 1970).

Clouston and Wills (1969, 1970) proposed that pressure inactivated spores by first allowing them to germinate and then killed the germinated cells. Evidence in support of the induction of germination comes from the findings that spores of *B. cereus* exposed to pressure suffer a loss of cortex similar to that found when spores are allowed to germinate normally (Gould and Sale, 1972). At low pressures, germination may be induced and the germinated forms not inactivated, although as shown in Table 8.3 they do become sensitive to mild heating (70°C, 30 min). Timson and Short (1965) proposed that pressures above 30 000 pounds per square inch (*ca.* 2000 atm) induced protein denaturation by ionization and the formation of ionic bonds between charged groups thereby altering protein solubility. It was further postulated that in spores DPA protected proteins against solvation and excessive ionization, which accounted for their increased resistance as compared to vegetative cells. It is, however, pertinent to point out that germination is induced at pressures well below those needed to cause denaturation and cause inactivation of the germinated forms (Gould and Sale, 1972).

Another possible "target site" in the bacterial cell is DNA (Heden, 1964; Rutberg, 1964a,b,c; Landau, 1967). Since there are optimal levels for inactivation by pressure at specified pH (Section III.B) and temperature (Section III.C), it is, however, unlikely that effects on protein or DNA are entirely responsible for the lethal effects of pressure. If they were, then increases in pressure should cause more inactivation (Sale *et al.*, 1970).

Pressurized spores release DPA, calcium and hexosamine-containing material and become phase-bright (Sale *et al.*, 1970). This finding, taken in conjunction with the information presented above, suggests that the hypothesis that hydrostatic pressure induces germination and then inactivates the germinated spores is likely to be correct. It does not, however, explain the paradoxical effect of higher pressures on spores.

V. *Possible Applications of Hydrostatic Pressure*

A combination of hydrostatic pressure with heat or radiation reduces the degree of heat or radiation dose required for sterilization (Wills, 1974) and such a combined treatment could have potential value in the sterilization of thermal- or radiation-sensitive materials. Examples of the use of pressure-radiation combinations are provided by Wills (1975).

There may, however, be limitations to the actual uses of hydrostatic pressure. "Superdormant" spores, which may be present in the tail of a germination curve, are also more resistant to germination induced by pressure; spores found in nature are more dormant than laboratory ones, and may be inactivated to a much smaller extent, even when exposed to high pressures at high temperatures (Gould, 1973).

VI. *Conclusions*

Studies during the late 1960s and during the 1970s have shown that hydrostatic pressure, for long considered a process to which spores were inordinately resistant, exerts some interesting changes in bacterial spores at much lower doses than those originally described as being without effect on these forms. The sporicidal effect involving germination of the spores, followed by destruction of the germinated cell is highly dependent on temperature.

Hydrostatic pressure is a useful process since it enables investigations to be made of germination in the absence of physiological germinants. Its reduced effect against "superdormant" spores, however, raises doubts as to its possible applications. Further information is needed about the possible use of combined pressure–radiation treatments.

References

Clouston, J. G. and Wills, P. A. (1969). *Journal of Bacteriology* **97**, 684–690.
Clouston, J. G. and Wills, P. A. (1970). *Journal of Bacteriology* **103**, 140–143.

Dring, G. J. (1976). *In* "Inhibition and Inactivation of Vegetative Microbes" (F. A. Skinner and W. B. Hugo, eds), pp. 257–277. Society for Applied Bacteriology Symposium Series No. 5. Academic Press, London and New York.

Gould, G. W. (1970). *Journal of Applied Bacteriology* **33**, 34–49.

Gould, G. W. (1973). *Acta Alimentaria* **2**, 377–383.

Gould, G. W. and Sale, A. J. H. (1970). *Journal of General Microbiology* **60**, 335–346.

Gould, G. W. and Sale, A. J. H. (1972). *In* "The Effects of Pressure on Living Organisms" (M. A. Sleigh and A. G. McDonald, eds). *Symposium of the Society for Experimental Biology* **26**, 147–157. Academic Press, London and New York.

Heden, C.-G. (1964). *Bacteriological Reviews* **28**, 14–29.

Johnson, F. and Zobell, C. E. (1949). *Journal of Bacteriology* **57**, 353–358.

Knaysi, G. and Curran, H. R. (1961). *Journal of Bacteriology* **32**, 691–694.

Landau, J. V. (1967). *Biochimica et Biophysica Acta* **149**, 506–512.

Marquis, R. E. and Matsumara, P. (1978). *In* "Microbial Life in Extreme Environments" (D. J. Kushner, ed.), pp. 105–158. Academic Press, London and New York.

Murrell, W. G. and Wills, P. A. (1977). *Journal of Bacteriology* **129**, 1272–1280.

Rode, L. J. and Foster, J. W. (1960). *Proceedings of the National Academy of Sciences, U.S.A.* **46**, 118–128.

Rutberg, L. (1964a). *Acta Pathologica et Microbiologica Scandinavica* **61**, 81–90.

Rutberg, L. (1964b). *Acta Pathologica et Microbiologica Scandinavica* **61**, 91–97.

Rutberg, L. (1964c). *Acta Pathologica et Microbiologica Scandinavica* **61**, 98–105.

Sale, A. J. H., Gould, G. W. and Hamilton, W. A. (1970). *Journal of General Microbiology* **60**, 323–334.

Timson, W. J. and Short, A. J. (1965). *Biotechnology and Bioengineering* **7**, 139–159.

Wills, P. A. (1974). *Atomic Energy of Australia* **17**, 2–10.

Wills, P. A. (1975). *In* "Radiosterilization of Medical Products 1974", pp. 45–61. International Atomic Energy Agency, Vienna.

Zimmerman, A. M. (1970). "High Pressure Effects on Cellular Processes". Academic Press, London and New York.

Zobell, C. E. and Johnson, F. H. (1949). *Journal of Bacteriology* **57**, 179–189.

9

Effects of Combined Treatments on Bacterial Spores

I. *Introduction*

Several attempts have been made to improve the efficacy of a given sterilization process by using it in conjunction with another process, chemical or physical. In actual fact, a combined treatment could lead to a potentiation of activity or alternatively to an equivalent activity as a result of employing reduced "doses" of each component in unison. The latter could mean a lessened effect on a product being sterilized whilst maintaining the lethal quality of the process. In another context, the combination of two chemicals could result in an enhanced sporicidal effect.

There are various types of combined treatments. One that has long been used in the United Kingdom utilizes the known potentiation of activity of bactericides by raising the temperature (Russell, 1974, 1982) and employing this combination in the sterilization of certain parenteral and eye products (Russell *et al.*, 1967). More recently, there has been a resurgence of interest in thermoradiation, and studies with triple combinations (heat + radiation + bactericide) have also been made. These and other combined processes are discussed in subsequent sections of this chapter. The interested reader is referred to the review by Deasy (1972) for earlier information.

II. *Thermochemical Effects*

A. General Comments

It has long been known that the bactericidal activity of a bactericide usually increases as the temperature rises. A measurement of this effect can be obtained from a knowledge of the temperature coefficient (θ) which is a measure of the increase in bactericidal activity per 1°C rise in temperature. By convention, for ease of administration and to demonstrate more clearly differences between bactericides, in practice θ^{10} (or Q_{10}) is employed, a term which denotes the increase in activity per 10°C rise. Examples of θ^{10} values are listed in Table 9.1, which is based in part on Bean (1967, 1972).

As a case in point, chlorocresol may be considered. The temperature coefficient (θ) per 1°C for this agent is 1·1. Thus, if the temperature is increased from 20° to 100°C, then (assuming that θ is the same over the entire temperature range):

$$\theta^{100-20} = \theta^{80} = 1 \cdot 1^{80} = 2104$$

which means an increase of more than 2000-fold in bactericidal activity.

Table 9.1. Temperature coefficients (θ^{10} values) of some antimicrobial agents[a]

Substance	θ^{10} value (Q_{10})
Formaldehyde	1·5
Aliphatic alcohols	30–50
Phenols and cresols	3–5
Ethylene oxide	2·7[b]
β-propiolactone	2–3

[a] Based in part on Bean (1967).
[b] For additional information, see Table 9.2.

Many diverse chemicals have an increased sporicidal activity at high temperatures, including betadine (Sykes, 1970), domiphen bromide (Sykes, 1970), nisin and subtilin (Anderson and Michener, 1950; Lewis *et al.*, 1954; Michener *et al.*, 1959a,b), pharmaceutical preservatives (considered in Section B below) and miscellaneous compounds (Bose and Roy, 1959, 1960; Michener *et al.*, 1959a,b). Nisin and subtilin (see also Chapter 6, Section III) reduce the heat resistance of *Cl. sporogenes* PA 3679 spores (Anderson and Michener, 1950; Lewis *et al.*, 1954; cf. Denny *et al.*, 1959) and *B. stearothermophilus* spores (Anderson and Michener, 1950; Lewis *et al.*, 1954). The effect of nisin on heat resistance may, however, be more apparent than real as it has been suggested that nisin is adsorbed on to *B. stearothermophilus* spores and that, unless desorbed by means of the enzyme trypsin, the adsorbed antibiotic carried over into the subculture medium can prevent colony formation, thereby leading to erroneous conclusions (Thorpe, 1960; Tramer, 1964). This point does not appear to have been considered by Anderson and Michener (1959a,b) who also showed that heat potentiated the activity of hydrogen peroxide, formaldehyde and silver nitrate but not of several other common antibacterial agents.

B. Potentiation of Disinfectant Activity

1. *Liquid-phase disinfectants*

Most antibacterial agents lack significant sporicidal activity (Chapter 6). Of those that possess such activity, such as chlorine, glutaraldehyde and formaldehyde, it will always be important to attempt to achieve ways of increasing this property. An obvious policy is to investigate the effect of increasing temperatures on the disinfectant. Two aspects must be considered: first, the potentiation of sporicidal activity; second, the stability of the disinfectant molecule.

Chlorine-treated spores of *Cl. perfringens* and *Cl. bifermentans* are more sensitive to subsequent heat treatment than are untreated spores, although spores of the latter organism appear to have a low intrinsic resistance to high temperatures (Dye and Mead, 1972). The sporicidal activity of formaldehyde is temperature-dependent, especially over the range 40–60°C (Trujillo and David, 1972). Likewise, formaldehyde base disinfectants dissolved in water show a temperature-dependent sporicidal effect (Trujillo and Lindell, 1973). Tego compounds (amphoteric surfactants) are not normally considered as being sporicidal, but become so at elevated temperatures (Sykes, 1970; Tsuchido *et al.*, 1975). These few examples serve to illustrate the profound changes that can occur in sporicidal properties when chemical disinfectants are used at high temperatures.

Probably the best known example is, however, glutaraldehyde (pentanedial), and several studies have been made to measure the interplay of temperature and pH on sporicidal activity and changes in molecular stability. As pointed out in Chapter 6 (Section IV), glutaraldehyde is most stable at acid pH but most active against microorganisms when made alkaline ("activated"). Unfortunately, under alkaline conditions, the dialdehyde has only a short shelf-life. Differences in sporicidal activity between the acid and alkaline forms begin to disappear at temperatures of about 40°C (Thomas and Russell, 1974) and at higher temperatures there is equivalent activity. Further information will be found in Chapter 6 and in the review by Gorman *et al.* (1980).

2. Gaseous disinfectants

As pointed out in Chapter 7 (Section II), the sporicidal activity of gaseous disinfectants increases as the temperature is raised. Although the Q_{10} value of 2·7 is usually associated with ethylene oxide, it may be seen from Table 9.2 that in fact some disagreement exists over the actual value. Ernst and Shull (1962), in fact, obtained two Q_{10}-values for each concentration of ethylene oxide tested in different temperature ranges. If, however, an average Q_{10}-value is obtained in the lower temperature range (*ca.* 5–40°C) it can be seen that this is 2·7–2·8 and that their values do not disagree strongly with that Q_{10}-value obtained by Phillips (1949) who used a much narrower temperature range.

A process that has given promising results is the use of saturated steam at subatmospheric pressure in the presence of formaldehyde; this is better known as low temperature steam with formaldehyde (LTS/F). This process has been described by Alder *et al.* (1966, 1971), Alder

Table 9.2. Temperature coefficients of ethylene oxide

Concentration (mg/l) of ethylene oxide	Temperature range (°C)	Q_{10}-value[a] (θ^{10})	Reference
22–884	5–37	2·7	Phillips (1949)
440	20–40	3·1	
	40–55	1·8	Ernst and Shull (1962)
880	20–35	2·5	
	35–55	1·8	
1500	20–55	1·8	

[a] Over the approximate range 5–40°C, the mean Q_{10}-value is $\frac{1}{3}(2·7 + 3·1 + 2·5)$, i.e. $2·7 - 2·8$, and the value of 2·7 is usually quoted by other authors.

(1968), Line and Pickerill (1973), Gibson (1971), Handlos (1977), Marcos and Wiseman (1979) and Deverill and Cripps (1981). The principle is that low temperature steam is itself bactericidal but not highly sporicidal (although it is more effective than hot water at the same temperature: Alder, 1968) whereas the addition of low (sublethal) formaldehyde concentrations produces a LTS/F mixture that is highly sporicidal to various organisms, including the heat-resistant *B. stearothermophilus* (Alder, 1968). Nevertheless, there have been conflicting results published, especially with *B. stearothermophilus* spores (Blake *et al.*, 1977). These differences have been attributed to differences in LTS/F cycle characteristics and the lack of standardization of the test organism (Alder and Simpson, 1982). Thus, despite the potential value of LTS/F in the sterilization of heat-sensitive equipment and porous loads, it is obvious that the discrepancies have yet to be explained satisfactorily.

C. Antimicrobial Agents in Pharmaceutical Products

The general principles of the inclusion of antimicrobial agents in pharmaceutical products have been discussed by Russell *et al.* (1967) and Grundy (1977). In the context of sporicidal activity, only two types of product need to be considered, viz. injections and eye-drops.

The sporicidal activity of a chemical compound is enhanced at elevated temperatures. This has been shown with phenylmercuric nitrate (Berry *et al.*, 1937), chlorocresol (Briggs and Yazdany, 1974) and phenol (Russell and Loosemore, 1964). The first two compounds are used in conjunction with heat as a British method of sterilizing some types of injections. Phenylmercuric nitrate, phenylmercuric acetate, benzalkonium chloride and chlorhexidine diacetate may be employed in conjunction with heat as one method of sterilizing eye-drop formulations. Further information can be obtained by consulting the Pharmaceutical Codex (1979).

D. Curing Agents in Foods

The activity of sodium nitrite against spores, and in particular the Perigo effect, was discussed in detail in Chapter 6 (Section IV). The possible roles of nitrite in inhibiting *Cl. botulinum* spores and in maintaining the stability of cured meat products have been ascribed by Johnston *et al.* (1969) to one or more of the following possibilities:

(a) an enhancement of spore destruction by heat;
(b) an increase in spore germination during heat processing, with subsequent thermal death of the germinated cell;
(c) an inhibition of germination of spores that survive thermal processes;
(d) a reaction with some component of the meat to form an antimicrobial compound.

Sodium nitrite has various functions, including its effect on meat colour and flavour, its antioxidant properties and the fact that it will retard the growth of a toxin formation by *Cl. botulinum* (Ingram, 1976; Sofos *et al.*, 1979; Sofos and Busta, 1981). Amongst the methods of preventing botulism are the destruction of the organisms in food by a suitable thermal or radiation process (see the comments in Chapter 4 on radappertization), and a process involving mild heat treatment combined with appropriate food preservatives to retard growth of heat-injured spores (Sofos *et al.*, 1979). In unheated systems, nitrite is more inhibitory to spores or vegetative bacteria at an acid pH, although there is a triple interaction between pH, sodium chloride and soium nitrite (Roberts, 1975).

The 12-D concept ($12 \times D$-value) for the thermal and radiation processing of foods to confer protection against *Cl. botulinum* has been discussed in Chapters 2 (Section IV.C) and 4 (Section III.E) respectively. In the case of heat processing, the time at 121°C (250°F) to achieve this effect is 2·78 min ($F_0 = 2·78$; Sofos *et al.*, 1979) or *ca.* 0·5 min at 121°C ($F_0 = 0·5$) in cured meats (Ingram and Roberts, 1971). The lower F_0 value for most cured meat products is adequate because of the additional effects of salt, nitrite and also the low numbers of anaerobic bacteria in raw meat (see Roberts, 1975).

The exact role of nitrite has yet to be fully elucidated. The results of Ingram and Roberts (1971) and of Labbe and Duncan (1970) are, however, of particular interest. *Clostridium botulinum* spores heated in

Table 9.3. Inhibition of bacterial spores by sodium nitrite

Possible effect of NaNO$_2$ against spores	Evidence for	Evidence against
(1) Enhancement of thermal process		Rate of death of spores the same in presence or absence of nitrite
(2) Perigo effect	Occurs in heated laboratory media containing nitrite	Not always observed in heated foods containing nitrite
(3) Increase in germination during heating		Nitrite does not affect spore germination of *Cl. botulinum* (Sofos *et al.*, 1979). See also (1) above and Labbe and Duncan (1970)
(4) Inhibition of post-heating germination and/or outgrowth	Heat-injured spores rendered more sensitive to nitrite (Ingram and Roberts, 1971)	

water or in water containing salt and nitrite are killed at approximately the same rate. On the other hand, spores heated in either environment become more sensitive to curing agents in the recovery medium, indicating an inhibition of the development of heated spores by the curing salts *after* heating. Additionally, nitrite heated in the recovery medium before use is more inhibitory to heated spores than is medium containing filter-sterilized nitrite (Ingram and Roberts, 1971). Nitrite induces germination of bacterial spores but only at higher concentrations than those permitted legally in foods (Labbe and Duncan, 1970). The Perigo factor (formed by heating nitrite in culture media) is not always produced in meats (see Chapter 6, Section IV.J for a full discussion). The most likely conclusion to date (summarized in Table 9.3) is that heat treatment results in injury to spores so that they become less tolerant to salt and nitrite. Possibly, this involves outgrowth rather than germination (Duncan, 1970).

E. Acid-heat Treatments

Despite some early discrepancies, it is now accepted that the pH of the medium in which spores are heated influences their sensitivity to temperature (Sognefest *et al.*, 1948; Xezones and Hutchings, 1975; Steinbuch, 1975; Chapter 2, Section V.H). In fact, the heat resistance of mature spores of *Bacillus* spp. (Alderton and Snell, 1963, 1969a,b,

1970; Alderton *et al.*, 1964) and of *Cl. botulinum* type A and B (Alderton *et al.*, 1976) is a manipulative property, with increased thermal sensitivity at acid pH (Lowik and Anema, 1972; Mazokhina *et al.*, 1973; Gould, 1978; Wallace *et al.*, 1978; El-Mabsout and Stevenson, 1979).

Canned foods have been divided into various groups on the basis of their pH (Cameron, 1940): low acid foods (pH > 5·3), medium acid foods (5·3–4·5), acid foods (4·5–3·7) and high acid foods (<3·7). It is now generally agreed that spores are more susceptible to heat when at low pH than in alkaline conditions, although the actual composition of the heating menstruum should also be borne in mind. Putrefaction, caused by *Cl. nigrificans*, and flat-sour spoilage (caused by various bacilli, especially *B. thermoacidurans*) may be found in low-acid foods; "TA" spoilage ("thermophilic anaerobe not producing H_2S") induced by *Cl. thermosaccharolyticum*, which is a sugar-splitting organism thereby producing acid and gas, may occur in low- and medium-foods (Frazier, 1958). High-acid foods do not ordinarily undergo spoilage by microorganisms.

Spores exhibit a base exchange behaviour which will reduce, restore or enhance the thermal resistance of fully formed spores (Alderton and Snell, 1963). The spore exchanger is then considered as being a weak cation exchange system, so that the H^+ ion, possessing the greatest exchange potential would displace other ions. Mature spores can be manipulated by means of appropriate pre-treatment to states that are sensitive and resistant to moist heat (Alderton and Snell, 1963; Alderton *et al.*, 1964; Kovacs-Proszt and Farkas, 1976), to dry heat (Alderton and Snell, 1969b) and to heat at intermediate water activity (Alderton and Snell, 1970). Sensitization of the spores involves converting them to the hydrogen (H) form by treatment with hydrochloric acid to pH 3 or less. The H form spores can be converted to the resistant calcium (Ca) form by treatment with calcium acetate at alkaline pH. The dry heat resistance of lyophilized *B. subtilis* spores varies in a rhythmic manner as a function of time between acidification (but not alkalinization) and freezing (Heckley and Dimatteo, 1975).

H-form spores of *Cl. perfringens* type A strains are more sensitive to lysozyme-induced germination than native spores, but lysozyme resistance can be restored by calcium loading (Ando, 1975).

III. *Combination of Chemicals and Irradiation*

The presence of various substances during the irradiation process may increase the sensitivity of bacteria to the process so that a lower radiation dose may be employed to achieve a sporicidal effect. Another aspect that will be considered in this section will be the influence of chemical agents that will either sensitize bacterial spores to, or protect them from, the consequences of ionizing radiation.

A. Irradiation and Antimicrobial Agents

The presence of nisin (100 parts/10^6) or tylosin (1 part/10^6) has been shown to reduce by 75% the radiation dose required to sterilize a pea extract (Farkas *et al.*, 1967). A combination of tylosin lactate and ionizing also increases the storage life of blanched peas as compared to irradiated controls (antibiotic absent) (Farkas *et al.*, 1967).

Other additives have also been tested: sodium chloride, calcium chloride, alkyl isothiocyanate, nutmeg, sodium citrate, sodium nitrate, sodium nitrite, and EDTA all reduce the radiation dose required to inactivate *Cl. botulinum* spores in beef (Krabbenhoft *et al.*, 1964; Anderson *et al.*, 1967).

Various types of *Bacillus* spores surviving irradiation treatment are more readily inactivated by heating with a bactericide such as chlorocresol or phenylmercuric nitrate (Deasy *et al.*, 1968, 1970, 1971, 1977; Deasy, 1972). This process has not, as yet, found any application.

B. Sensitization and Protection

Certain chemical compounds have the property of either sensitizing bacterial spores to ionizing radiation or of protecting them from the lethal activity of radiation. Studies with such compounds have been of value in obtaining information about the lethal effects of radiation.

It was pointed out in Chapter 4 (Section IV.D) that the presence of oxygen during or after an irradiation process can influence markedly the response of bacterial spores, with highest sensitivity being shown in the presence of oxygen or air and highest resistance when irradiation is carried out under anoxic conditions. During the past decade or so, several investigations have been carried out to examine the sensitization to radiation of spores exposed to various chemicals.

Ketonic agents (acetone, acetophenone and *p*-nitroacetophenone (PNAP)) of widely differing electron affinities sensitize bacterial spores in anoxic buffer suspension to subsequent radiation (Tallentire and Jacobs, 1972; Ewing *et al.*, 1974; Fielden *et al.*, 1974; Ewing, 1975). The maximum sensitization achieved, however, is only about 40% of that achieved in oxygen alone, although this does increase to about 58% with the nitroxyl sensitizer nor-pseudopelletierine-*n*-oxyl (NPPN:

Table 9.4. Sensitivity of *B. megaterium* spores in 0·067 M phosphate buffer, pH 7, to ionizing radiation[a]

Irradiation in	Presence of 10^{-3} M PNAP[b]	Approx. D-value (krad $\times$ 10^{-2})
N_2	No	2·7
N_2	Yes	2·1
N_2O	Yes	1·75
N_2O	No	1·5
O_2	No	1·25

[a] Calculated from the graphical data of Ewing *et al.* (1974).
[b] *p*-Nitroacetophenone.

Fielden *et al.*, 1974). A summary of the sensitizing effect of PNAP is presented in Table 9.4, which has been derived from the graphical data of Ewing *et al.* (1974). Tertiary butanol (tert-butanol) is an hydroxyl radical (·OH) scavenger (Powers *et al.*, 1972; Ewing, 1976) and at lower PNAP concentrations, where there is a submaximal sensitizing effect, tert-butanol will eliminate the effect of the ketonic agent, although this does not occur at higher PNAP concentrations (Ewing *et al.*, 1974). ·OH scavengers, such as tert-butanol or high concentrations (0·8 M) of ethanol, can however, reduce but not completely eliminate the maximum amount of sensitization (Ewing, 1975). Nitrous oxide (dinitrogen (I) oxide, N_2O) produces radiosensitization in bacterial spores, but this can be completely reversed by tert-butanol. PNAP and N_2O appear to sensitize by different mechanisms and when tested together PNAP reduces the N_2O effect whilst maintaining its own sensitizing ability (Ewing *et al.*, 1974). N_2O may act by increasing the yield of ·OH, by scavenging solvated electrons in the presence of water, thus (Powers and Cross, 1970):

$$N_2O + e^-_{aq} \xrightarrow{\text{H}_2\text{O}} N_2 + OH^- + \cdot OH.$$

Dilute solutions of ethanol partially, and concentrated solutions completely, prevent this sensitizing action (Powers and Cross, 1970).

Cross *et al.* (1972) have proposed that hydrogen peroxide is associated with the lethal effect under anoxic conditions. They postulate a two-step mechanism for anoxic radiation sensitization of spores in an aqueous environment that requires the presence of ·OH in order to complete an initial step which then allows sufficiently high concentrations of H_2O_2 to finish off, as it were, the damaging sequence. This is

Table 9.5. Accumulation of H_2O_2 in irradiated suspensions of *B. megaterium* spores[a]

Additive	Gas environment	H_2O_2 accumulation[b]	Inactivation constant k[c] $(\times 10^2)$
None	N_2	+	1·3
	N_2O	4+	1·9
	O_2	5+	2·6
Formate	N_2	+	1·4
	N_2O	+	1·3
	O_2	5+	2·4
Catalase	N_2	2+	1·6
	N_2O	2+	1·7
	O_2	2+	2·6

[a] Based on the data of Cross *et al.* (1973).
[b] +, $<6 \times 10^{-7}$ M; ++, $<2 \times 10^{-7}$ M; +++, $>10^{-6}$ M; ++++, $>10^{-5}$ M; +++++, $>10^{-4}$ M.
[c] Expressed as krad^{-1}.

clearly depicted in Table 9.5, which is a simplified version of their findings. In particular, the values of the inactivation constant (k) in the presence of catalase under anoxic and oxic conditions are most interesting. Thus, sensitizing agents appear to act by removing electrons from the aqueous medium within the cells and thereby prevent the conversion of the hydroxyl radical (·OH) into the hydroxyl ion (OH$^-$) which is harmless to the spore (Richmond and Powers, 1974). Fielden *et al.* (1974) and Ewing *et al.* (1974) envisage that PNAP at high concentrations enhances the lethality of the "direct effects" of radiation, with only a negligible contribution from "indirect effects".

Other agents will also affect the response of bacterial spores to ionizing radiation. Cobalt (III) complexes bring about a sensitization which is strictly additive to the oxygen effect, and ethanol reverses the sensitization in anoxic but not in oxic conditions, whereas tert-butanol exerts no protective effect (Richmond *et al.*, 1975). Some inorganic ions, such as Ag$^+$ and MnO$_4^-$, will also in the absence of oxygen sensitize spores to ionizing radiation, and the sensitization maximum is equal to the full O$_2$ effect (Tallentire and Jones, 1973; Richmond and Powers, 1974; Richmond *et al.*, 1975). Within the oxygen effect, the effects of sub-maximum oxygen and potassium permanganate are additive, since MnO$_4^-$ does not increase the sensitivity of spores that have been oxygenated fully (Tallentire and Jones, 1973). Finally, it has

K

been shown that the inactivation constant for Fe^{2+}-sensitized spores in nitrogen is actually greater than that in oxygen (Richmond *et al.*, 1975).

Investigations into the sensitization of spores to ionizing radiation have thus provided some highly interesting results. Bacterial spores have been selected for these studies because of their relative metabolic inertness. It must, however, be asked whether the findings have any value as a possible sterilization process. The answer must, at least at present, be in the negative, but what the investigations have achieved or will achieve is a better understanding of the possible ways in which the lethal effects of radiation are brought about.

IV. *Thermoradiation*

The combined effects of heat and radiation, i.e. thermoradiation, on bacterial spores can conveniently be considered under three headings, viz. preliminary heat-shocking followed by irradiation; irradiation at various temperatures, i.e. simultaneous use; and pre-irradiation followed by heating. The term "thermoradiation" is, however, correctly applied only to the simultaneous use of heat plus radiation.

A. Pre-heating

Morgan and Reed (1954) and Kempe (1955) found that a preliminary heat-shocking treatment did not affect the lethal effect of subsequent irradiation on spores of *Cl. botulinum* whereas Anderson *et al.* (1967) showed that heated spores of *Cl. botulinum* type A were more resistant than unheated spores to radiation.

B. Pre-irradiation

This aspect has been studied by many authors, and it has been shown that spores of *Cl. sporogenes* PA 3679 (Morgan and Read, 1954; Kempe, 1955, 1960; Kempe *et al.*, 1957; Kan *et al.*, 1957), *Cl. botulinum* type A (Gombas and Gomez, 1978), *B. cereus* (Kan *et al.*, 1957; Farkas and Roberts, 1976) and *B. subtilis* (Licciardello and Nickerson, 1963; Stegeman *et al.*, 1977) are more sensitive to heat following exposure of spores to sublethal doses of ionizing radiations. Some dissension has, however, been expressed with this view, and Deasy *et al.* (1968, 1970a,b, 1971) and Briggs and Yazdany (1974) have demonstrated that prior irradiation of the spores of *B. subtilis*, *B. subtilis* var. *niger*, *B. pumilus* and *B. stearothermophilus* brings about only a slight increase in their subsequent sensitivity to moist heat. Nevertheless, the currently available opinion is that prior irradiation sensitizes spores to heat. Interestingly, it was shown many years ago (Curran and Evans, 1938) that exposure of spores to UV radiation rendered them more sensitive to subsequent high temperatures.

Gamma-irradiated spores heated in the presence of high concentrations of sucrose do not become heat-sensitive (Gomez *et al.*, 1980). This finding, viewed in the light of the expanded cortex theory of Gould and Dring (1975), is not unexpected, since sucrose reimposes dehydration of the spore core. It suggests additionally, however, that prior irradiation reduces the ability of spores to maintain the dehydrated state of the cortex. The sensitizing mechanism of pre-irradiation has been suggested as being the result of radiation-induced chain breaks in the peptidoglycan polymer (Stegeman *et al.*, 1977).

C. **Simultaneous Heat and Irradiation (Thermoradiation)**

There has been some divergence of opinion on the effect of temperature on irradiation. Ingram and Thornley (1961) studied the effect of various temperatures ($-75, 0$ and $18°C$) on the inactivation by irradiation of *Cl. botulinum* spores in minced pork, and concluded that low temperatures had little effect on the sterilizing dose of ionizing radiation. Likewise, Denny *et al.* (1959) found that there was only a relatively small reduction in radiation sensitivity of these spores at $-78°C$ in comparison to $0°C$. In contrast, it has been shown that the radiation sensitivity of spores of *Cl. botulinum* 33A in phosphate buffer or in ground beef increases with increasing temperature over the range $-196°$ to $0°C$ (Grecz *et al.*, 1965, 1967) whereas in pork pea broth, however, temperatures has virtually no effect on radiation sensitivity of the spores over this range (Grecz *et al.*, 1967). It has further been observed (El-Bisi *et al.*, 1967) that lower irradiation doses are needed to inactivate spores of *Cl. botulinum* 53B in food as the temperature increases in the range $-196°$ to $20°C$. Possible applications of low temperature irradiation of foods are described by Anellis *et al.* (1972, 1977a,b).

The effect of higher temperature during irradiation often results in an increase in spore resistance to radiation (Denny *et al.*, 1959; Anderson *et al.*, 1967). With *Cl. botulinum* 33A spores, Grecz (1965) found that the radiation sensitivity increased with a rise in temperature in the range $-50°$ to $30°C$, whereas between $30°$ and $80°C$, there was a sudden increase in radiation resistance (Table 9.6). At temperatures above $80°C$, there was a rapid increase in sensitivity. This effect has been termed "paradoxical inversion" (Grecz *et al.*, 1971) or "thermorestora-

Table 9.6. Effect of temperature during irradiation on the radiation sensitivity in tris buffer of *Cl. botulinum* 33A spores[a]

Irradiation temp (°C)	Approx. % of spores surviving treatment[b]
−200	10
−100	10
− 50	10
0	1
30	0·6
80	>10
90	0·1

[a] Calculated from the graphical data of Grecz (1965).
[b] Initial no. taken as 100%.

Table 9.7. Comparative effects of irradiation at different temperatures on spores and vegetative cells of *B. subtilis*[a]

Irradiation temperature (°C)	D-value (krad) with *B. subtilis*		Ratio (A/B)
	Spores (A)	Vegetative cells (B)	
15	—	10·3	—
25	158	10·3	15·34
35	158	6·2	25·48
45	158	3·8	41·58
55	158	—	—
75	158	—	—
85	129	—	—
90	94	—	—

[a] Based on results of Pallas and Hamdy (1976).

tion" (Friedman and Grecz, 1973), but although it has been found in the model systems described above, it does not necessarily occur when spores are irradiated in foods at various temperatures (Grecz *et al.*, 1971) nor does it always occur in model systems themselves (Pallas and Hamdy, 1976; see Table 9.7). Friedman and Grecz (1973) suggested that a typical thermorestoration survival pattern involved at least six phases of response to a single radiation dose ranging from below 0°C (high radiation resistance), through 0°C (highly lethal conditions), 0–15°C (rapid increase in resistance), 15–50°C (resistance still increasing but at a reduced rate), 50–65°C (*B. cereus*) or 50–75°C (*B. stearothermophilus*) where complete saturation occurred, and finally a highly lethal terminal range.

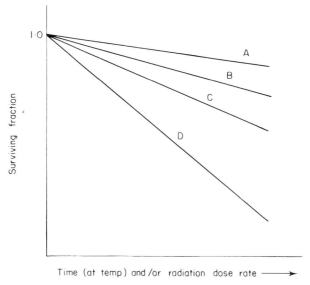

Fig. 9.1   Diagrammatic representation (not to scale) of the effects on spores of ionizing radiation and dry heat used alone or simultaneously. A, radiation only; B, high temperature only; C, additive effect of combination; D, synergistic effect of combination.

Figure 9.1 is a diagrammatic representation of the simultaneous use of dry heat and ionizing radiation on bacterial spores, and is based on the findings of Sivinski and Reynolds (1972), Sivinski *et al.* (1973) and Trauth and Sivinski (1975). For the sake of clarity, the assumption is made in Fig. 9.1 that a logarithmic order of death is operative in each case. Curve A denotes the effect of radiation alone, B elevated temperature alone and D the effect of the combination, whereas C represents the result that would have been obtained if the combined effect had been merely additive in nature. Thus the area between C and D depicts a synergistic effect. Examples of the results obtained (Sivinski *et al.*, 1973) are given in Table 9.8, from which it can be seen that a definite synergism results from use of a combination of dry heat and radiation. Combined processes exhibit a dose-rate effect which is of importance in designing sterilization cycles involving combinations of heat and ionizing radiation (Trauth and Sivinski, 1975). Examples of the effect of dose-rate on D-values at 105°C (Reynolds and Garst, 1970) are shown in Table 9.9.

Naturally occurring spores in soil, with a high resistance to dry heat (D-value at 125°C = 29 h) show a D-value of *ca.* 0·2 Mrad when exposed

Table 9.8. Synergistic vs. additive effects on dry heat and ionizing radiation in combination on *B. subtilis* spores[a]

Situation	Dry heat (°C)	Radiation (krad/h)	D-value (h)
A	95	—	12
B	—	11	7
C[b]	95	11	4·5
D[c]	95	11	2·28
A	105	—	4·5
B	—	27	3·3
C[b]	105	27	1·8
D[c]	105	27	0·7

[a] From the graphical data of Sivinski *et al.* (1973).
[b] Hypothetical result of an additive effect.
[c] Actual result, denoting synergism.

Table 9.9. Effect of irradiation of dose-rate on dry heat inactivation of *B. subtilis* var. *niger* spores[a]

Irradiation dose rate (krad/h)	D-value (h) at 105°C
0	4·5
2	2
5	1·6
13	1·1
22	0·9
35	0·7
50	0·6

[a] Derived from the graphical data presented by Reynolds and Garst (1970). At low irradiation dose-rates, there is a considerable reduction in D-values at 105°C but at higher rates there is a much smaller effect on D-values.

to ionizing radiation; however, the simultaneous application of dry heat and radiation (dose rate 76 krad/h) reduces the D-value to 1 h (Reynolds *et al.*, 1974), which is less than one-third of an additive effect. In dry heat thermoradiation, the degree of synergism is dependent on the RH (Fisher and Pflug, 1977).

There is no evidence that increases in spore resistance to radiation occur at different dry heat temperatures, although the situation is not, of course, strictly comparable to that described earlier.

The synergism between heat and radiation has been quantified by Fisher and Pflug (1977) in terms of a synergism index (SI), in which:

SI = *TR* destruction rate/(*T* destruction rate + *R*/rate) destruction *TR* denoting thermoradiation, *T* thermal, and *R* radiation.

Despite the convincing evidence, presented above, of the synergism noted by means of a thermoradiation process, Emborg (1974) has concluded that thermoradiation is likely to be of little practical use in the sterilization of medical products. Certainly additional data are needed before this conclusion can be substantiated or rejected.

V. *Hydrostatic Pressure*

It was shown in Chapter 8 (Section IV) that hydrostatic pressure initiates germination of bacterial spores and that the germinated spores are then destroyed by this process. Several attempts have been made to potentiate the effect of hydrostatic pressure, and these are considered briefly here.

A. Compression Plus Temperature

One of the most critical parameters affecting the sensitivity of bacterial spores to compression is temperature (Sale *et al.*, 1970; Murrell and Wills, 1977) and the temperatures (°C) required to produce a 50% change in spores compressured to 630 atm for 30 min are as follows (Wills, 1974): *B. cereus* 9, *B. pumilus* 25, *B. subtilis* 39, *B. licheniformis* 47, *B. stearothermophilus* 63. Spores that are highly resistant to heat are usually more resistant to compression and a classical example occurs with *B. stearothermophilus* spores in which germination is not initiated at 25°C by as high a dose as 1500 atm (Wills, 1974). The actual optimum temperature depends on the suspending menstruum (Wills, 1975).

Compressed spores are more susceptible to heat than are control (uncompressed) spores, this degree of subsequent sensitivity to moist heat increasing as the dose and period of compression increase and depending also on the suspending medium (Wills, 1975).

Thus, precompression treatments have reduced the subsequent heat resistance of highly thermoresistant spores such as *B. stearothermophilus*. Additionally, when spores of some species are sublethally heated (below about 65°C) prior to pressurization, they become more sensitive to pressure at the lower temperatures and pressures (Sale *et al.*, 1970).

B. Compression Plus Irradiation

Because of the problem that some spores always appear to survive hydrostatic pressure, Wills (1974, 1975) investigated a combination of hydrostatic pressure plus radiation on *B. pumilus* spores in various menstrua. Compressed spores were found to remain viable until a pressure of 600 atm was reached, but thereafter an increasing lethal effect was observed as the pressure increased to about 1350–1800 atm (depending on menstruum). When pressure and radiation were applied simultaneously, a pressure of only 500 atm was required before the radiation sensitivity of the spores was affected (Wills, 1974). The effect, however, is an additive one, rather than a synergistic one (Wills, 1974, 1975). Pre-irradiation of spores renders the survivors more sensitive to pressure (Sale *et al.*, 1970; Gould, 1973).

Exposure of spores to hydrostatic pressure at the optimum temperatures reduces their subsequent resistance to ionizing radiation.

C. Conclusions

The main problem associated with hydrostatic pressure is the fact that it cannot be relied upon to kill all treated spores (Chapter 8, Section V) and thus cannot be considered alone as a suitable sterilizing treatment. The possibility exists, however, of using it in conjunction with a reduced degree of heat or of radiation dose for sensitive materials.

IV. *Combinations of Chemical Agents*

Insufficient attention appears to have been devoted to the employment as sporicides of chemical agents acting in combination, although there is evidence that two compounds which, individually, are not sporicidal (or are only poorly so) can, when combined, be lethal to spores. This point is well illustrated by the fact that alcohol is not sporicidal and that only high concentrations (9%) of hydrochloric acid are sporicidal, whereas acid alcohol (1% HCl in 70% alcohol) kills spores in 4 h (Coulthard and Sykes, 1936; Sykes, 1970). The hypochlorites are sporicidal agents (Kelsey *et al.*, 1974) but a potentiation of this activity can be achieved in the presence of methanol and other alcohols (Coates and Death, 1978; Death and Coates, 1979) as described more fully in Chapter 6 (Section IV.C). The presence of alcohol does not always result in potentiation, however, since it has been shown that the sporicidal activity of alcoholic solutions of iodine is less than that of aqueous solutions (iodine plus potassium iodide to aid solubility) (Sykes, 1970).

Glutaraldehyde is itself a sporicide but its action may be potentiated by non-ionic surfactants and by metal cations (discussed by Gorman *et al.*, 1980).

VII. *Ultrasonics and Chemical Agents*

There have been several reports of the potentiation of antimicrobial activity by ultrasonic waves.

Ultrasonic waves alone are not sporicidal (Ahmed and Russell, 1975; Boucher, 1979). Probably the most significant findings in relation to

Table 9.10. Sporicidal activity of ultrasonic waves and hydrogen peroxide[a]

Spores	Treatment[b] (at 35°C)	D-value (min)	k value (sec^{-1})
B. cereus	Ultrasonics	—[c]	—[c]
	H_2O_2	13·5	$7·6 \times 10^{-3}$
	Combined (S)	12·0	$19·2 \times 10^{-3}$
	Combined (M)	9·25	$21·9 \times 10^{-3}$
Cl. sporogenes	Ultrasonics	—[c]	—[c]
	H_2O_2	13·0	$16·0 \times 10^{-3}$
	Combined (S)	12·0	$21·9 \times 10^{-3}$
	Combined (M)	6·5	$21·9 \times 10^{-3}$

[a] Based on the data of Ahmed and Russell (1975).
[b] Combined (S) . . . single bottle treated; Combined (M) . . . many bottles treated.
[c] Ultrasonic waves alone had no effect.

Table 9.11. Potentiation by ultrasonic waves of sporicidal activity of disinfectants[a]

Treatment	Result
1. Ultrasonics alone	Not sporicidal
2. Ultrasonics plus	
(a) Glutaraldehyde (alkaline pH)	Not tested?
(b) Glutaraldehyde (acid pH, potentiated)	Sporicidal effect, 60°C
(c) Benzalkonium chloride	Poor sporicidal effect
(d) Hydrogen peroxide	Sporicidal effect
(e) Iodophors	Poor sporicidal effect

[a] Based in part on Boucher (1979).

their possible use in augmenting disinfectant activity have been those made by Shaner (1964), Sierra and Boucher (1971), Ahmed and Russell (1975) and Boucher (1979). A combination of ultrasonic waves with hydrogen peroxide is more lethal than hydrogen peroxide alone to spores of *B. cereus* and *Cl. sporogenes* (Table 9.10).

Glutaraldehyde at acid pH is less active as a sporicidal agent than when used at alkaline pH, but the combination of potentiated acid dialdehyde plus ultrasonics at 60°C is a potent sporicidal mixture.

A summary of the effects of ultrasonic waves in conjunction with different disinfectants is provided in Table 9.11.

VIII. *Other Combined Treatments*

Other combined treatments have also been studied and although it is difficult to come to any firm conclusions as yet, they are worthy of mention.

Ultrasonic waves were shown in Section VII to have little sporicidal activity, and they and sonic waves have, in fact, been employed to separate spore and vegetative forms (Heiligman *et al.*, 1956; Goodenough and Solberg, 1972). Although ultrasonic waves do not affect the heat resistance of some strains of *Bacillus* spores (Ordonez and Burgos, 1976) there is evidence that with other strains the heat resistance decreases significantly (Burgos *et al.*, 1972). Sonically treated spores retain their heat resistance (Berger and Marr, 1960; Goodenough and Solberg, 1972).

A synergistic effect of hydrogen peroxide and UV irradiation has been found to occur (Bayliss and Waites, 1979a,b), although this synergism occurs only when the two agents are used together. It was pointed out in Chapter 6 (Section IV.I) that activation of peroxide to hydroxyl radicals is necessary for sporicidal action. Irradiation of H_2O_2 with far UV also produces hydroxyl radicals, and this might well be the reason for the synergistic response.

IX. *Conclusions*

The various types of combined treatments that have been studied have been considered in this chapter. Two probably stand out as having, over the years, made a significant contribution to safety. The first is the use of bactericidal agents at elevated temperatures, a method which, as described, has important pharmaceutical applications. The other is the incorporation of curing agents into various foods with a view to controlling *Cl. botulinum.*

Of the other combined treatments described, thermoradiation, low temperature steam and formaldehyde, and acid-heat treatment are distinctly useful processes, and of course ways of potentiating the sporicidal activity of liquid- and vapour-phase disinfectants must continue to be investigated.

References

Ahmed, F. I. K. and Russell, C. (1975). *Journal of Applied Bacteriology* **39**, 31–40.

Alder, V. G. (1968). *In* "COSPAR Technique Manual Series No. 4" (P. H. A. Sneath, ed.), pp. 141–155. COSPAR Secretariat, Paris.

Alder, V. G. and Simpson, R. (1982). *In* "Principles and Practice of Disinfection, Preservation and Sterilization" (A. D. Russell, W. B. Hugo and G. A. J. Ayliffe, eds), pp. 433–453. Blackwell Scientific Publications, Oxford.

Alder, V. G., Brown, A. M. and Gillespie, W. A. (1966). *Journal of Clinical Pathology* **19**, 83–89.

Alder, V. G., Bose, E., Gillespie, W. A. and Swann, A. J. (1971). *Journal of Applied Bacteriology* **34**, 757–763.

Alderton, G. and Snell, N. S. (1963). *Biochemical and Biophysical Research Communications* **10**, 139–143.

Alderton, G. and Snell, N. (1969a). *Science, New York* **163**, 1212–1213.

Alderton, G. and Snell, N. (1969b). *Applied Microbiology* **17**, 745–749.

Alderton, G. and Snell, N. (1970). *Applied Microbiology* **19**, 565–572.

Alderton, G., Thompson, P. A. and Snell, N. S. (1964). *Science, New York* **143**, 141–143.

Alderton, G., Ito, K. A. and Chen, J. K. (1976). *Applied and Environmental Microbiology* **31**, 492–498.

Anderson, A. A. and Michener, H. D. (1950). *Food Technology* **4**, 188–189.

Anderson, A. W., Corlett, D. A. and Krabbenhoft, K. L. (1967). *In* "Botulism 1966" (M. Ingram and T. A. Roberts, eds), pp. 76–88. Chapman and Hall, London.

Ando, Y. (1975). *Journal of Bacteriology* **122**, 794–795.

Anellis, A., Berkowitz, D., Swantak, W. and Strojan, C. (1972). *Applied Microbiology* **24**, 453–462.

Anellis, A., Shattock, E., Mori, M., Srisara, B., Qvale, S., Rowley, D. B. and Ross, E. W., Jr. (1977a). *Applied and Environmental Microbiology* **34**, 823–831.

Anellis, A., Shattuck, E., Latt, T., Songpaserchal, S., Rowley, D. B. and Ross, E. W., Jr. (1977b). *In* "Spore Research 1976" (A. N. Barker, J. Wolf, D. J. Ellar, G. J. Dring and G. W. Gould, eds), pp. 631–647. Academic Press, London and New York.

Bayliss, C. E. and Waites, W. M. (1979a). *Journal of Applied Bacteriology* **47**, 263–269.

Bayliss, C. E. and Waites, W. M. (1979b). *FEMS Microbiology Letters* **5**, 331–333.

Bean, H. S. (1967). *Journal of Applied Bacteriology* **30**, 6–16.

Bean, H. S. (1972). *Journal of the Society of Cosmetic Chemists* **23**, 703–720.

Berger, J. A. and Marr, A. G. (1960). *Journal of General Microbiology* **22**, 147–157.

Berry, H., Jensen, E. and Silliker, F. K. (1937). *Quarterly Journal of Pharmacy and Pharmacology* 11, 729–735.

Blake, G. C., Cornick, D. E. R. and Vidic, J. (1977). *Hospital Engineering* 22, 19–21.

Bose, A. N. and Roy, A. K. (1959). *Journal of Scientific and Industrial Research* 18C, 248–250.

Bose, A. N. and Roy, A. K. (1960). *Journal of Scientific and Industrial Research* 19C, 277–279.

Boucher, R. M. G. (1979). *Canadian Journal of Pharmaceutical Sciences* 14, 1–12.

Briggs, A. and Yazdany, S. (1974). *Journal of Applied Bacteriology* 37, 623–631.

Burgos, J., Ordonez, J. A. and Sala, F. A. (1972). *Applied Microbiology* 24, 497–498.

Cameron, E. J. (1940). *Journal of the Association of Official Agricultural Chemists* 23, 607–608.

Coates, D. and Death, J. E. (1978). *Journal of Clinical Pathology* 31, 148–152.

Coulthard, C. E. and Sykes, G. (1936). *Pharmaceutical Journal* 139, 79–81.

Cross, M. H., Simic, M. and Powers, E. L. (1972). *Nature New Biology* 238, 260–261.

Curran, H. R. and Evans, F. R. (1938). *Journal of Bacteriology* 36, 455–465.

Deasy, P. B. (1972). *Manufacturing Chemist and Aerosol News* 43(4), 21–24.

Deasy, P. B., Kuster, E. and Timoney, R. F. (1968). *Applied Microbiology* 16, 810–811.

Deasy, P. B., Kuster, E. and Timoney, R. F. (1970). *Applied Microbiology* 20, 461–464.

Deasy, P. B., Kuster, E. and Timoney, R. F. (1971). *Applied Microbiology* 22, 567–570.

Deasy, P. B., Bhagwan, L. B. and Fitzmaurice, M. P. (1977). *In* "Spore Research 1976" (A. N. Barker, J. Wolf, D. J. Ellar, G. J. Dring and G. W. Gould, eds), pp. 589–602. Academic Press, London and New York.

Death, J. E. and Coates, D. (1979). *Journal of Clinical Pathology* 32, 247–252.

Denny, C. B., Bohrer, C. W., Perkins, W. E. and Townsend, C. E. (1959). *Food Research* 24, 44–50.

Deverill, C. E. A. and Cripps, N. F. (1981). *Journal of Hospital Infection* 2, 175–180.

Duncan, C. L. (1970). *Journal of Applied Bacteriology* 33, 60–73.

Dye, M. and Mead, G. C. (1972). *Journal of Food Technology* 7, 173–181.

El-Bisi, H. M., Snyder, O. P. and Levin, R. E. (1967). *In* "Botulism 1966" (M. Ingram and T. A. Roberts, eds), pp. 89–107. Chapman and Hall, London.

El-Mabsout, Y. E. and Stevenson, K. E. (1979). *Journal of Food Science* 44, 705–709.

Emborg, C. (1974). *Applied Microbiology* 27, 830–833.

Ernst, R. R. and Shull, J. J. (1962). *Applied Microbiology* 10, 337–341.

Ewing, D. (1975). *International Journal of Radiation Biology* 28, 165–176.

Ewing, D. (1976). *Radiation Research* 68, 459–468.

Ewing, D., Fielden, E. M. and Roberts, P. B. (1974). *Radiation Research* 58, 481–488.

Farkas, I., Kiss, I. and Andrassy, E. (1967). *In* "Radiosterilization of Medical Products", pp. 343–354. Proceedings of a Symposium, International Atomic Energy Agency, Vienna.

Fielden, E. M., Ewing, D. and Roberts, P. B. (1974). *Radiation Research* 58, 489–497.

Fisher, D. A. and Pflug, I. J. (1977). *Applied and Environmental Microbiology* 33, 1170–1176.

Frazier, W. C. (1958). "Food Microbiology". McGraw-Hill, New York.

Friedman, Y. S. and Grecz, N. (1973). *Acta Alimentaria* 2, 209–227.

Gibson, G. L. (1977). *Journal of Clinical Pathology* 30, 269–274.

Gombas, D. E. and Gomez, R. F. (1978). *Applied and Environmental Microbiology* 36, 403–407.

Gomez, R. F., Gombas, D. E. and Herrero, A. (1980). *Applied and Environmental Microbiology* 39, 525–529.

Goodenough, E. and Solberg, M. (1972). *Applied Microbiology* **23**, 429–430.

Gorman, S. P., Scott, E. M. and Russell, A. D. (1980). *Journal of Applied Bacteriology* **48**, 161–190.

Gould, G. W. (1973). *Acta Alimentaria* **2**, 377–383.

Gould, G. W. (1978). *In* "Spores VII" (G. Chambliss and J. C. Vary eds), pp. 21–26. American Society for Microbiology, Washington, D.C.

Gould, G. W. and Dring, G. J. (1975). *Nature, London* **285**, 402–405.

Grecz, N. (1965). *Journal of Applied Bacteriology* **28**, 27–35.

Grecz, N., Snyder, O. P., Walker, A. A. and Anellis, A. (1965). *Applied Microbiology* **13**, 527–536.

Grecz, N., Upadhyay, J. and Tang, T. C. (1967). *Canadian Journal of Microbiology* **13**, 287–293.

Grecz, N., Walker, A. A., Anellis, A. and Berkowitz, D. (1971). *Canadian Journal of Microbiology* **17**, 135–142.

Grundy, W. E. (1977). *In* "Disinfection, Sterilization and Preservation" (S. S. Block, ed.), 2nd end, pp. 757–767. Lea and Febiger, Philadelphia.

Handlos, V. (1977). *Archiv for Pharmaci og Chemi Scientific Edition* **5**, 163–169.

Heckley, R. J. and Dimatteo, J. (1975). *Applied Microbiology* **29**, 565–566.

Heiligman, F., Desrosier, N. W. and Broumand, H. (1956). *Food Research* **21**, 63–69.

Ingram, M. (1976). *In* "Microbiology in Agriculture, Fisheries and Food", Society for Applied Bacteriology Symposium Series No. 4 (F. A. Skinner and J. G. Carr, eds), pp. 1–18. Academic Press, London and New York.

Ingram, M. and Roberts, T. A. (1971). *Journal of Food Technology* **6**, 21–28.

Ingram, M. and Thornley, M. J. (1961). *Journal of Applied Bacteriology* **24**, 94–103.

Johnston, M. A., Pivnick, H. and Samson, J. M. (1969). *Canadian Institute of Food Technology Journal* **2**, 52–55.

Kan, B., Goldblith, S. A. and Proctor, B. E. (1957). *Food Research* **22**, 509–518.

Kelsey, J. C., Mackinnon, I. H. and Maurer, I. M. (1974). *Journal of Clinical Pathology* **27**, 632–638.

Kempe, L. L. (1955). *Applied Microbiology* **3**, 346–352.

Kempe, L. L. (1960). *Nucleonics* **18**, 108–112.

Kempe, L. L., Graikoski, J. T. and Bonventre, P. F. (1957). *Applied Microbiology* **5**, 292–295.

Kovacs-Proszt, G. and Farkas, J. (1976). *Acta Alimentaria* **5**, 179–188.

Krabbenhoft, K. L., Corlett, D. A., Jr., Anderson, A. W. and Elliker, P. R. (1964). *Applied Microbiology* **12**, 424–427.

Labbe, R. G. and Duncan, C. L. (1970). *Applied Microbiology* **19**, 353–359.

Lewis, J. C., Michener, H. D., Stumbo, C. R. and Titus, D. S. (1954). *Journal of Agricultural and Food Chemistry* **2**, 298–302.

Licciardello, J. L. and Nickerson, J. T. R. (1963). *Applied Microbiology* **11**, 216–219.

Line, S. J. and Pickerill, J. K. (1973). *Journal of Clinical Pathology* **26**, 716–720.

Lowik, J. A. M. and Anema, P. J. (1972). *Journal of Applied Bacteriology* **35**, 119–121.

Marcos, D. and Wiseman, D. (1979). *Journal of Clinical Pathology* **32**, 567–575.

Mazokhina, N. N., Naidenova, L. P., Rozanova, L. I. and Dashevskaya, T. V. (1973). *Acta Alimentaria* **2**, 385–391.

Michener, H. D., Thompson, P. A. and Lewis, J. C. (1959a). *Applied Microbiology* **7**, 166–173.

Michener, H. D., Thompson, P. A. and Lewis, J. C. (1959b). *Agricultural Research Service*, ARS-74-11. United States Department of Agriculture.

Morgan, B. H. and Reed, J. M. (1954). *Food Research* **19**, 357–366.
Murrell, W. G. and Wills, P. A. (1977). *Journal of Bacteriology* **129**, 1272–1280.
Ordonez, J. A. and Burgos, J. (1976). *Applied and Environmental Microbiology* **32**, 183–184.
Pallas, J. E. and Hamdy, M. K. (1976). *Applied and Environmental Microbiology* **32**, 250–256.
Pharmaceutical Codex (1979). Pharmaceutical Press, London.
Phillips, C. R. (1949). *American Journal of Hygiene* **50**, 280–288.
Powers, E. L. and Cross, M. (1970). *International Journal of Radiation Biology* **17**, 501–514.
Powers, E. L., Cross, M. and Simic, M. (1972). *International Journal of Radiation Biology* **22**, 237–243.
Reynolds, M. C. and Garst, D. M. (1970). *Space Life Sciences* **2**, 394–399.
Reynolds, M. C., Lindell, K. F., David, T. J., Favero, M. S. and Bond, W. W. (1974). *Applied Microbiology* **28**, 406–410.
Richmond, R. C. and Powers, E. L. (1974). *Radiation Research* **58**, 470–480.
Richmond, R. C., Simic, M. and Powers, E. L. (1975). *Radiation Research* **63**, 140–148.
Roberts, T. A. (1975). *Journal of the Science of Food and Agriculture* **26**, 1755–1760.
Russell, A. D. (1974). *Microbios* **10**, 151–174.
Russell, A. D. (1982). *In* "Principles and Practice of Disinfection, Preservation and Sterilization" (A. D. Russell, W. B. Hugo and G. A. J. Ayliffe, eds), pp. 107–133. Blackwell Scientific Publications, Oxford.
Russell, A. D. and Loosemore, M. (1964). *Applied Microbiology* **12**, 403–406.
Russell, A. D., Jenkins, J. and Harrison, I. H. (1967). *Advances in Applied Microbiology* **9**, 1–38.
Sale, A. J. H., Gould, G. W. and Hamilton, W. A. (1970). *Journal of General Microbiology* **60**, 323–334.
Shaner, E. O. (1964). *Journal of the Acoustics Society of America* **36**, 2238–2239.
Sierra, G. and Boucher, R. M. G. (1971). *Applied Microbiology* **22**, 160–164.
Sivinski, H. D. and Reynolds, M. C. (1972). *Life Sciences and Space Research* **10**, 33–34.
Sivinski, H. D., Garst, D. M., Reynolds, M. C., Trauth, C. A., Trujillo, R. E. and Whitfield, W. J. (1973). *In* "Industrial Sterilization" (G. B. Phillips and W. S. Miller, eds), pp. 305–335. Duke University Press, Durham, North Carolina.
Smelt, J. P. P. M., Santos da Silva, M. J. and Haas, H. (1977). *In* "Spore Research 1976" (A. N. Barker, J. Wolf, D. J. Ellar, G. J. Dring and G. W. Gould, eds), pp. 469–485. Academic Press, London and New York.
Sofos, J. N., Busta, F. F. and Allen, C. E. (1979). *Journal of Food Protection* **42**, 739–770.
Sofos, J. N. and Busta, F. F. (1982). *In* "Principles and Practice of Disinfection, Preservation and Sterilization" (A. D. Russell, W. B. Hugo and G. A. J. Ayliffe, eds), pp. 306–342. Blackwell Scientific Publications, Oxford.
Sognefest, P., Hays, G. L., Wheaton, E. and Benjamin, H. A. (1948). *Food Research* **13**, 400–416.
Stegeman, H., Mossel, D. A. A. and Pilnick, W. (1977). *In* "Spore Research 1976" (A. N. Barker, J. Wolf, D. J. Ellar, G. J. Dring and G. W. Gould, eds), pp. 565–587. Academic Press, London and New York.
Steinbuch, E. (1977). *In* "Spore Research 1976" (A. N. Barker, J. Wolf, D. J. Ellar, G.

J. Dring and G. W. Gould, eds), pp. 451–468. Academic Press, London and New York.

Sykes, G. (1970). *Journal of Applied Bacteriology* **33**, 147–156.

Tallentire, A. and Jacobs, G. P. (1972). *International Journal of Radiation Biology* **21**, 205–213.

Tallentire, A. and Jones, A. B. (1973). *International Journal of Radiation Biology* **24**, 345–354.

Thomas, S. and Russell, A. D. (1974). *Applied Microbiology* **28**, 331–335.

Thorpe, R. H. (1960). *Journal of Applied Bacteriology* **23**, 136–145.

Tramer, J. (1964). *4th International Symposium on Food Microbiology*, pp. 25–33. SIK, Göteborg, Sweden.

Trauth, C. A. and Sivinski, H. D. (1975). *In* "Radiosterilization of Medical Products" 1974, pp. 25–42. International Atomic Energy Agency, Vienna.

Trujillo, R. and David, T. (1972). *Applied Microbiology* **23**, 618–622.

Trujillo, R. and Lindell, K. F. (1973). *Applied Microbiology* **26**, 106–110.

Tsuchido, T., Kanda, K. and Shibasaki, I. (1975). *Journal of Fermentation Technology* **12**, 862–868.

Wallace, M. J., Nordsiden, K. L., Wolf, I. D., Thompson, D. R. and Zoltola, E. A. (1978). *Journal of Food Science* **43**, 1738–1740.

Wills, P. A. (1974). *Atomic Energy of Australia* **17**, 2–10.

Wills, P. A. (1975). *In* "Radiosterilization of Medical Products" 1974, pp. 45–61. International Atomic Energy Agency, Vienna.

Xezones, H. and Hutchings, I. J. (1965). *Food Technology* **19**, 113–115.

10

Recovery and Revival of Damaged Spores

I. *Introduction*

This brief chapter serves as a means of bringing together those principles involved in the methods of examining bacterial spores that are injured but not yet dead. In accordance with common practice, the term "recovery" is used in the sense of "getting back" from a sublethal environment, whereas "revival" is employed in its true meaning of resuscitating damaged organisms. "Repair" is used to denote the method(s) by which cells can set aright (repair) the damage inflicted.

An obvious indication that spores are damaged by a process can be obtained by comparing post-treatment counts on different media, e.g. basal media with supplemented media. Spores are complex entities and the germination/outgrowth systems of injured spores may be highly sensitive to agents present in recovery media that have no effect on undamaged cells. This is undoubtedly of academic interest and additionally may serve to pin-point reasons for the increased sensitivity of damaged organisms. Moreover, in a practical sense such findings serve a most important function, since (a) a more accurate assessment of the value of a chemical or physical process can be obtained (as with the employment of biological indicators (BIs) or sterility testing or other procedures to check sterilization methods), (b) the possibility of the presence of damaged spores that are capable of revival in a "sterilized" medical product intended for introduction into the human body or in canned foods meant for human consumption could have serious consequences.

Much time and effect have thus been devoted to investigating those factors that influence the revival of injured bacterial spores, and useful information has accrued. This information, insofar as it applies to the revival of bacterial spores injured by exposure to chemical and physical processes, has often been obtained in a somewhat haphazard, often unscientific, manner. Nevertheless, valuable information has been obtained.

The subject of injured microorganisms is a fascinating one that is now occupying the activities of many microbiologists and of biochemists and molecular biologists who are interested in repair of injury. Several reviews in this field have appeared notably those by Schmidt (1955), Harris (1963), Russell (1964), Corry *et al.* (1977), Hurst (1977), Mossel and Corry (1977), Witter and Ordal (1977), Adams (1978a,b), Busta (1976, 1978), Ray (1979) and Speck and Ray (1979). Many of these papers considered the repair of injury in sporulating and non-sporulating bacteria.

II. *Revival after Thermal Injury*

A. Nature of Thermal Injury

The thermal destruction of non-sporulating cells by moist heat has been attributed to one or more causes, in particular to RNA degradation, DNA degradation, membrane damage and protein coagulation (Allwood and Russell, 1970; Tomlins and Ordal, 1976). Repair of damage in *Staph. aureus* has been linked to a recovery of salt tolerance and may involve regeneration of ribosomal RNA (Tomlins and Ordal, 1976).

In bacterial spores, inactivation by moist heat has been correlated by several authors with DPA leakage (see Chapter 2, Section VII.A, for a comprehensive discussion) but it now appears likely that rehydration of a dehydrated spore core may be a dominant feature in the thermal inactivation of these highly resistant cell forms. This was discussed in more detail in Chapter 2.

B. Factors Influencing Recovery and Revival of Spores

In general terms, bacteria which have survived a treatment harmful to the majority of organisms in that suspension often, but not invariably, require additional factors before they revive and commence multiplication. Some of these cells may produce colonies on "ordinary" (i.e. unsupplemented) agar, and are considered to have been unharmed by the treatment; others will not produce colonies on any media tested, and are thus considered to be "non-viable"; still others will produce colonies only on supplemented agar, and these are termed "damaged" bacteria.

1. *Revival after moist heat*

The revival of heated spores depends on the following factors.

(a) **Composition of recovery medium.** Dickinson *et al.* (1925) found that the germination time of *Cl. botulinum* spores which had survived a heating process could be greatly delayed, even when the spores were placed in an environment suitable for their growth. The value of enrichment substances in the recovery medium in eliminating spore dormancy was noted by Süpfle and Dengler (1916) and Morrison and Rettger (1930a,b). An intensive study of this phenomenon was made by Curran and Evans (1937), who demonstrated that spores which survived drastic treatments, including heat, were more fastidious in their nutritional requirements than untreated spores. A somewhat similar statement, in that the nutritional requirements of thermally-induced sublethally damaged spores are greatly changed, was made by Ernst (1968). Nelson (1943) showed that heat-treated spores of *B. subtilis* gave different counts in different recovery agars. The source of agar may also be important (Harris, 1963).

The early findings thus demonstrated that revival of injured spores was influenced by the composition of the recovery medium. Subsequent studies have confirmed and extended this work. The usefulness of enriched media in enhancing the revival of heat-treated spores has been observed for *B. subtilis* (Edwards *et al.*, 1965a,b), *B. anthracis* (Amaha and Sakaguchi, 1957), *B. stearothermophilus* (Campbell *et al.*, 1965) and PA 3679 (Frank and Campbell, 1955; Augustin and Pflug,

Table 10.1. Influence of recovery medium on the apparent inactivation of *Bacillus stearothermophilus* spores, strain 1518-S, held at 121°C for 12 min[a]

Recovery agar	Additive	Number of survivors[b]
GT[c]	None	$4·96 \times 10^4$
Minimal	None	$2·2 \times 10^1$
Minimal	Casein hydrolysate, 0·5%	$1·4 \times 10^4$
Minimal	Amino acid mixture	$3·42 \times 10^3$
GT[c]	None	$4·87 \times 10^4$
Minimal	None	$2·5 \times 10^1$
Minimal	L-glutamic acid	$1·96 \times 10^3$
Minimal	L-lysine	$5·2 \times 10^1$

[a] Data of Campbell *et al.* (1965).
[b] Original number of spores = 8×10^8.
[c] GT, glucose tryptone agar.

1967). The paper by Campbell *et al.* (1965) is particularly interesting (see Table 10.1) since it suggested to the authors that the requirements for heat-damaged spores were for germination and not for outgrowth (see also Hashimoto *et al.*, 1972). In this context, also, the more recent paper by Kadota *et al.* (1978) should be considered, as these authors found that the repair of injury in heated *B. subtilis* could occur on one type of synthetic medium (Schaeffer's) but not on another (Demain's minimal agar), the main difference between the two being that the former contained a fuller complement of amino acids than the latter. Spores could not form colonies on Demain's minimal agar unless it was supplemented with glycine, threonine or homoserine. However, measurement of colony formation only does not give conclusive evidence for the involvement of germination rather than outgrowth (or vice versa) in the repair process. Nevertheless, the findings that the presence of a known germination stimulant, calcium dipicolinate, stimulates the numbers of stressed *B. subtilis* spores that are able to form colonies (Edwards *et al.*, 1965a,b), and the more detailed studies by Busta and Adams (1972), and Adams and Busta (1972a,b) suggest that in these spores germination is involved in the repair process. Sodium bicarbonate accelerates germination of several *Clostridium* species, and its inclusion in recovery media increases the colony counts of heat stressed *Clostridium* spores (Roberts, 1970).

Stage V forespores of *B. cereus*, sublethally injured by heat, can be revived from the injured state when sucrose or Mg^{2+} is added to the recovery medium (Busta *et al.*, 1976, 1977). Sucrose can be replaced by other agents such as sodium chloride or glycerol, although these are less effective, which suggests that the effect is an osmotic one.

An important finding was made by Cassier and Sebald (1969) who reported that heat-stressed spores of *Cl. perfringens* type A required treatment with lysozyme before injury could be repaired. This work has been confirmed and extended by others (Duncan *et al.*, 1972; Barach *et al.*, 1974; Ando, 1975; Flowers and Adams, 1976; Adams, 1974). Pre-treatment with EDTA may be necessary for lysozyme sensitization (Bradshaw *et al.*, 1977). The same finding has been found to occur markedly with *Cl. botulinum* type E spores, but to a much smaller extent with type A (Sebald and Ionesco, 1974; Alderton *et al.*, 1974). Unheated spores, in contrast, do not require lysozyme for germination, and germination by lysozyme requires pre-treatment with reagents that disrupt disulphide bonds (Gould and Hitchins, 1963; see also Chapter 1). It has also been shown, however, that EDTA or NaOH rapidly sensitizes spores of *Cl. perfringens* type A to lysozyme (Adams, 1973a,b; Barach *et al.*, 1975). Lysozyme does not increase colony counts of heat-damaged *Cl. bifermentans* spores (Waites and Wyatt, 1974). Interestingly, revival of heat-injured spores of *Cl. perfringens* (Cassier and Sebald, 1969) or *B. stearothermophilus* (Labbe, 1969) occurs in agar containing a sterile culture filtrate.

(b) **Presence of inhibitors.** Heat-injured spores of *Cl. perfringens* type A are highly sensitive to mercuric chloride (Toda, 1970), formaldehyde (Toda, 1970) polymyxin, neomycin and kanamycin, but less so to sulphadiazine and D-cycloserine (Barach *et al.*, 1974). With some media in which antibiotics are present, recovery of survivors may still occur because they contain egg yolk emulsion (lysozyme present); conversely, the addition of lysozyme to other media does not improve the numbers of heat-injured spores recovered because the selective agents present in these media interfere with lysozyme action (Barach *et al.*, 1974). Spores injured by UHT or lower heat treatment are unable to outgrow in the presence of neomycin and polymyxin (Chumney and Adams, 1980) and such injured spores show increasing sensitivity to surface-active agents, including quaternary ammonium compounds (Barach *et al.*, 1974; Flowers and Adams, 1976; Adams, 1978a,b). Injured spores undergo repair during outgrowth in a medium lacking antibiotics and during this repair regain resistance simultaneously to these agents (Flowers and Adams, 1976).

Certain recovery media are unsuitable for the revival of heat-damaged spores as certain constituents may be inhibitory to injured spores. Thus, Ernst (1968) has stated that thioglycollate broth is definitely inhibitory to the outgrowth of the *Bacillus* species used for monitoring steam and dry heat sterilization processes. It is, then, of interest in this context to note that thioglycollate inhibits the germination or outgrowth of various *Clostridium* species (Segner *et al.*, 1966; Mossel and Beerens, 1968). Fluid Thioglycollate Medium, U.S.P. is unsuitable for monitoring saturated steam sterilization processes involving *B. stearothermophilus* as the test organism (Davis *et al.*, 1979) possibly because of its inhibitory effect on repair of injury in damaged spores, and has been shown to be inhibitory to the revival of severely heated PA 3679 spores (Wheaton *et al.*, 1959; Wheaton and Pratt, 1961).

Odlaug and Pflug (1977) compared the recovery of heat-treated *Cl. botulinum* spores in yeast extract agar, pork infusion agar and modifications of these media and presented evidence to show that the presence of sodium bicarbonate and sodium thioglycollate in the recovery media gave higher colony counts. Sodium bicarbonate is known to stimulate germination of spores of this organism (Treadwell *et al.*, 1958), some strains of *Cl. butyricum* (Sarathchandra *et al.*, 1974) and of other species of clostridia (Roberts, 1970) and its inclusion in recovery media increases the colony count of heat-stressed *Clostridium* spores (Roberts, 1970). The above finding with sodium thioglycollate is in disagreement with the results, quoted earlier in this section, that show it to be inhibitory.

Other constituents of recovery media that may be inhibitory to heat-damaged spores include bromocresol purple, sodium chloride and sodium nitrite. Bromocresol purple present in Oxoid brand Dextrose Tryptone Broth is harmful to heated spores of *B. stearothermophilus* (Cook and Brown, 1960). Bromothymol blue is likewise inhibitory to heat-stressed spores (Bühlmann *et al.*, 1973). The sodium chloride content of the recovery medium influences the colony counts of heated aerobic and anaerobic spores (Roberts and Ingram, 1966; Roberts *et al.*, 1966a,b; Cook and Gilbert, 1968a,b,c; Pivnick and Thacker, 1970; Ingram and Roberts, 1971; Farkas and Roberts, 1976), the heating process rendering the spores considerably more sensitive to subsequent inhibition by this substance and sodium nitrite (Roberts and Ingram, 1966; see also Jarvis *et al.*, 1976). In actual fact, it is likely that there is an interaction occurring between the various curing agents, pH value and the thermal process (Roberts and Ingram, 1973; Jarvis *et al.*, 1976). The role of nitrite, including heated nitrite in the recovery medium (the "Perigo effect": Perigo *et al.*, 1967), was discussed in Chapter 6 (Section IV.J) and will thus not be repeated in detail here, although a few brief comments will be made. *Clostridium botulinum* type B spores heated at pasteurizing temperatures (70–80°C) become sensitive only to high concentrations of sodium chloride; however, spores heated at higher temperatures become sensitive to lower NaCl concentrations (Jarvis *et al.*, 1976). Sodium chloride, at high concentrations, may also prevent outgrowth of undamaged *Cl. botulinum* spores (Emodi and Lechowich, 1969a,b).

Murrell *et al.* (1950) reported that, as the period of heating increased, surviving spores became increasingly sensitive to the inhibitors present in the recovery medium. Starch (Olsen and Scott, 1946, 1950; Schmidt, 1955; Wynne and Foster, 1948), charcoal and serum albumin (Olsen and Scott, 1950) improved the effectiveness of most of the recovery media to which they were added. Although the reason for the effectiveness of starch is not fully known, it has been shown that small quantities of unsaturated fatty acids inhibited germination of *Cl. botulinum* spores, and that this inhibition could be overcome by the addition of starch (Foster and Wynne, 1948). It thus seems likely that starch and the other materials adsorb inhibitory substances present in the recovery media. The stimulatory effect of pea extract on the recovery and revival of heat-stressed putrefactive anaerobe spores is likely to result from the presence of starch, since the effect is eliminated by α-amylase (Ashton, 1971).

Thus, in conclusion, it appears that there are various types of factors present in recovery media that can influence the revival or repair of sublethally heat-injured bacterial spores. These are the requirements for non-nutrient germination stimulants (Adams, 1978a); the fact that the spores may become increasingly sensitive to their nutritional environment (Augustin and Pflug, 1967; Adams, 1978a,b); and the presence of substances that are inhibitory to injured, but not to normal, spores.

Examples of recovery media used by various authors are given in Table 10.2 (see also Table 10.3). It is worthy of note that, despite the investigations described above, several authors give no reason for choosing a particular medium, so that it is often not known whether the use of an alternative medium would have considerably altered their findings.

(c) **pH of recovery media.** There is comparatively little information available on the effect which the pH of the recovery medium has on the revival of sublethally heated bacterial spores. With heated non-sporing bacteria, the optimum pH of the medium is approximately 6–6·5 (Allwood *et al.*, 1968). Yokoya and York (1965) found that the composition of the recovery medium affected the apparent heat resistance of *B*.

stearothermophilus spores when the pH of the recovery medium was 7, but not 6·5. The optimum pH for the recovery of *B. stearothermophilus* spores is considered to be 7·4 (Cook and Brown, 1965a,b,c), although no reasons for this were given. Similar findings have been made by Roberts (1970).

(d) **Temperature of incubation.** When heat-damaged cells of non-sporulating bacteria such as *Staph. aureus* or *E. coli* are transferred to an appropriate recovery medium, revival occurs to a greater extent at incubation temperatures below those considered optimal for unheated cells (Allwood *et al.*, 1968). From the limited data available (Sugiyama, 1952; Williams and Reed, 1942; Edwards *et al.*, 1965a,b), it appears that a similar conclusion applies to heated spores of *Cl. botulinum* and *B. subtilis*. The reason for this finding is not known, but may be connected with a repair of thermal injury (Edwards *et al.*, 1965a,b). Futter and Richardson (1970a,b; 1972) observed that optimum recovery of therm-ally-injured spores of *Cl. perfringens* occurred at 27°C; Cook and Gilbert (1968a,b) found optimum recovery with *B. stearothermophilus* at 45–50°C. In both instances, these recovery temperatures were below the optimum for unheated spores.

More recent studies using a gradient temperature incubator (Prentice and Clegg, 1974) showed that unheated *B. subtilis* spores showed similar counts at 16–48°C whereas thermally injured spores had an optimum recovery temperature of 30°C. As a result of this investiga-tion, it was concluded by the authors that outgrowth rather than germination was sensitive to temperature (*cf.* earlier).

(e) **Period of incubation.** Following exposure to deleterious processes, spores may require longer periods than usual to germinate, and in consequence, growth (turbidity, colony count) of vegetative cells may be delayed. This is a point which should obviously not be overlooked when survivor levels from heated spores are being determined.

In a practical context, this can be an important factor in the assess-ment of food can spoilage, in the evaluation of BIs, in fractional exposure validation studies and in sterility testing procedures.

2. *Revival and recovery after dry heat*

Russell (1971) pointed out that there was then little information available as to the effect of the composition and pH of the recovery medium, of the incubation temperature, on the recovery of bacterial spores exposed to dry heat. At that time, it was considered that the most

Table 10.2. Examples of recovery conditions for determining the survival of some thermally treated strains of bacterial spores

Organism	Recovery[a] media	Incubation temp range (°C)	References
B. stearothermophilus	DTB; DTB without BCP; AA + S; DTA	50–56	Cook and Brown (1960, 1965a,b); Cook and Gilbert (1965); Fields and Finley (1962); Briggs (1966)
B. subtilis	TYE + NaCl; "P" medium + S; Blood agar base; Modified TA + S; TDSS; TGE; FNA; CNA; PCA; BHI agar; NA ± 6% NaCl	30–45 (16–48: Prentice and Clegg, 1974)	Walker et al. (1961); Lechowich and Ordal (1962); Licciardello and Nickerson (1963); Walker and Matches (1966); Briggs (1966); Put and Aalsberberg (1967); Busta and Adams (1972); Prentice and Clegg (1974); Tsuchido et al. (1975)
B. cereus	TYE + NaCl; "P" medium + S; AA	30–37	Walker et al. (1961); Walker and Matches (1966); Briggs (1966); Walker and Matches (1966)
B. megaterium	"P" medium + S; TYE + NaCl; Blood agar base; NA + 0·1% YE	30–37	Walker et al. (1961); Levison and Hyatt (1964)
B. polymyxa	"P" medium + S; TYE + NaCl	30	Walker et al. (1961); Walker and Matches (1966)
B. coagulans	TA + S; modified TA + S	45	El-Bisi and Ordal (1956); Lechowich and Ordal (1962)
Various Clostridium species	RCA	30	Roberts et al. (1966a)
Cl. sporogenes	RCA; various media	37	Wheaton and Pratt (1961); Roberts et al. (1966b); Augustin and Pflug (1967)
Cl. botulinum Type E	PIA + T; RCA	30	Marshall et al. (1963); Roberts and Ingram (1965); Wheaton et al. (1959); Marshall et al. (1963); Odlaug and Pflug (1977)
Type B	PIA + T; YE agar; PIA; various	30–37	

Table 10.2. (cont.)

Type A	YE agar; PIA	32	Odlaug and Pflug (1977)
Cl. perfringens	BHI + FT; RCA or RCM; TS; TYCS ± lysozyme	37	Barnes et al. (1963); Nakamura and Converse (1967; Barach et al. (1974, 1975); Adams (1973, 1974)
Cl. tyrobutyricum	RCA	37	Cerf et al. (1967)
Cl. bifermentans	PIA + T	30	Marshall et al. (1963)

[a] DTB, dextrose tryptone broth; AA, antibiotics assay medium; S, 0·1% soluble starch; DTA, dextrose tryptone agar; TYE, trypticase yeast extract; NA, nutrient agar; TDSS, tryptone-dextrose-soluble starch-sterile soil; TGE, tryptone glucose extract; TA, thermoacidurans agar; RCA, reinforced clostridial agar; RCM, reinforced clostridial medium; PIA, pork infusion agar; T, 0·1% sodium thioglycollate; BHI, brain heart for infusion; TS media, tryptone sulphite agar + antibiotics; TYCS, trypticase-yeast extract-citrate-sulphite agar; FNA, fortified nutrient agar; CNA, FNA + CaCl$_2$ + sodium dipicolinate; PCA, plate count agar; BHI agar, brain heart infusion agar; BHI + FT, brain heart infusion + thioglycollate.

Table 10.3. Influence of recovery medium and incubation temperature on D-values of B. stearothermophilus exposed to moist heat[a,b]

Treatment temp (°C)	Highest D-value (min) at recovery temp of (°C)				Lowest D-value (min) at recovery temp of (°C)			
	50	57	62	65	50	57	62	65
116	7·57	7·45	6·87	5·54	3·31	2·91	3·16	2·39
121	2·04	1·88	1·77	1·43	0·7	0·64	0·68	0·51
132	0·17	0·16	0·15	0·12	0·05	0·04	0·04	—

[a] Dervied from the data of Davis et al. (1973).
[b] Four recovery media were tested, viz. Trypticase soy broth, Columbia broth, Eugonbroth and Fluid thioglycollate medium. The highest D-values were always recorded in Eugonbroth and the lowest in Fluid thioglycollate medium.

Table 10.4. Influence of recovery medium and incubation temperature on D-values of *B. subtilis* var. *globigii* exposed to dry heat or ethylene oxide[a]

Treatment and temp (°C)		Highest D-value (min) at recovery temp of (°C)			Lowest D-value (min) at recovery temp of (°C)		
		30	37	42	30	37	42
Dry heat	130	12·43T[b]	12·22C	10·85E	6·53F	6·28F	5·85F
	140	7·11C	6·49C	6·19C	3·72F	3·53F	3·14F
	150	3·35C	3·46C	3·41C	2·17F	2·22F	2·17F
Ethylene oxide	54	3·69ET[c]	3·24E	3·93C	1·73F	1·68F	1·58F
	63	2·46E	2·19C	1·95C	1·63F	1·08F	0·96F
	71	1·37C	1·25C	1·09C	0·82F	0·84F	0·78F

[a] Derived from the data of Davis *et al.* (1979).
[b] Four recovery media were tested: T, Trypticase soy broth; C, Columbia broth; E, Eugonbroth; F, Fluid thioglycollate medium.
[c] Same value obtained in Eugonbroth and Trypticase soy broth.

important findings had been made by Augustin and Pflug (1967) and these are considered below together with more recent information.

Most authors appear to use Trypticase soy agar (or broth) or Tryptone glucose extract agar as the recovery medium. Occasionally, the latter may be reinforced by the addition of soluble starch (0·1%) and yeast extract. Some authors use Plate count agar. Few if any reasons are published to explain why a particular medium is chosen, but recent work does in fact provide evidence to show that Tryptone glucose is a far better recovery medium for damaged *Bacillus* spores than are other media, especially a minimal one (Gurney and Quesnel, 1980). The recent findings of Davis *et al.* (1979), presented in Table 10.4, are of especial interest, because they demonstrate clearly that:

(i)   Thioglycollate medium is inhibitory to spores damaged by dry heat;

(ii) Columbia broth is generally the best of the four media tested (the composition of the media is considered in Section IV.B);

(iii) higher D-values are obtained when recovery media are incubated at lower temperatures.

Eugonbroth and a synthetic medium had previously been shown to be less suitable than other media for the recovery of dry heat-damaged spores of PA 3679 (Augustin and Pflug, 1967; Table 10.5).

There is still, however, a comparative paucity of information on recovery and revival and on repair processes in spores following damage by dry heat.

Table 10.5. Effect of subculture medium on the dry heat resistance of spores of PA 3679[a]

Treatment temp (°C)	*D*-value (min) in various subculture media						
	Beef infusion	Liver infusion	Pea infusion	Yeast extract	Trypti-case	Eugon-broth	Synthetic medium
123·9[b]	133	125	134	138	140	96	—
123·9[c]	181	189	179	183	174	150	143

[a] Data of Augustin and Pflug (1967).
[b] Freshly prepared spores used.
[c] Spores stored for 5–9 months before use.

III. *Revival after Radiation Injury*

Considerably less information is available on the recovery and revival of irradiated bacterial spores than with thermally injured spores. Various recovery media and incubation have been used by various authors for determining the survival of irradiated bacterial spores. Examples of such conditions are proved in Table 10.6, which indicates that authors are sometimes less than specific with regard to their details for determining survival. Woese (1958) found that there was no effect on survival of X-irradiated spores of *B. subtilis*, *B. brevis* and *B. mesentericus* if the post-irradiation counting medium was changed from a yeast extract medium to a chemically defined one, and Freeman and Bridges (1959) and Bridges (1964) pointed out that the composition of the recovery medium did not influence the survival counts of irradiated spores of *B. subtilis*. These findings might suggest that irradiated spores are insensitive to the recovery conditions used, whereas various authors have shown that certain irradiated spores are, in fact, sensitive to such environments. Roberts *et al.* (1965) found that whereas the presence of sodium chloride during irradiation was without effect on the radiation resistance of spores of *Cl. sporogenes* and *Cl. oedematiens* type C, increasing doses of γ-radiation rendered the spores increasingly sensitive to post-irradiation inhibition by sodium chloride in the plating medium. This has been confirmed for *Cl. botulinum* (Chowdhury *et al.*, 1976; Rowley *et al.*, 1974). The more radiation-resistant *Cl. botulinum* strains are also more resistant to sodium chloride than are radiation-sensitive ones (Kiss *et al.*, 1978). Thioglycollate medium, inhibitory to thermally damaged spores, is also harmful to radiation-damaged spores of *B. pumilus* E601 (Kereluk, 1977). Optimal recovery of radiation-

Table 10.6. Examples of recovery conditions for determining the survival of some irradiated strains of bacterial spores

Organism	Recovery media[a]	Incubation temperature (°C)	References
Various *Bacillus* species	TSB	37	Pepper *et al.* (1956)
B. subtilis	BA; TGY; NA; NA + G; TGES	30–37	Christensen and Sehested (1964), Christensen and Holm (1964), Terano *et al.* (1971), Deasy *et al.* (1970), Härnulv and Snygg (1973)
B. globigii	BA; TGY	?	Christensen and Sehested (1964), Christensen and Holm (1964)
B. stearo-thermophilus	NB; TGES	55–60	Darmady *et al.* (1961), Härnulv and Snygg (1973)
B. pumilus	NA; SW; BA; TGY; CB[b]; TSA	30–37[b]	Burt and Freeman (1963), Farkas *et al.* (1967) Christensen and Holm (1964), [b]Kereluk (1977), Prince (1978)
B. cereus	SW	30	Farkas *et al.* (1967)
B. megaterium	NA + Y; NA + G	30–37	Levinson and Hyatt (1960), Tallentire and Jacobs (1972), Tallentire and Powers (1963), Tallentire *et al.* (1963)
B. coagulans	SW	45	Farkas *et al.* (1967)
Various *Clostridium* species	RCM	37	Roberts and Ingram (1965)
Cl. tetani	RMB[c]	37	Darmady *et al.* (1961)
Cl. oedematiens type C	RCM	37	Roberts *et al.* (1965)
Cl. sporogenes	RCM; CMM; EB; FTM; Fortified BHI	37	Pepper *et al.* (1956) Roberts *et al.* (1965), Borick and Fogarty (1967)
Cl. botulinum	WA; WBA; MWB; Thiotone; PPI	30–37	Anellis *et al.* (1965, 1967), Grecz *et al.* (1967), Riemann (1960), Durban *et al.* (1974), Kiss *et al.* (1978), Rowley *et al.* (1974)

[a] TSB, trypticase soy broth; TSA, trypticase soy agar; BA, blood agar; TGY tryptone glucose yeast extract agar; NB, nutrient broth; NA, nutrient agar; NA + G, nutrient agar + glucose; SW, sweet whey + yeast extract + meat extract + peptone ± 2% agar; NA + Y, nutrient agar + yeast extract; RCM, reinforced clostridial medium; CMM, cooked meat medium; EB, eugonbroth; FTM, fluid thioglycollate medium; BHI, brain heart infusion; WA, Wynne's agar; WBA, Wynne's broth + 1·5% agar; MWB, modified Wynne's broth; PPI, pork pea infusion; TGES, tryptone-glucose-extract agar + 0·1% soluble starch.
[b] CB (Columbia broth) was found by Kereluk (1977) to be far superior to any other recovery medium tested, with an optimum incubation temperature of 32°C.
[c] RMB, Robertson's meat broth, followed by subculture on to blood agar under anaerobic conditions.

exposed spores of this organism occurs in Columbia broth at pH 7–8 (Kereluk, 1977). Farkas *et al.* (1967) found that irradiation increased the sensitivity of *B. pumilus* E601 and *B. cereus* to the pH of the recovery medium.

Irradiated aqueous suspensions of *B. subtilis* spores survive better at a post-treatment temperature of 20°C than at 0°C (Cook and Roberts, 1963). There is, in fact, a comparative dearth of information on the influence of post-irradiation incubation temperature, although working with *Cl. botulinum* 62A spores, Chowdhury *et al.* (1976) have shown that whereas colony formation with unirradiated spores was not influenced by temperature, irradiated spores had an optimum temperature of 40°C. Highest counts of irradiated *Bacillus F* spores are obtained with media of acid pH (Roberts, 1970) although the reasons for this are unclear. In contrast, with *Cl. perfringens*, highest counts are achieved with media of alkaline pH (Futter, 1968).

The method of determining survivors may also be of importance, since surface-spread counts on agar have been shown to be much greater than tube dilution counts by the most probable number (MPN) method (Cook *et al.*, 1964).

These relatively few reports suggest that more attention should be paid to the problem of revival of irradiated spores. It is, of course, conceivable that authors have determined the optimum recovery conditions for the particular strain used, although the impression which is often, if not invariably, conveyed to the reader is that a particular set of recovery conditions has been used merely on account of a personal preference. The particular instance of *B. pumilus* E601 in Table 10.6 is a case in point: would each of the media tested by the authors cited give the same survival counts? In the light of the recent findings of Kereluk (1977), the answer to this question is probably not. In general terms, if counts on different media differ markedly, how do these differences affect the shape of dose–survivor curves, *D*-values, IF values and—most importantly—the safety of any consumable or medically employed product? Russell (1971) opined that too much time and effort could be spent on investigating a whole range of recovery conditions, although both he and Goldblith (1967) considered that more information on radiation damage, recovery media and above all, repair processes, was needed. Since then, some light has been shed on the nature of the repair processes in radiation sublethally-injured spores. Radiation-injured spores of *Cl. botulinum* 62A are better capable of repair at 40°C than at other temperatures; repair is associated with outgrowth and is prevented by inhibitors of protein synthesis, but not by cell wall inhibitors (Chowdhury *et al.*, 1976). In contrast, in *B. subtilis*, rejoining of radiation-induced single-strand breaks in DNA occurs in germinating spores (Terano *et al.*, 1969, 1971), although it has also been claimed that direct enzymatic repair can take place in dormant spores in the absence of germination (Durban *et al.*, 1974).

IV. *Recovery and Revival after Chemically-induced Injury*

A. Liquid Phase Disinfectants

Information on the recovery revival of spores after exposure to chemicals is still sparse. This can at least partly be ascribed to the fact that many agents do not induce a significant reduction in colony forming units and consequently there has been little point in investigating optimum recovery conditions. When the sporicidal activity of such agents is enhanced, however (e.g. at elevated temperatures: Chapter 9, Section II.B), or when true sporicidal agents are being studied, it would seem logical to investigate the factors influencing the recovery and revival of the treated spores.

The composition of the recovery agar may influence the apparent numbers of survivors. The inclusion of germination stimulants such as L-alanine and D-glucose has been shown to increase the numbers of colony forming units of *B. subtilis* spores exposed to high phenol concentrations at elevated temperatures (Russell and Loosemore, 1964). Following exposure to hydrogen peroxide, spores of *B. cereus* recover best in Plate Count Agar (PCA) containing starch (Neal and Walker, 1977), PA 3679 spores in PCA containing glutathione (Neal and Walker, 1977) and *B. subtilis* var. *niger* in W (Wang *et al.*, 1964) medium (Wallen and Walker, 1979). The findings of Wallen and Walker (1979) suggested to the authors that the sporicidal action of peroxide was less than previously considered. Most types of chlorine-treated clostridial spores recover equally well on Reinforced Clostridial Agar (RCA) and Sulphite-Polymyxin-Sulphadiazine (SPS) agar (Dye and Mead, 1972). Tego compounds (amphoteric surfactants) have no sporicidal properties at ordinary temperatures, but are markedly sporicidal to *B. subtilis* var. *niger* spores at elevated temperatures. Spores surviving this combined treatment lose their salt tolerance and are highly sensitive to sodium chloride (Tsuchido *et al.*, 1975).

The pH of the recovery medium should also be considered, as should the temperature and period of incubation. Maximum recovery of peroxide-treated spores occurs around neutrality (Neal and Walker, 1977; Wallen and Walker, 1979) and at this optimum level recovery takes a shorter period than at other pH values (Wallen and Walker, 1979). Incubation temperature seems to have no important role (Dye and Mead, 1972; Wallen and Walker, 1979).

This necessarily brief report indicates that perhaps a better knowledge of spore recovery and revival is needed.

B. Gaseous Disinfectants

The value of gaseous disinfectants, in particular ethylene oxide (EO) was discussed in Chapter 7. An important factor in assessing their sporicidal activity is the composition of the recovery medium (Table 10.4) and Doyle *et al.* (1968) showed that thioglycollate broth did not support the growth of *B. subtilis* var. *niger* spores which were entrapped or held, whereas trypticase soy broth was a suitable recovery medium. The inhibitory effect of thioglycollate on the recovery and revival of ethylene oxide-damaged spores is well depicted in Table 10.4 (based on the data of Davis *et al.*, 1979). *D*-values of spores recovered in thioglycollate medium are well below those in the other test media, and generally the highest values are recorded in Columbia broth. A comparison of Columbia broth (presumably Columbia agar without the agar component), Eugonbroth and Trypticase soy broth (all BBL, Cockeysville, Maryland, U.S.A.) does not, in fact, provide any real clue as to why it should be the most effective.

Whitbourne and Reich (1979) in their studies on biological indicators for monitoring ethylene oxide sterilization recommend the use of Trypticase soy broth as recovery medium.

Also of interest from Table 10.4 is the fact that post-treatment incubation temperature is important, the highest *D*-values occurring at the lowest (30°C) of the three temperatures tested. *Cl. perfringens* spores exposed to EO recover better at 31°C than at 37°C and there is evidence that prolonged incubation may be needed to obtain maximum revival (Futter and Richardson, 1972c). This may be associated with the fact that ethylene oxide, at sublethal concentrations, induces a delay in outgrowth of spores, although germination is unaffected (Reich, 1980).

V. *Summary and Conclusions*

There is no doubt that recovery conditions for estimating numbers of spores surviving an inimical treatment are of considerable importance in assessing its sporicidal efficacy. In particular, the composition of the recovery medium, notably the presence of inhibitory substances (e.g.

sodium chloride, sodium thioglycollate) or of germination stimulants, plays a significant role. Damaged spores may be sensitive to substances that have no effect on untreated spores, and it cannot be emphasized too strongly that this can have very important applications in the pharmaceutical and food contexts (see Section I). The various factors that have been shown to play an important part in assessing sporicidal activity of the available processes are summarized in Table 10.7.

Some comments should, perhaps, be devoted to sodium thioglycollate. Ever since the use of thioglycollate by Brewer (1939), media containing this compound have been used for the growth of anaerobic

Table 10.7. Factors in the recovery and revival of spores following exposure to chemical or physical processes

Process	Factors

Moist heat	1. Composition of recovery medium
	  (a) *Nutritional factors*
	    Complex
	    Minimal + amino acids
	  (b) *Non-nutrient germination stimulants*
	    Lysozyme
	    Calcium dipicolinate[a]
	    Sodium bicarbonate (for *Clostridium* spp.)
	  (c) *Presence of inhibitors*
	    Thioglycollate
	    Sodium nitrite
	    Sodium chloride
	    Dyes
	  (d) *Removal of some inhibitors*
	    Starch, pea extract
	  (e) *Other considerations*
	    Sucrose
	    Mg^{2+}
	2. pH of recovery medium
	  Below or at optimum for undamaged spores?
	3. Temperature of incubation
	  Below optimum for undamaged spores

Dry heat	1. Composition of recovery medium
	  (a) *Nutritional factors*
	    Complex
	  (b) *Presence of inhibitors*
	    Thioglycollate
	    Others?
	2. pH of recovery medium
	3. Temperature of incubation
	  Below optimum for undamaged spores

Table 10.7—*contd.*

Process	Factors

Ionizing radiation	1. Composition of recovery medium
	   (a) *Nutritional factors*
	   (b) *Presence of inhibitors*
	      Thioglycollate
	      Sodium chloride

Ionizing radiation	2. pH of recovery medium pH 7–8? 3. Temperature of incubation

Liquid-phase disinfectants	1. Composition of recovery medium
	   (a) *Germination stimulants*
	   (b) *Presence of inhibitors*
	2. pH of recovery medium
	3. Temperature of incubation
	   No important role?

Gaseous disinfectants	1. Composition of recovery medium
	   (a) *Nutritional factors*
	      Columbia broth?
	   (b) *Presence of inhibitors*
	      Thioglycollate
	      Others?
	2. pH of recovery medium?
	3. Temperature of incubation
	     Below optimum for undamaged spores
	4. Period of incubation

[a] Although DPA and analogues of dipicolinate di-anion induce germination of undamaged spores of *B. stearothermophilus* (Lewis and Colman, 1974), dipicolinate does, in fact, inhibit elongation and vegetative growth in this organism (Fields and Frank, 1973).

organisms. Various workers have, however, claimed that thioglycollate is inhibitory to "normal" clostridia spores, as pointed out earlier, and there is little doubt that it can be inhibitory to injured spores, especially when *Bacillus* spores are involved. Clark (1943) pointed out that growth of unspecified thermophilic anaerobes was retarded in thioglycollate media, whereas Ting and Fung (1972) noted that the simultaneous presence of sodium thioglycollate and sodium glutamate was necessary for sporulation and growth of *Cl. perfringens* strains.

Thus, it would be logical to avoid media containing sodium thioglycollate for recovering or enumerating injured bacterial spores, unless it can be shown that thioglycollate is not inhibitory to the test organisms. Some of the published discrepancies could, in fact, be the result of

L

differences in response to thioglycollate, and thioglycollate appears to be non-toxic to the germination of *Cl. tetani* spores (Shoesmith and Holland, 1972).

The process of repair in injured spores is complicated and generally only poorly understood. Evidence has been presented which shows that dormant spores can repair strand breaks in DNA induced by ionizing radiation, but more usually repair is associated with germination or outgrowth.

References

Adams, D. M. (1973a). *Applied Microbiology* 26, 282–287.

Adams, D. M. (1973b). *Journal of Bacteriology* 116, 500–502.

Adams, D. M. (1974). *Applied Microbiology* 27, 797–801.

Adams, D. M. (1978a). *In* "Spores VII" (G. Chambliss and J. C. Vary, eds), pp. 15–16. American Society for Microbiology, Washington, D.C.

Adams, D. M. (1978b). *Advances in Applied Microbiology* 23, 245–261.

Adams, D. M. and Busta, F. F. (1972a). *In* "Spores V" (H. O. Halvorson, R. Hanson and L. L. Campbell, eds), pp. 368–377. American Society for Microbiology, Washington D.C.

Adams, D. M. and Busta, F. F. (1972b). *Applied Microbiology* 24, 418–423.

Alderton, G., Chen, J. K. and Ito, K. A. (1974). *Applied Microbiology* 27, 613–615

Allwood, M. C. and Russell, A. D. (1970). *Advances in Applied Microbiology* 12, 89–119.

Allwood, M. C., Harries, D. and Russell, A. D. (1968). Unpublished data.

Amaha, M. and Sakaguchi, K. (1957). *Journal of General and Applied Microbiology* 3, 163–192.

Ando, Y. (1975). *Journal of Bacteriology* 122, 794–795.

Anellis, A., Grecz, N. and Berkowitz, D. (1965). *Applied Microbiology* 13, 397–401.

Anellis, A., Berkowitz, D., Jarboe, C. and El-Bisi, H. M. (1967). *Applied Microbiology* 15, 166–177.

Ashton, D. H. (1971). *Applied Microbiology* 21, 38–40.

Augustin, J. A. L. and Pflug, I. J. (1967). *Applied Microbiology* 15, 266–276.

Barach, J. T., Adams, D. M. and Speck, M. L. (1974). *Applied Microbiology* 28, 793–797.

Barach, J. T., Flowers, R. S. and Adams, D. M. (1975). *Applied Microbiology* 30, 873–875.

Barnes, E. M., Despaul, J. E. and Ingram, M. (1963). *Journal of Applied Bacteriology* 26, 415–427.

Borick, P. M. and Fogarty, M. G. (1967). *Applied Microbiology* 15, 785–789.

Bradshaw, J. G., Peeler, J. T. and Twedt, R. M. (1977). *Applied and Environmental Microbiology* 34, 280–284.

Brewer, J. H. (1939). *Journal of the American Medical Association,* 112, 2009–2018.

Bridges, B. A. (1964). *Progress in Industrial Microbiology* 5, 283–326.

Briggs, A. (1966). *Journal of Applied Bacteriology* 29, 490–504.

Bühlmann, X., Gay, M. and Schiller, I. (1973). *Pharmaceutica Acta Helvetiae* 48, 223–244.

Burt, M. M. and Freeman, F. J. (1963). *Journal of Applied Bacteriology* **26**, 484–489.

Busta, F. F. (1976). *Journal of Milk and Food Technology* **39**, 138–145.

Busta, F. F. (1978). *Advances in Applied Microbiology* **23**, 195–200.

Busta, F. F. and Adams, D. M. (1972). *Applied Microbiology* **24**, 412–417.

Busta, F. F., Baillie, E. and Murrell, W. G. (1976). *Applied and Environmental Microbiology* **32**, 312–314.

Busta, F. F., Baillie, E. and Murrell, W. G. (1977). *In* "Spore Research 1976" (A. N. Barker, J. Wolf, D. J. Ellar, G. J. Dring and G. W. Gould, eds), pp. 431–451. Academic Press, London and New York.

Campbell, L. L., Richards, C. M. and Sniff, E. E. (1965). *In* "Spores III" (L. L. Campbell and H. O. Halvorson, eds), pp. 55–63. American Society for Microbiology, Washington, D.C.

Cassier, M. and Sebald, M. (1969). *Annales de L'Institut Pasteur* **117**, 312–324.

Cerf, O. (1977). *Journal of Applied Bacteriology* **42**, 1–19.

Cerf, O., Bergere, J. L. and Hermier, J. (1967). *Journal of Dairy Research* **34**, 221–229.

Chowdhury, M. S. U., Rowley, D. B., Anellis, A. and Levinson, H. S. (1976). *Applied and Environmental Microbiology* **21**, 172–178.

Christensen, E. A. and Holm, N. W. (1964). *Acta Pathologica et Microbiologica Scandinavica* **63**, 253–264.

Christensen, E. A. and Sehested, K. (1964). *Acta Pathologica et Microbiologica Scandinavica* **62**, 448–458.

Chumney, R. K. and Adams, D. M. (1980). *Journal of Applied Bacteriology* **49**, 55–63.

Clark, F. M. (1943). *Food Research* **8**, 327–336.

Cook, A. M. and Brown, M. R. W. (1960). *Journal of Pharmacy and Pharmacology* **12**, 116T–118T.

Cook, A. M. and Brown, M. R. W. (1965a). *Journal of Pharmacy and Pharmacology* **17**, 1S–6S.

Cook, A. M. and Brown, M. R. W. (1965b). *Journal of Pharmacy and Pharmacology* **17**, 7S–11S.

Cook, A. M. and Brown, M. R. W. (1965c). *Journal of Applied Bacteriology* **28**, 361–364.

Cook, A. M. and Gilbert, R. J. (1968a). *Journal of Pharmacy and Pharmacology* **20**, 626–629.

Cook, A. M. and Gilbert, R. J. (1968b). *Journal of Pharmacy and Pharmacology* **20**, 803–804.

Cook, A. M. and Gilbert, R. J. (1968c). *Journal of Applied Bacteriology* **32**, 96–102.

Cook, A. M. and Gilbert, R. J. (1975). *Journal of Pharmacy and Pharmacology* **17**, 205–215.

Cook, A. M. and Roberts, T. A. (1963). *Journal of Pharmacy and Pharmacology* **15**, 345–346.

Cook, A. M., Roberts, T. A. and Widdowson, J. P. (1964). *Journal of General Microbiology* **34**, 185–193.

Corry, J. E. L., Doorne, H. van and Mossel, D. A. A. (1977). *In* "Antibiotics and Antibiosis in Agriculture" (M. Woodbine, ed.), pp. 174–196. Butterworths, London.

Curran, H. R. and Evans, F. R. (1937). *Journal of Bacteriology* **34**, 179–189.

Darmady, E. M., Hughes, K. E. A., Jones, J. D., Prince, D. and Tuke, W. (1961). *Journal of Clinical Pathology* **14**, 38–44.

Davis, S. B., Carls, R. A. and Gillis, J. R. (1979). *Developments in Industrial Microbiology* **20**, 427–438.

Deasy, P. B., Kuster, E. and Timoney, R. F. (1970). *Applied Microbiology* **20**, 461–464.

Dickinson, E. C., Burke, G. S., Beck, D. and Johnston, J. (1925). *Journal of Infectious Diseases* **36**, 472–483.

Doyle, J. E., Mehrhof, W. H. and Ernst, R. R. (1968). *Applied Microbiology* **16**, 1742–1744.

Duncan, C. L., Labbe, R. G. and Reich, R. R. (1972). *Journal of Bacteriology* **109**, 550–559.

Durban, E., Grecz, N. and Farkas, J. (1974). *Journal of Bacteriology* **118**, 129–138.

Dye, M. and Mead, G. C. (1972). *Journal of Food Technology* **7**, 173–181.

Edwards, J. L., Busta, F. F. and Speck, M. L. (1955a). *Applied Microbiology* **13**, 851–857.

Edwards, J. L., Busta, F. F. and Speck, M. L. (1965b). *Applied Microbiology* **13**, 858–864.

El-Bisi, H. M. and Ordal, Z. J. (1956). *Journal of Bacteriology* **71**, 1–9.

Emodi, A. S. and Lechowich, R. V. (1969a). *Journal of Food Science* **34**, 78–81.

Emodi, A. S. and Lechowich, R. V. (1969b). *Journal of Food Science* **34**, 82–87.

Ernst, R. R. (1968). *In* "Disinfection, Sterilization and Preservation" (C. A. Lawrence and S. S. Block, eds), pp. 703–740. Lea and Febiger, Philadelphia.

Farkas, J. and Roberts, T. A. (1976). *Acta Alimentaria* **5**, 289–302.

Farkas, J., Kiss, I. and Andrassy, E. (1967). *In* "Radiosterilization of Medical Products", pp. 343–345. Proceedings of a Symposium, International Atomic Energy Agency, Vienna.

Fields, M. L. and Finley, N. (1962). *University of Missouri College of Agriculture Research Bulletin* 807.

Fields, M. L. and Frank, H. A. (1973). *Journal of Bacteriology* **114**, 878–879.

Flowers, R. S. and Adams, D. M. (1976). *Journal of Bacteriology* **125**, 429–434.

Foster, J. W. and Wynne, E. S. (1948). *Journal of Bacteriology* **55**, 495–501.

Frank, H. A. and Campbell, L. L. (1955). *Applied Microbiology* **3**, 300–302.

Freeman, B. M. and Bridges, B. A. (1959). U.K. Atomic Energy Authority, Research Group Report AERE-R3204. H.M.S.O. London.

Futter, B. V. (1968). Ph.D. Thesis. Cited by Roberts, 1970.

Futter, B. V. and Richardson, G. (1970a). *Journal of Applied Bacteriology* **33**, 321–330.

Futter, B. V. and Richardson, G. (1970b). *Journal of Applied Bacteriology* **33**, 331–341.

Futter, B. V. and Richardson, G. (1972). *Journal of Applied Bacteriology* **35**, 301–307.

Goldblith, S. A. (1967). *In* "Radiosterilization of Medical Products", pp. 3–22. Proceedings of Symposium, International Atomic Energy Agency, Vienna.

Gould, G. W. and Hitchins, A. D. (1963). *Journal of General Microbiology* **33**, 413–423.

Grecz, N., Upadhyay, J. and Tang, T. C. (1967). *Canadian Journal of Microbiology* **13**, 287–293.

Gurney, T. R. and Quesnel, L. B. (1980). *Journal of Applied Bacteriology* **48**, 231–247.

Härnulv, B. G. and Snygg, B. G. (1973). *Journal of Applied Bacteriology* **35**, 615–624.

Harris, N. D. (1963). *Journal of Applied Bacteriology* **26**, 387–397.

Hashimoto, T., Frieben, W. R. and Conti, S. F. (1972). *In* "Spores V" (H. O. Halvorson, R. Hanson and L. L. Campbell, eds), pp 409–415. American Society for Microbiology, Washington, D.C.

Hurst, A. (1977). *Canadian Journal of Microbiology* **23**, 936–944.

Ingram, M. and Roberts, T. A. (1971). *Journal of Food Technology* **6**, 21–28.

Jarvis, B., Rhodes, A. C., King, S. E. and Patel, M. (1976). *Journal of Food Technology* **11**, 41–50.

Kadota, H., Uchida, A., Sako, Y. and Harada, K. (1978). *In* "Spores VII" (G. Chambliss and J. C. Vary, eds), pp. 27–30. American Society for Microbiology, Washington, D.C.

Kereluk, K. (1977). *Developments in Industrial Microbiology* **18**, 373–385.

Kiss, I., Rhee, C. O., Grecz, N., Roberts, T. A. and Farkas, J. (1978). *Applied and Environmental Microbiology* **35**, 533–539.

Labbe, R. G. (1979). *Journal of Applied Bacteriology* **47**, 457–462.

Lechowich, R. V. and Ordal, Z. J. (1962). *Canadian Journal of Microbiology* **8**, 287–295.

Levinson, H. S. and Hyatt, M. T. (1960). *Journal of Bacteriology* **80**, 441–451.

Levinson, H. S. and Hyatt, M. T. (1964). *Journal of Bacteriology* **87**, 876–886.

Lewis, J. C. and Colman, R. (1974). *Journal of Bacteriology* **117**, 1350–1353.

Licciardello, J. T. and Nickerson, J. T. R. (1963). *Applied Microbiology* **11**, 216–219.

Marshall, B. J., Murrell, W. G. and Scott, W. J. (1963). *Journal of General Microbiology* **31**, 451–460.

Morrison, E. W. and Rettger, L. F. (1930a). *Journal of Bacteriology* **20**, 299–311.

Morrison, E. W. and Rettger, L. F. (1930b). *Journal of Bacteriology* **20**, 312–342.

Mossel, D. A. A. and Beerens, H. (1968). *Journal of Hygiene, Cambridge* **66**, 269–272.

Mossel, D. A. A. and Corry, J. E. L. (1977). *Alimenta* 19–34.

Murrell, W. G., Olsen, A. M. and Scott, W. J. (1950). *Australian Journal of Scientific Research* **3**, 234–244.

Nakamura, M. and Converse, J. D. (1967). *Journal of Hygiene, Cambridge* **65**, 359–365.

Neal, N. D. and Walker, H. W. (1977). *Journal of Food Science* **42**, 1600–1602.

Nelson, F. E. (1943). *Journal of Bacteriology* **45**, 395–403.

Odlaug, T. E. and Pflug, I. J. (1977). *Applied and Environmental Microbiology* **34**, 377–381.

Olsen, A. M. and Scott, W. J. (1946). *Nature, London* **157**, 337.

Olsen, A. M. and Scott, W. J. (1950). *Australian Journal of Scientific Research* **3**, 219–233.

Pepper, R. E., Buffa, N. T. and Chandler, V. L. (1956). *Applied Microbiology* **11**, 384–388.

Perigo, J. A., Whiting, E. and Bashford, T. E. (1967). *Journal of Food Technology* **2**, 141–148.

Pivnick, H. and Thacker, C. (1970). *Canadian Institute of Food Technology Journal* **2**, 141–148.

Prentice, G. A. and Clegg, L. F. L. (1974). *Journal of Applied Bacteriology* **37**, 501–513.

Put, H. M. C. and Aalsberberg, W. I. J. (1967). *Journal of Applied Bacteriology* **30**, 411–419.

Ray, B. (1979). *Journal of Food Protection* **42**, 346–355.

Reich, R. (1980). *Journal of the Parenteral Drug Association* **34**, 200–211.

Riemann, H. (1960). *Nordic Veterinery Medicine* **12**, 86–104.

Roberts, T. A. (1970). *Journal of Applied Bacteriology* **33**, 74–94.

Roberts, T. A. and Ingram, M. (1965). *Journal of Applied Bacteriology* **28**, 125–139.

Roberts, T. A. and Ingram, M. (1966). *Journal of Food Technology* **1**, 147–163.

Roberts, T. A. and Ingram, M. (1973). *Journal of Food Technology* **8**, 467–475.

Roberts, T. A., Ditchett, P. J. and Ingram, M. (1965). *Journal of Applied Bacteriology* **28**, 336–348.

Roberts, T. A., Gilbert, R. J. and Ingram, M. (1966a). *Journal of Food Technology* **1**, 227–235.

Roberts, T. A., Gilbert, R. J. and Ingram, M. (1966b). *Journal of Applied Bacteriology* **29**, 549–555.

Rowley, D. B., Anellis, A., Wierbicki, E. and Baker, A. W. (1974). *Journal of Milk and Food Technology* **37**, 86–93.

Russell, A. D. (1964). *Laboratory Practice* **13**, 114–122.

Russell, A. D. (1971). *In* "Inhibition and Destruction of the Microbial Cell" (W. B. Hugo, ed.), pp. 451–612. Academic Press, London and New York.

Russell, A. D. and Loosemore, M. (1964). *Applied Microbiology* **12**, 403–406.

Sarathchandra, S. U., Barker, A. N. and Wolf, J. (1974). *In* "Spore Research 1973" (A. N. Barker, G. W. Gould and J. Wolf, eds), pp. 207–231. Academic Press, London and New York.

Schmidt, C. F. (1955). *Annual Review of Microbiology* **9**, 387–400.

Sebald, M. and Ionesco, H. (1972). *C. R. Academie des Sciences* **275D**, 2175–2177.

Segner, W. P., Schmidt, C. F. and Boltz, J. K. (1966). *Applied Microbiology* **14**, 49–54.

Shoesmith, J. G. and Holland, K. T. (1972). *Journal of General Microbiology* **70**, 253–261.

Speck, M. L. and Ray, B. (1979). *Journal of Food Protection* **40**, 333–336.

Sugiyama, H. (1952). *Journal of Bacteriology* **62**, 81–96.

Süpfle, K. and Denger, A. (1916). *Archives of Hygiene* **85**, 189–197.

Tallentire, A. and Jacobs, G. P. (1972). *International Journal of Radiation Biology* **21**, 205–213.

Tallentire, A. and Powers, E. L. (1963). *Radiation Research* **20**, 270–287.

Tallentire, A., Dickinson, N. A. and Collett, J. H. (1963). *Journal of Pharmacy and Pharmacology* **15**, 180T–181T.

Terano, H., Tanooka, H. and Kadota, H. (1969). *Biochemical and Biophysical Research Communications* **37**, 66–71.

Terano, H., Tanooka, H. and Kadota, H. (1971). *Journal of Bacteriology* **106**, 925–930.

Ting, M. N. and Fung, D. Y. C. (1972). *Applied Microbiology* **24**, 755–759.

Toda, K. (1970). *Journal of Fermentation Technology* **48**, 811–818.

Tomlins, R. I. and Ordal, Z. J. (1976). *In* "Inactivation of Vegetative Microbes" (F. A. Skinner and W. B. Hugo, eds), pp. 153–190. Symposium No. 5, Society for Applied Bacteriology. Academic Press, London and New York.

Treadwell, P. E., Jann, G. J. and Salle, A. J. (1958). *Journal of Bacteriology* **76**, 549.

Tsuchido, T., Kanda, K. and Shibasaki, I. (1975). *Journal of Fermentation Technology* **12**, 862–868.

Waites, W. M. and Wyatt, L. R. (1974). *Journal of General Microbiology* **84**, 235–244.

Walker, H. W. and Matches, J. R. (1966). *Journal of Food Science* **30**, 1029–1036.

Walker, H. W., Matches, J. R. and Ayres, J. C. (1961). *Journal of Bacteriology* **82**, 960–966.

Wallen, S. E. and Walker, H. W. (1979). *Journal of Food Science* **44**, 560–563.

Wang, D. I. C., Scherer, J. and Humphrey, A. E. (1964). *Applied Microbiology* **12**, 451–454.

Wheaton, E. and Pratt, G. B. (1961). *Journal of Food Science* **26**, 261–268.

Wheaton, E., Pratt, G. B. and Jackson, J. M. (1959). *Food Research* **24**, 134–145.

Whitbourne, J. E. and Reich, R. R. (1979). *Journal of the Parenteral Drug Association* **33**, 132–143.

Williams, O. B. and Reed, J. M. (1942). *Journal of Infectious Diseases* **71**, 225–227.

Witter, L. D. and Ordal, Z. J. (1977). *In* "Antibiotics and Antibiosis in Agriculture" (M. Woodbine, ed.), pp. 131–138. Butterworths, London.
Woese, C. (1958). *Journal of Bacteriology* 75, 5–8.
Wynne, E. S. and Foster, J. W. (1948). *Journal of Bacteriology* 55, 61–68.
Yokoya, F. and York, G. K. (1965). *Applied Microbiology* 13, 993–999.

Index

B

DNA
  heat-induced degradation, 293
  hydrostatic pressure, 264
  interaction with
    β-propiolactone, 249
    formaldehyde, 200–201
    propylene oxide, 250
  ionizing radiation and, 134–137
  release from ethylene oxide-treated
    spores, 244, 245
  spore core, 5, 6
  synthesis, 11, 15, 177
    inhibitors, 185–187
  T_m value, 263
  transforming,
    UV and, 160
  UV resistance and, 160, 161–165
Domiphen bromide, 269
Dose–survivor curves
  ionizing radiation, 112–116
    exponential inactivation, 113
    non-exponential inactivation,
      113–114
    resistant tail, 114–115
    target theory, 115–116
  ultraviolet radiation, 153–154
DPA, *see* Dipicolinic acid
Dressings, 137
Dry heat, 90–109
  D-values, 92, 95–97, 98, 281, 282,
    302, 303
  factors influencing sensitivity,
    100–103
  F- and F_o-values, 92
  ionizing radiation and, 281, 282, 283
  mathematical aspects, 92–100
  mechanisms of spore inactivation,
    103–105
    induction of mutants, 104
    oxidation, 103
    role of water, 104–105
  process types, 91–92, 101–102
  revival of spores from, 299–303
  spore carrier, 102–103
  testing of sterilizers, 106
  uses, 105–106
  z-values, 98, 99
D-values
  dry heat, 92, 95–97, 98, 281, 282,
    302, 303

ethylene oxide, 302, 307
ionizing radiation, 116–121, 275
moist heat, 38–46, 52, 60, 61, 72, 73,
  74, 75, 301
nisin and heat resistance, 177
thermoradiation, 280, 281, 282
D_{10}-value, *see* D-value
Dyes
  and heat-damaged spores, 308

E

EDTA, 60, 215, 275, 296
Engulfment, 12, 13
Erythrobate, 214
Erythromycin, 173, 180
Escherichia coli
  antibacterial agents, 170, 171, 196,
    201
  gases, 244
  ionizing radiation, 121
  moist heat, 300
  ultraviolet radiation, 154, 155, 156
Ethanol, *see* Ethyl alcohol
Ethidium bromide, 214
Ethyl alcohol (ethanol), 191–192, 193,
  216, 217, 284
  inhibition of germination, 193, 216
  OH scavenger, 276
  separation of spores and cells, 191
Ethylenediamine tetraacetic acid, *see*
  EDTA
Ethylene oxide,
  antibacterial activity, 235–242
    concentration, 234–236, 242
    condition of organism, 240–242
    D-values, 302, 307
    exposure time, 236–237, 242
    RH, 238–240, 241, 242, 243, 244
    temperature, 236, 237, 242
    temperature coefficient, 269, 271
    type of organism, 237
    type of sterilizer, 237–238
  chemical structure, 233
  crystals, 244
  desiccation and, 238
  "dwell" period, 239
  indicators, 245–246
  "microenvironment", 239